"It is amazing how vivid and inevitable Mr. Lamb makes all this. . . . The background is history for all to read, Omar's speech is guided through echoes of his own poems."

—*Books*

". . . the product of a gifted imagination. . . . Old Persia lives and moves before us with all the vivid picturesqueness of a land seen and a people known."

—*Boston Transcript*

". . . Mr. Lamb is well fitted to play the role of guide along old caravan tracks of Western and Middle Asia."

—*Saturday Review of Literature*

OMAR KHAYYAM
A LIFE

by

Harold Lamb

LEISURE BOOKS, INC.

LEISURE BOOKS

**THIS BOOK CONTAINS THE COMPLETE TEXT
OF THE HARDCOVER EDITION**

First Leisure Book printing February 1971

Copyright 1934 by Harold Lamb
All rights reserved

Reprinted by arrangement with Doubleday & Company, Inc.

ISBN 0-8439-0014-8

COVER ILLUSTRATION BY JAMES DIETZ

Published by Leisure Books, Inc.
6340 Coldwater Canyon
North Hollywood, California 91606

CONTENTS

DEDICATED TO THOSE PERSIANS
WHO SHARED THEIR HOMES AND
THOUGHTS WITH ME AND IN
SO DOING MADE POSSIBLE
THIS BOOK.

PART I

The Street of the Booksellers in the old city of Nisapur, in the Land of the Sun. The year 1069 by the calendar of the Christians.

THE STREET LED from the Friday mosque down to the park. It had a grape arbor over it, to keep out the sun's glare. Half way down, where the street turned, stood a giant plane tree with a fountain beneath it.

Here the women who came to fill their water jars liked to sit. They put down their jars and whispered together, while the men dozed in the open book stalls and the boys from the mosque academy ran by, shouting, "Wake up, O sellers of old books!"

This shout always made Yasmi squirm. The boys never paid any attention to her, since she wore a child's white half veil. They went by with manly strides, and occasionally they threw stones at Yasmi's gray kitten. Some of them had the light hairs of beards on their chins.

Yasmi was twelve years old and beautiful, in her own eyes. So she resented the child's veil. If she could wear a full veil and look out at the boys from the shutters of the harem part of the house, they would notice her readily enough.

Instead of that she waited upon her father in the book stall, and he was old and irresolute because he was nearly blind with much poring over finely written manuscripts. He thought more of an illuminated page of Avicenna than he did of his daughter. And the wives of the house only noticed Yasmi when they remembered tasks she could do.

7

Yasmi listened sometimes when her father read to the boys, but got little satisfaction out of it. How could she understand such matters as the shape of the Wild Geese in the night sky, or the veil that hangs before the Invisible? Wisdom of that nature belonged to men; girls, it seemed, had no souls — after life left them they would be wherever the horses and cats were.

Yasmi swept out the stall for her father, and found for him the things he could not see, and ran errands for him back and forth into the interior of the house. Between whiles she embroidered idly on a headcloth, or played with the gray kitten, sitting where she could watch all that went up and down the Street of the Booksellers.

Two of the older boys stopped often at the stall. The taller of them, Rahim — Rahim Zadeh, the son of the landowner — had a red and brown robe that caught Yasmi's eye; the other would bend over books until the sunset hour when the light failed and the shopkeepers came out for the evening prayer.

The evening that Rahim bought the illuminated book, her father went to the corner and came back with a square of mastic for Yasmi. While she was eating it, gratefully — because candy was a treat in a house of poverty — her father meditated.

"Rahim really wanted the painting on the back of the cover. It was a sultan on horseback, cutting down an infidel with his sword."

All this belonged to the world of men, of which Yasmi knew nothing. She had a fancy that she cherished, a concept of a quiet and kingly amir who would wear velvet and damask robes, who would ride a white horse through the Street of the Booksellers, with a dozen Turkish swordsmen at his tail. This dignified prince would thereupon observe Yasmi with passionate eyes, and bestow gifts of silver and alabaster upon her father in return for carrying her, Yasmi, away with him to his palace up the river where he would sequester her in a pavilion with white swans, and silk hangings and silver plates of sugared fruits. The rider of the white horse would always be so passionately devoted to her that he would care nothing for his other wives, and her children would be his favorites. He would never laugh at her. . . .

"Rahim laughs so much," she observed.

"Well —" her father considered. "He does. But why not,

when he is noble-born, with body servants to run hither and yon for him?"

That would be nice, Yasmi thought, and for a moment she considered Rahim in the rôle of the amir of the white horse. Still, Rahim remained Rahim. Once he had flung her a copper coin, and she had polished it until it looked almost like gold. She wondered why he always went about with his friend the son of Ibrahim.

"The son of Ibrahim," she suggested, restraining the gray kitten from an excursion out into the street, "is silent and fierce. I do not like him."

This other boy had never so much as looked into her eyes. He would hasten down the street with his *abba* flying out from his broad shoulders and his headcloth in disarray, as if he had not taken any thought about his dress. He would hurry through strings of donkeys and under camels' necks, as if nothing could check his course. When he was in her father's shop he would read with that same intentness, taking up one book after the other, while Rahim and her father talked.

"The son of Ibrahim?" her father muttered. "Oh, he is not silent at the school. He argues and mocks. By God's will, no good ever came of that."

Yasmi knew well enough what mockery was — she had her share of it in the women's apartments. But the day of the stoning of the gray kitten she had something else to think about.

The kitten had wandered out and Yasmi called "Maleki, Maleki" in vain until she discovered her pet in the branches of the small plane tree at the street turning. Maleki would not come down for good reason. A half-dozen students were flinging pebbles at her, idly at first, then savagely as the lust to slay grew upon them.

"Stop!" Yasmi cried shrilly.

When they did not stop the girl began to sob. Maleki was so helpless, crouching there in the branches. Yasmi pushed through the boys and stamped her foot, the tears dripping down her cheeks. Then, desperately, she rushed at the tree and scrambled up into the branches.

She climbed until she reached the kitten. Once she had picked it up in her arms the stones ceased cutting through the branches. The boys were no longer interested. They went away, down the street.

But when Yasmi descended to the lower branches, she felt frightened. She was so far above the ground. How she had got there she did not know. It was impossible to jump down with the kitten in her arms. The men of the shops were trooping off toward the mosque and no one paid any attention to a girl-child in a tree. Except the boy who came and stood beneath her. "Jump," he said gravely, holding out an arm.

It was the son of Ibrahim, and Yasmi did not want to jump. "No," she shook her head.

"*Yah bint!*" He leaped and caught the branches, swinging himself beside her. "Oh, girl."

Holding her fast, he let himself go. Yasmi gasped, and the gray kitten whined and clawed at his headcloth. Then they were on the ground, and Yasmi's heart thumped against her ribs. The son of Ibrahim was smiling down at her, his dark eyes amused. He was disengaging Maleki from his clothing. "*Y'allah,*" he said, "both of you hold tight enough!"

Yasmi wiped her cheeks, and cried out: "Do not mock me!"

Then she felt dismayed, and ran away into the shadows under the trellis. All that evening she thought of his eyes smiling down at her, and the restless muscles of his arms holding her.

From that time Yasmi thought of nothing but the son of Ibrahim. Instead of watching the riders pass along the park at the foot of the street, she sat where she could see the school gate of the mosque enclosure and when his uncouth figure came striding down among the other youths, Yasmi turned away with her cheeks burning. None the less, she watched him from the corners of her eyes. She noticed for the first time how straight he stood and how firmly he planted his sandals on the smooth stones. His lips were full and dark, and when he smiled at her, his dark face became gentle.

Yasmi tried various ways of attracting his attention. Once she experimented with the powder cloth of her elder sister and blackened her lids and lashes with *kohl*. Then she worked at a wreath of jasmine blossoms, and let it fall — she had seen her sister do that — when he came by the shop. He picked it up and put it back in her lap and went on — and Yasmi hid away from everyone for an hour, from sheer excitement and fear that she had been too forward.

10

Then she studied herself in her mother's bronze mirror, and decided that she was beautiful. She imagined herself veiled and seductive, and sought by men as if she were the daughter of an amir. She confided all this to the gray kitten in the hours of the night when the women thought her asleep on her quilt in the corner. But she wanted the son of Ibrahim to speak to her.

When he was in the shop she watched his every action — how he settled down in a corner of the rug in the sunlight to read, what books he favored, how he frowned and twisted his fingers over the written pages. There was one book he always looked for. Yasmi examined it when she had the shop to herself and found that it had many pictures with circles and lines and strange squares cut into parts. She could not read it, but she knew this book well, and one day she ventured to hide it among some larger manuscripts.

When Rahim and the son of Ibrahim came in, she smiled at the tall student and both of them looked at her. "Eh, Yasmi," said Rahim, "what new moon or what houri of paradise could vie with thy beauty?"

That, she thought, was a very pretty speech. She dropped her eyes and raised them suddenly so that Rahim could appreciate them.

"I have no shield," he laughed, "I have no shield to ward off such destroying darts. Be merciful!"

Yasmi smiled, but she was listening to the son of Ibrahim searching for his book. She pretended to upset the pile of manuscripts, and snatched up the red book with the drawings. In doing so she managed to tear a page across, just as she heard her father's slow steps approaching. He had not seen the tragedy — her heart thumped painfully when she remembered that this was one of his cherished volumes — but he noticed the torn page projecting from the edge.

"I have done that," said the son of Ibrahim suddenly. "So I will buy it. What is the price?"

"The Euclid with all the diagrams?" Her father looked surprised. It was a costly manuscript, and both he and Rahim knew that the son of Ibrahim had little money to spend.

"The library of the Nisapur school hath not such a copy with all the diagrams," began her father.

"Oh," Rahim broke in, "I will buy it, because I meant to make a gift of it to this scatterbrain Omar, son of Ibrahim of the Tentmakers."

Omar flushed and took the red book in his strong fingers.

"But do not say, O Seller of Old Books," Rahim laughed, "that this was the copy of Sultan Mahmoud, the one he kept always by his golden throne. It is worth no more than fourteen *dinars* because it is the work of an infidel Greek a long time dead."

"Nay," her father began to bargain, "the written text without the diagrams is worth twice that. And this binding —"

For an hour they discussed the price, while Yasmi listened eagerly, understanding that Omar was longing to possess the book. At the end Rahim bought it for his friend, for nineteen dinars of gold and some copper coins. Nothing more was said about the torn page.

When the two students left, Yasmi saw Omar stop and draw his pencase from his girdle cloth. It was a finely painted case. He thrust it into Rahim's hand and ran off, refusing to take back the pencase.

That evening was a memorable one for the son of Ibrahim of the Tentmakers. He hurried through his supper, washing his hands at the fountain and wiping them carefully on a clean sheepskin. Borrowing an extra lamp and lighting it at the courtyard fire, he went to his room.

It was a clay shed on the roof of the house, intended for drying onions and sweet grass. The boy occupied it because it cost only a few coppers a moon and because it gave him seclusion at night, with a clear view of the stars. When the night wind breathed across the plain, the bunches of grass and strings of onions rustled as if touched with life. Lying on his quilt Omar could look over the roofs to the round tower of the Sultan's palace.

Now he sighed thankfully because there was no wind. He lighted the other lamp, and placed the two in niches in the wall. With the copy of Euclid resting on a polished board on his knees, he turned the pages slowly. This was so much better than the parrot-like repetition of the schoolroom.

His eyes, under the strong, arched brows, became intent. His hand reached out for ink and pen, and a sheet of cotton paper from which he had erased the faded writing of years before. With ruler and compass he drew a cone, divided it swiftly into segments.

Lines of numerals formed under his fingers, as his mind drifted into calculation. The shed, the lamps, even the book, passed from his mind as he worked . . . the familiar cadence of a voice interrupted him for a moment.

It was the voice calling to the night prayer, and a vague unrest seized upon the boy. He ought to make the prayer — this book was the work of an infidel. He blinked at the lamps and settled down to a fresh calculation.

Before midnight he was disturbed again. He heard shuffling feet in the street below, the snapping of torches, and a hoarse voice. Going to the parapet he saw a crowd gathered about a gaunt figure in a black headcloth.

"O believers!" The figure spread out its arms and Omar recognized a Hanbalite, a zealot of Islam.

"O believers! The day cometh swiftly when ye who have tasted of ease shall be summoned by a warner. The day cometh when ye shall take up the sword against unbelievers. When that day is at hand, ye will hear a blast of trumpets bidding you rise from the beds of ease and take up the sword, to drive the unbelievers as a great wind drives sand before it. Give heed to the warning!"

The ragged Hanbalite beat his chest, driving his voice out into the night, and the idlers who followed him muttered among themselves. Omar listened with appreciation, for the man was eloquent. But, war! Was the Sultan not always at war?

When the Hanbalite had passed on and the "O believers!" dwindled into the vagrant sounds of the roof-tops, Omar stared up at the star groups. Suddenly he yawned. Stretching his long arms, he blew out the lamps; he flung himself down on his quilt, pulling the camel's hair blanket over his shoulders. In another moment he was asleep.

Chance gave to Yasmi the opportunity for which she had longed. Her mother had sent her up the street to fill a jar at the fountain. It was easy to carry the empty jar to the trickle of water under the plane tree; when the jar was filled, Yasmi dawdled about before struggling to raise it to her small head.

Presently Omar appeared and stopped to drink from his hand. He had no books, he was arguing with no friends, and he saluted Yasmi gravely.

"Eh, say," she remarked instantly, before he could pass.

"What shall I say?"

She considered, fearful that he would go on his way. "My father says you are a mocker. Why do you come to a bad end?"

Omar looked at her as if she had been a parrot that had suddenly given tongue.

"It is much better," she hurried on, "to be sweet to people, and not to mock them — then they give you candy at times. How old are you? What do you do when you are not at the school, or thinking, or sitting with Rahim?"

"Well," Omar smiled, "I am seventeen years old. Sometimes I visit the shop of my father, who was of the tentmakers' guild. Now he is dead. But Rahim — Rahim is going away."

Yasmi wriggled with interest. She looked up at the boy shyly and made room for him to sit on the rock beside her. "Tell me," she said impulsively, "what you would like to do? What you do in your mind, when you aren't carrying water or children, or washing cloths —"

With dismay she realized that a student who contradicted masters at the school and chanted verses from the Koran that he knew by heart had other occupations than her humble self. But her mistake proved fortunate because Omar sat down.

"I would like," he meditated, "to have an observatory."

She did not know what this might be, but she was careful not to make a second slip. "And then what?"

"Oh, a globe of the sky-sphere, and a copy of Ptolemy's star tables."

There was a lot more, it seemed, needed to complete an observatory. Yasmi perceived that what Omar longed for was a tower of seclusion that would belong to him — something like the pavilion with the white swans of her own dreams.

"I know!" she nodded. "You want to be a conjurer like Sidi Ahmed, and read fate in the stars."

The older women of her house patronized Sidi Ahmed, the soothsayer.

Omar was not pleased. His brows drew together and he gritted his teeth. "The father of fools, the braying donkey — with his abracadabra mumblings, and his horoscopes!"

14

It appeared that Omar did not believe in soothsayers. What he wanted to do was vague in Yasmi's agile mind. He wanted to use his observatory to measure Time. Yasmi's notion of Time began with sunrise and the first of the five prayers, and it ended with starlight. There was the moon, of course, to mark the months.

Omar, however, was not content with the moon. The moon went on its way and left many hours of Time behind each year. Why should men lose these hours from the year? The moon was to blame, but they would not forsake the moon to make a true count of the hours.

Yasmi nodded wisely, thinking of other things. If Omar could have his observatory, and if — and if he could love her a little, she would sweep it out and wash his turban cloths for him, and embroider his slippers. The two of them would live all their hours in the observatory.

Because Yasmi no longer wanted to go home. She wanted to listen to the voice of the son of Ibrahim, to watch the shadows flecking his smooth skin, while his eyes flashed and darkened. Without Omar, she would be empty and nothing — nothing would please her, ever. She edged a little closer to him, clutching the rose that she had picked to try in her hair.

"Would you like this?" she said faintly, when he had exhausted the misdemeanors of the moon.

"What? Oh, that! Why —" He took it in his fingers and smelled it. "It is yours?"

"But I want you to take it," she said urgently, "and keep it."

(Once her sister had thrown such a rose from the lattice of the balcony, and Yasmi had seen a youth of Baghdad pick it up and press it to his heart.) The son of Ibrahim merely looked at his rose; his mind was off somewhere with the moon. Yasmi brought it back to earth and herself again.

"When you have your observatory —" Yasmi thought it must be something like the round tower of the Castle. "I — I will be glad."

Then Omar smiled. "How old are you, Yasmi?"

"Almost thirteen," she whispered. She had heard her mother and the other wives say that a girl could be married at thirteen.

"When you are thirteen I will send you roses, lots of them."

15

He went away then, wondering how he had come to say so much to that child in the striped dress with the hungry eyes. But Yasmi sat where she was, her eyes dark with excitement. Her whole body ached with delight. She heard the jingling of donkey bells and the cries of men as if from some remote place. All the street had altered, all these men were strangers. And she had a feeling deep within her that they would never change back to ordinary things again. . . . She did not mind when the women slapped her for dawdling with the water at the fountain.

After a while she ran out and picked herself a rose from the small hedge, and she carried it with the gray kitten to her sleeping quilt that night.

"It is time," one of the women observed the next day, "that Yasmi wore the veil and kept to the *anderun*. My soul — she was seen hanging around a beardless student for an hour at the fountain."

"No longer shall she wait in the shop," her mother agreed.

Yasmi said nothing. This was to be expected. At last she would wear the veil of a marriageable woman. She felt sure that walls and lattices would not keep her love penned up.

But Omar went away.

A serai in the mountains by the great Khorasan road, three weeks' journey of a laden camel train to the west of Nisapur.

NO ONE SLEPT during the first watch of the night, because no one could sleep. Fires of thorn bush crackled in the open courtyard; camels grunted and sighed in their kneeling places; horses munched dried grass in the corners, while beggars went about with their bowls and their endless *"Ya hu ya hak!"*

Around the empty stew pots men sat licking the last of the grease and rice from their fingers, pausing to toss dried fruit or copper coins into the beggars' bowls. They were in a charitable mood because they were bound on a journey, a dangerous journey, and the giving of alms was a pious propitiation of fate.

The serai keeper alternately cried out that he was not Moses to provide water where the last of the water had been used up, and counting the coins in his wallet on the sly. These were hectic days for the resthouse on the Khorasan road; even now, in midwinter, hundreds were riding in daily, all bound west to join the army.

Men had spread their sheepskins upon every foot of the covered gallery around the courtyard. Some were burning charcoal in braziers and the glow lighted up rings of bearded faces. Khorasanis, Persians, and Arabs huddled in quilted coat or furs, smiling and arguing — glad of the rest after enduring the bitter mountain wind. Only the smooth Turkish faces with small eyes and high cheekbones were impassive. Cold was nothing new to these hardy riders from the steppes of mid-Asia; they were accustomed to war and wandering, and they talked little in any case.

Rahim Zadeh, son of the Nisapur landowner, fortunately possessed a brazier, and he kept himself warm in a fine khalat lined with sable skins.

He had heard the cry of a fanatical Hanbalite one night in Nisapur when he had been drinking wine behind a locked door, and it had seemed to him to be a voice of warning. Rahim, usually indolent except where amusement was to be had, felt that he must draw his sword in this war, and he had come with his milk-brother Omar of the Tentmakers and a score of armed retainers to join the armed host of the Sultan, Alp Arslan, in the far west.

"At least," he observed, "it will be more exciting than chasing antelope on the plain."

Rahim's family belonged to the old Persian nobility, the Iranian aristocracy, more ancient than the Greeks. He had faultless manners, a taste for sugared wine. He played backgammon and polo well but he soon tired of a game.

"*Aiwallah,*" murmured one of his followers, "it is cold."

Rahim yawned. It was cold enough, and muddy. Moreover, bugs had got into his sleeping skins. He glanced up as the serai keeper appeared at his shoulder and did not go away.

"May it please the noble young lord," the fellow whispered, "we have women travelers in the house behind the serai."

The noble young lord gave no sign of displeasure, and the keeper bent closer. "Some of the girls are from Baghdad, very pleasant and well-trained." He dropped the fiction that the inmates of the other house were also travelers. "If the Amir of Swordsmen cares for amusement —"

Rahim hesitated and then got to his feet. "Say to the son of Ibrahim," he ordered his servants, "that I am gone awhile to — to talk with friends."

"On my head," muttered the man who was cold.

Enviously the men-at-arms looked after Rahim as he followed the serai keeper toward the stairs. There were no women here for the common born, but if Allah willed it, after the battle with the infidels, slaves would be hawked about for all. After warming themselves at the brazier they went to sleep.

It was late when Rahim came back, stepping over the prostrate forms shrouded like the dead. He was tired and out of humor.

Omar, kneeling on the sleeping robes, fanned the brazier red again and made room for his milk-brother. "Where wert thou?"

"May the breed of innkeepers go to all the seven hells and burn," muttered Rahim. "May they eat dirt!" He threw himself down, glad that Omar was awake to complain to. "Where wert thou?"

"Looking about. Oh, there is life upon this road." Omar smiled, because the highroad and above all the desert road always stirred him, who was desert born, with the blood of Arab wanderers in him. "Yonder is a great camp, and in the camp a tent as large as the Nisapur *kala't*. And the place full of Turks in armor with gold upon their helmets. I understand their talk a little. Some prince halted there the night. I saw him."

Rahim sighed. Whatever Omar did, he did with all his intensity, plunging into things, getting messed up in them. Warfare was something new to the son of Ibrahim, and he went out of his way to look at strange horsemen, to ask questions at the halting places and even to examine the baggage bales offloaded from the camels. Omar found adventure in crossing a river, whereas he, Rahim, merely got wet. "Who?" he asked.

"I did not hear. The lord was sitting on a red cloth by the fire in the tent, talking with some doctors of the law, his tutors. He is two years younger than thou, and he wears a white ermine kaftan. The doctors told him that a certain star he had seen was Suhail, but I knew it was not. No man can see Suhail from this spot at this hour —"

"I know," Rahim lied hastily. "Isn't there a proverb —"

"That the sight of Suhail is fortunate — yes."

"Thou hast dared to speak before the Turks? But how?"

"In Arabic," explained Omar, amused. "The boy *tarkhan* went from the tent with me, to be shown the constellations. Those doctors were fools, mouthing folly —"

"Nay, scatterbrain, thou wert a greater fool to gainsay them. Wilt never learn not to deny the word of one who can set his slipper on thy lips?" Rahim was half-provoked, half-fearful. "What said the prince?"

"He asked if the stars held any portent for the war."

"Ah, and do they?"

The young student was silent, tracing signs absently with a dagger sheath in the dried mud. "If we knew, Rahim," he responded quietly, "we would be wiser than the Magi. If we could read human fate! And still — I showed the boy where the planets stood in their houses —"

"Thou hast no need to show me," cried his foster-brother impatiently. "How stands the omen?"

Omar shook his head. "Harken to Zarathustra! Two kings are going into battle and the heavens declare that the destiny of the king in the east is rising, and that of the monarch of the west is falling. But — listen to the prophecy — the portent of death hangs over both of them." Suddenly he laughed. "It's nonsense, to say that. But the lion cub stared as if he had seen a ghost."

"The lion cub!" Rahim's eyes opened wide. "What —"

"The prince, the one with the white coat. At least they called him that."

"My father's beard!" Rahim sighed. "Hast thou never heard of the Lion Cub?"

"Nay."

"May Allah the Compassionate befriend thee. There is but one! He is the eldest son of our Sultan, of Alp Arslan, the Valiant Lion. Thou hast prophesied victory to the prince-royal."

"I did not know him."

"Would any one believe? And more, thou hast foretold the

death of his father, which" — Rahim's agile mind delved into possibilities — "no soothsayer in his senses would do, in public, anyway. Still, it means the throne to the Lion Cub. What said he?"

"He asked my name, and I told him. He asked whom I served, and I said no one, being a student of the Nisapur *madrasse.*"

"Hmm. Well, if I know these Turks our masters, and *if* Alp Arslan dies, thou mayest go to this same Lion's Cub and claim the post of astrologer to the King. Then appoint me thy carpet spreader, at a rich salary."

Omar shook his head.

"I think," Rahim insisted, "the making of a fine soothsayer is in thee, scatterbrain. Everyone believes thee. Oh, Yarmak —" He kicked at one of his sleeping servants. "Yarmak, fetch me the jar in the leather case. A goblet."

It was wine that Yarmak poured out into the cup that Rahim held. Forbidden wine. Rahim, who craved it, whispered that such a small sin would not count against the sanctity they would attain by fighting in the holy war. Omar, who cared little for it but who loved his foster-brother, would not gainsay him.

"Still," he pointed out as he took the cup, "we may lose the battle."

"Not we," cried Rahim. "Our Turkish Sultan may be a common soldier, but he wins all his battles. That, at least, was a sound prophecy."

The sweet wine refreshed him and he took a second cup. He fancied himself at the battlefield, riding recklessly in advance of the Sultan's red banner, mounted on his big black horse — sweeping forward between the lines of the two armies, and meeting hand-to-hand a chosen hero of the Christians, some knight in splendid armor. He visioned himself cutting down the infidel champion, while the Moslems shouted his praise. He thought of taking the head of his enemy and casting it down before the horse of his Sultan. . . .

"Hark to this, Omar," he urged.

But the milk-brother lay rolled up in the camel hair rug, sleeping as soundly as though combat and glory and royal favor did not exist.

The valley of the Arsanas River within sight of the blue Lake Van in the Armenian mountains, five weeks' journey of a laden camel to the west of Nisapur. Early spring of the year 1071 of the Christian calendar.

JAFARAK, the King's jester, sat in meditation upon his white donkey. His short legs projected on either side the donkey's ribs. A scarlet cloak covered his wizened body. Only his clear brown eyes moved restlessly from side to side.

For Jafarak, who did his best to keep near that grim Sultan, his master, was aware that this would be no ordinary battle.

They had told him to wait by the baggage train, with the assemblage of mullahs, the priests of Islam. That, they had said, would be the safest place. But Jafarak had said, no. "The safest place," he had retorted, "is behind my master's back, for the Moslems will send no arrows there and the Christians will never see it."

This had pleased his master, the Sultan Alp Arslan, the Seljuk, Lord of the World, and King of the East and the West. So Jafarak kept his place by the red standard and the imperial parasol that was held by armed slaves over the head of Alp Arslan. Alp Arslan no longer laughed, in these last days that tried the patience of the Moslem warriors.

For Alp Arslan had planted his standard near the head of the valley, beside the walls of the town of Malasgird. In front of him stretched the rolling, fertile valley. Up this valley was advancing the host of the Christians, of the accursed *Roumis*, the host commanded by the Emperor of Constantinople himself — the Emperor whose ancestors had been the arch foes of Islam for four centuries.

Until now Alp Arslan had contented himself with making inroads far into the dominion of the Emperor — thrusting spearheads of horsemen into the vitals of Asia Minor, so long the stronghold of Asiatic Rome. These spear thrusts had wounded and angered the *Roumis*, until at last the Emperor had assembled all his power to strike back at the wary Turk who had challenged him so boldly, whose ancestors, sons of Tokak the Bowman, had emerged from the fastness of mid-Asia to ride victoriously almost within sight of Constantinople. Now the Emperor was advancing with his mailed cavalry, and his heavy infantry, his mercenary Bulger archers, throngs of fierce Georgian swordsmen and friendly Armenians fighting to defend their land against the advance of Islam. A huge, slow-moving host, hybrid as the array of Sennacherib. Seventy thousand souls, men said, crawling up the valley after the retreating Turks fifteen thousand strong.

The Emperor of the Christians, a fine soldier, was impatient to come to grips with the Turkish horsemen who had eluded him for so many months. And now, to the surprise of his own officers, Sultan Alp Arslan had planted his standard in the ground, and had quartered his cavalry regiments across the valley, to await the coming of the Emperor.

It seemed a strange thing to Jafarak that fifteen thousand should sit down to wait when they were pursued by seventy thousand.

He heard some of the amirs say, when they thought no one was listening — no one except the Court fool in his motley — that even the veteran Turkish cavalry could not withstand the charge of the heavier *Roumi* mailed lancers. And still Alp Arslan waited there with his cavalry, while the advancing standards of the Christians came nearer, moving slowly over the muddy fields. Jafarak knew that many officers were afraid of being penned up; they were accustomed to attack and pursuit, or swift retreat.

"That will not be," Alp Arslan said in his deep, slow voice. "The camp of the Roumis is already placed far down the valley. They have pressed on to overtake us, and we are here. It is decided, it is written. And what is written will come to pass."

Jafarak, who was sitting by the eldest prince, noticed that the boy glanced toward his father as if frightened by these words.

Perhaps, thought the jester, the issue of the morrow's battle was already decided, as the pious mullahs proclaimed and as the learned astrologers prophesied. He thought of the impatience of the great Christian Emperor, of the muddy, bare fields, and the motionless horsemen of the Seljuk Turks who had never known defeat in battle. Perhaps it was decided, after all, and on the morrow they would only move hither and yon like pawns in a game foreordained.

But Alp Arslan did not sleep that night.

Before the first light Rahim was up, shivering with cold and excitement. He gave his sword to Yarmak to sharpen for the dozenth time, and set other men to grooming his black charger. Hastily he gulped down some dates and barley soaked in water. Now that the hour had come, it was not at all like the start of an antelope chase.

Nor was it in the least as Rahim had fancied it would be. Instead of being summoned to saddle at daybreak and rushing forward with a shout, Rahim could do nothing except fidget about his horse for hours, while the curtain of mist around him thinned away, and his men squatted down and threw dice. When he mounted his horse he could see the heads and lances of riders passing by at a walk. At times he heard a sound like wind rushing through a forest far away, and once beyond the haze in the valley a loud murmur rose, like the crowd pressing about the mosque of Nisapur on a feast day.

When a strange rider trotted by, Rahim cried out to him for news of the battle. The man, a Turk, merely looked at him and went on. Then, beside himself with impatience, Rahim trotted off to his commander, an amir who had the volunteer swordsmen of Nisapur gathered around his standard.

"Send us forward," he urged eagerly, "or we will not see the first blows struck."

To his astonishment he learned that fighting had been going on for hours down the valley. The Khorasanis had heard strange tidings. The Christians had sent demons encased in iron against the Moslems ... a whole regiment had been drowned in the river ... the Sultan had gone off to the mountains on the right, where hordes of Georgians and Armenians were pressing forward ... the valley, for leagues, was full of Christians.

"But no," cried someone, "there is our lord the Sultan. Look, yonder!"

Rahim rose in his stirrups and stared. He saw a cavalcade of horsemen trotting across a mound beside him. The leader of the cavalcade rode a white horse — a broad, powerful man with mustaches that curled up on either side his lined brown face beneath a towering black sheepskin hat. He held a white ivory baton in his rein hand, and a bowcase flapped against his hip as naturally as if he had been an archer of the palace guard.

"Where is the Sultan?" whispered Rahim, peering among the officers.

"*Wallahi,* that is he — there, the first one."

Rahim had expected to see silk robes fluttering in the wind of a headlong gallop — plumed helmets — a banner — drums beating — he did not know what. Deep disappointment filled him at beholding these ordinary quiet men, with a dwarf on a white donkey trotting after them. He went back to his place in silence.

At noon, when he felt both hungry and weary, Omar called him.

"The battle is coming nearer, Rahim. I have been watching from the mound, with the Turkomans. Come!"

When they climbed to the height over which the Sultan had passed, Rahim heard a humming as of a thousand beehives. A faint clattering of metal and drumming of horses' hoofs. The sun had cleared away the last of the mist and the whole valley lay open, with multitudes of tiny horsemen moving about it. At times they paced slowly, like grazing cattle. Then they would sweep back toward the mound as if driven by some irresistible wind.

For hours the Christian cavalry had been charging the Turks, who retired slowly, and crept back again. The arrows of the Turkish bowmen never ceased their hail. It seemed to Rahim as if these myriads of miniature riders had decided, all at once, to move down the valley.

"Look!" cried Omar.

Their own servants were standing up, waving at them. The regiment of Khorasanis had started to trot forward, the saddle drums muttering.

"At last," shouted Rahim, "they will charge."

"*Allah il-allah!*" shrieked a boy dragging a long spear after him, as he clutched Rahim's stirrup and tried to keep up with the horse.

This, thought Rahim, was the moment for which he had

waited. He drew his sword then sheathed it again presently because none of the others had done more than to draw on their shields. "Slay — slay!" sobbed the boy with the stolen spear, when he fell to the ground, no longer able to keep up with the charger. They were trotting across plowed earth, leaping channels of water.

An hour later they were still racing down the valley. But here their horses swerved from bodies that lay half buried in the mud. Riderless horses were trotting by them, while Arab tribesmen snatched at the loot that lay scattered about the plain.

"Now," exclaimed Rahim, eaten by impatience, "surely the Sultan will call for us to go into the battle."

Instead, they came at twilight to a regiment of Turkish cavalry dismounted in an abandoned garden, and here they were ordered to wait during the night. Although the Turks found dry brush somewhere and kindled great fires, the Khorasanis had neither fire nor food, and they drowsed through sheer weariness, until the first light when the clamor of distant trumpets roused them.

The trumpets were in the Christian camp, whither the Emperor had withdrawn the battered center of his host — the reserve in his rear had marched away during the darkness either from a misunderstanding or by treachery, and the infantry cut off upon his wings in the hills had surrendered to Alp Arslan's horsemen — and now, at dawn, the trumpets were summoning the mailed cavalry of Constantinople to a fresh charge. But Rahim and Omar knew nothing of this; they were heavy with sleep and stiff with the chill of the damp ground.

Their followers had saddled their chargers for them, and before they realized it they were in a mass of riders shouting and plunging over the ground at a gallop.

Omar's hands gripped the rein, and his head throbbed as if with fever. He saw the confusion about him only in glimpses of little things. A loosened turban cloth flapping about the head of a rider — a man running barefoot with his mouth open — a cart overturned, with a peasant crouching beneath it.

Suddenly at one side appeared a man crawling upon hands and knees. A rider reined in above him and thrust a lance down at the wounded man. The lance point stuck in the armor, and then thrust deep into the man's side. As it did so blood ran from his mouth and his head drooped, although he still tried to crawl away. And Omar thought with surprise that this must be a Christian soldier.

He turned his head, looking for Rahim. The rider with the loosened turban was holding fast to an arrow projecting from his hip. Omar heard him grunt with pain.

Then tents appeared on either hand. There was a sound of hammering upon iron, and a screaming. Omar noticed that foam lay upon the neck of his horse, and he loosened his grasp on the rein. He laughed when he thought that he had come through a battle and had not remembered to draw his sword.

Rahim was standing on the ground by a large tent. All around him the Khorasanis were dismounting to look for spoil. No one seemed to have ordered them to do that, but they were shouting and running about like children. Three of Rahim's followers came out of the tent with damask cloth and silver vessels in their arms. By the wrists they were leading a girl.

She stared about her as if bewildered, a mass of gleaming hair as light as ripe wheat falling about her eyes. She wore no veil, and the girdle that bound her slim waist was cloth-of-gold. The men-at-arms looked at her curiously; they had never encountered a Christian woman before.

"Ya, Omar," cried Rahim. "Allah hath favored us with victory."

Victory! It had a strange sound.

"This must be the slave of a Christian lord," continued Rahim gleefully. "I slew a dog of an infidel back there. Let us go into the tent —"

"Take care!" cried Yarmak suddenly. "Y'allah!"

Down between the tents came a band of men on muddy sweating horses. They were clutching swords and axes and galloping as if tormented by devils, their faces drawn and bleak under round iron helmets. Christian riders.

Omar caught at his rein and turned his horse, just as the riders swept upon him. The horse swerved and reared, throwing him back.

Something struck his shoulder, and the clashing hoofs of a charger passed over his head. Dirt stung his eyes and mouth, and after he had rubbed his eyes clear, he realized that he was on the ground. Unsteadily he got to his feet.

One of the servants twisted upon the earth, as if struggling with an invisible enemy. Close by him, Yarmak bent over Rahim, who was trying to lift himself to his knees.

Omar ran to him and caught his arms. Rahim was smiling in a strange way.

"Art thou hurt, O my brother?" cried Omar. "How?"

His foster-brother looked at him as if the words had no sense. Omar told Yarmak to bring a clean cloth. He let Rahim's wounded body gently down and began to raise the edge of the mail shirt to see the wound from which blood was running. It felt hot upon his hands, and a faint vapor rose from it into the damp air.

"O master," said Yarmak at his ear, "what would you do? Harken to the death rattle in his throat."

Standing up, Omar looked at his bloodied hands. The hot sunlight beat upon his hands and the trampled earth. Rahim's face was the color of clay, and he had ceased panting. Only that clacking sound came from his throat for a while and then ceased.

Then the servant Yarmak grunted like an animal and drew a curved knife from his girdle cloth. His lips twisted and he threw himself suddenly at the captive girl, who had stood motionless beside them during Rahim's death.

"Life for a life," Yarmak muttered, striking at the Christian.

She shrank away, the knife brushing her dress. Then she flung herself down before Omar, her hands clasping his legs, her body quivering. She made no sound, but her eyes stared up at him in agony.

"Fool!" Omar caught the servant's arm, and flung him away. Yarmak fell to the ground as if he had no strength in his limbs, and sobbed: *"Aiwallah aiwallah!"*

Omar told the Roumi girl to go into the tent, but she did not understand his words. When he pointed to the tent, she went into it slowly, looking over her shoulder. With the other servants Omar carried Rahim's body in and laid it upon the carpet. Uncertainly he wiped at his hands with a cloth and then ordered them to bring clean water.

With this he tried to wash the face of his milk-brother. After a while the girl knelt at his side and took the cloth from him. Deftly she bathed the dirt from Rahim's head and throat, as if she hoped to please Omar by doing so. Then she arranged the dead man's clothing. Omar thought that he would never have touched a dead Christian.

It seemed to him that there were so many things to do all at once. Nothing must be omitted that was necessary for Rahim.

Late that night the mullah with the gray beard looked at him wearily.

"My son," he said in his dry voice, "even the water of the sacred well of Zemzem must sink into the earth. Life comes from Allah, and to Allah return the souls of the believers upon that day when men's deeds are weighed in the scales of Judgment."

In his mind Omar saw the face of Rahim, the color of clay, lying upon the wet earth. Now Rahim lay in a clean shroud with his feet toward the holy city of Mecca, down there in the dark ground.

The mullah went away, having other burials upon his hands that night, and Omar sat down upon a stone. Yarmak came like a dog and sat by him, rocking gently forward and back. Now that his master was buried, Yarmak seemed satisfied. There was no help for it.

But to Omar, who had lost the foster-brother with whom he had grown up, it would be agony to go away from that place by the stone. Here Rahim must lie, washed by the rain, while the grass rose and the wheat was sown and reaped — through all the uncounted years until that day when the souls would rejoin their bodies at the Judgment seat. Behind the curtain of the Invisible, Rahim would wait for that day.

Omar sat, his chin on his hands, until the gray apparition of the dawn. He felt a little relief in his agony of mind, from the exhaustion of the last two days and nights.

"O Rahim," he whispered, "thy body is but a tent wherein the soul abides for a little. Then when the tent is struck, the soul goes forth on its long journey. O Rahim, I shall find thee, upon that journey,"

"Aman," assented Yarmak. "Peace!"

Within his tent Omar found a candle burning and he blinked at it, until the Roumi girl who had been sleeping among the garments thrown into a corner rose and poured a goblet of wine from a jar.

Omar raised his hand to strike it to the ground. Then he

remembered how Rahim had offered him a cup that night they had talked together in the serai on the Nisapur road. He took the goblet and drank it. A warmth crept through his chilled body. The girl filled the goblet again, and again Omar drank. He sighed and threw himself down on the rug, sinking into the stupor of exhaustion.

The captive girl blew out the candle. Seating herself beside him, she watched the dawn lighten the sky. When she could see everything clearly she picked up a bronze mirror and began to comb out her hair, looking reflectively into the mirror. It was not the first time that she had changed masters overnight.

Far down the valley the tent of the Sultan Alp Arslan had been pitched at last.

Turkish amirs thronged the entrance, on both sides of the carpet, straining for a sight of the three men at the head of the carpet. Jafarak, a privileged person, perched himself on a chest from which he could see the three — Romanus Diogenes, the Emperor of the Romans, and the mean little Moslem slave who had found the Emperor lying unconscious on the field and had brought him to the feet of Alp Arslan.

At first the spectators had watched Romanus, still in his armor, forced to kneel before the Sultan. Alp Arslan had set his foot once on the neck of the imperial captive, and then had lifted Romanus to a seat on the cushions at his right.

The listeners waited for the first word to be spoken between the commanders of the East and the West.

"Tell me," Alp Arslan asked casually, "what thou wouldst have done to me had I been brought captive thus before thee."

Romanus raised his head and thought for a moment, when the speech had been interpreted to him.

"I would have dealt with thee harshly," he said.

A smile lightened the dark face of the Sultan. "And what," he demanded, "dost thou expect from my hand?"

The captive Emperor looked at the intent faces of his enemies, and considered. "It may be that thou wilt slay me here, or place me in chains to be carried about thy kingdom. Or thou wilt accept ransom for me."

Alp Arslan found in his heart a liking for this Christian

monarch who did not lack courage. He was filled with exultation at his victory, and at having placed his foot upon the neck of a Caesar of Rome.

"Know," he said after a moment, "that I have decided what is to be done with thee."

From his place behind his father, the Lion Cub leaned forward, his hands clenched in his lap. He had not forgotten the prophecy that victory would come to the Moslems and that both the kings would die.

"From thee," Alp Arslan went on, "I shall take ransom, and a yearly tribute from thy people. And I will escort thee back to thy country with honor."

The Lion Cub breathed deep and settled back in his place. If Romanus had been slain here by the scimitar of an executioner, the Lion Cub would have expected the fulfillment of the prediction of a young student of Nisapur.

Omar could not sleep. In spite of the exhaustion of his body, his mind would not be quiet for long. The face of Rahim, smiling that strange smile, came before the eyes of his mind and would not go away. Then Rahim had still been Rahim; but after that he had become a thing like a wooden chest, to be lifted about on the tent floor and carried away. Try as he would, Omar could not keep from thinking of how they had carried Rahim, and how he had been wrapped up, in fold after fold of white cloth.

It was not easy to give orders in Rahim's place. As far back as he could remember, they had shared everything, being in this respect more like twins than ordinary brothers. Rahim had always seen to such things as food and servants and horses, and now, naturally, the men looked to Omar for orders.

It was time to start the journey back to Nisapur. Only the Seljuk Turks would remain in these mountains; already the Arabs and irregulars were on the march homeward, laden with spoil and captives.

When Yarmak and his surviving fellows had struck Omar's tent and packed it on the lead horses, Omar saw that each man had large sacks that did not belong to the baggage. They had spent these last days in gathering plunder, and in trading things they did not want. Now they were quite ready to go home with their new riches. But the son of Ibrahim had not so much as a dagger from the battlefield. He did not want anything to remind him of that.

Yarmak had saddled Rahim's black charger, and had made a bundle of his dead master's armor and weapons which he had tied behind the saddle. Omar looked at the black horse, and felt that he could not have it trotting beside him with an empty saddle all the way. On the other hand it must be taken back to Rahim's father.

"Perhaps," suggested Yarmak, "master, we could let the Roumi girl ride the charger. We have no litter for her."

The captive girl had to be taken along. She was Rahim's property and might be sold for a good price in the Nisapur slave market because she was young, with fine, silk-like hair. Omar, who had picked up a good many Greek words in his study of Plato's dialogues at the academy, had managed to find out a little about the girl.

Her name was Zoë, and she had no other because she had always been a slave, in Constantinople. She had been brought on the campaign by an officer who believed, like his Emperor, that the Moslems would be scattered and driven eastward without trouble.

"I will ride the charger," he said. "Give Zoë — give the Roumi girl my horse."

Although she wore a veil and rode behind Omar with the pack animals everyone who passed them on the road knew by her garments and light hair that she was a Christian captive, belonging to the young Khorasani warrior who rode alone and in silence.

It was hard for Omar at the first halting place. The caravanserai was so crowded that they had to set up the tent near a well occupied by the camp of an amir with a large following. The servants did nothing without being told — Omar had to show them where to picket the horses, and to bargain for barley and bread with the amir's men. He did not mind that because it kept him occupied, but when everything was done the memory of Rahim filled his mind.

So he sat upon his sleeping quilt until the fire by the tent pole died to embers. He remembered the wine that had brought forgetfulness for a few hours that first morning, but the wine was all used up and only the cup remained. Omar examined the sack to make sure, and held the silver vessel in his hand. Rahim had drained the cup of life so swiftly, and now he lay in the embrace of death.

Beside him the girl stirred in her sleeping robes, and sighed. Omar bent down and brushed the hair back from her eyes. They were dark and wet. Zoe had been crying to herself, for some reason of her own.

"Eh, what?" he asked gently.

Zoë's lips parted and she smiled. Evidently she did not want him to see her tears. For the first time he wondered what she was thinking about, in this long journey away from her own land. A slave had feelings as well as a sultan, but was not permitted to complain.

When he stroked the hair that tangled about her throat, it gave way softly under his fingers. Zoë glanced up at him curiously. She was no longer crying, and she moved away a little as if to make room for him beside her. The faint pulse in her throat quickened under his touch.

He took her into his arms and drew the covering over both of them, and lay looking up at the tent top from which the glow of the embers was slowly fading. He wondered if the trodden clay and the night wind and Rahim's strange smile would go from his mind now.

The girl stirred against him. When she raised herself to draw the heavy coils of her hair from beneath her shoulders, his lips brushed her throat. The warmth of her body, the scent of her hair soothed him, and then he felt her arms tighten about him. The warmth became a fever that drained the weariness from him and filled him with an intoxication that grew upon him with every motion of the girl.

In Zoë's arms that night he forgot death and the trodden clay, and he slept, breathing quietly, oblivious of the world.

PART II

*The house of the Mirror of Wisdom on the road to
the salt desert. The year after the victory of Sultan
Alp Arslan over the Christians.*

MASTER ALI was seventy-three years old. Next to the Koran
which he knew by heart, he lived for mathematics. Everything
in his household transpired with the regularity of the water
clock that dripped in the courtyard by the fish pool.

His assistants would say, "Now the master is washing his
feet and wrists; it is nearly time for the noon prayer." Or they
would say, "Now it is the third hour of the day, our master
will be copying the pages of his book."

The water clock, the five prayers, the two meals, the
twelve hours of work — all these moved in rotation with
the regularity of the constellations in the sky. Invariably
the same food appeared at each meal. No one had the
temerity to suggest to Master Ali, whose title was The
Mirror of Wisdom, that younger assistants might desire
dates and walnuts or pomegranates. So they bought
pomegranates secretly from the neighboring farmers and
gorged themselves, out of sight of the house.

At rare intervals Master Ali would clothe himself in his gray
brocade dress of honor and would depart for Nisapur on the
riding mule, with his parasol and a black slave to beat the mule.
His house was at the edge of the sown land, to the south of the
Nisapur plain, within sight of the white salt beds of the desert.
Here Master Ali had perfect seclusion for his labors.

He was finishing a treatise on *al-jebr w'al muqabala* — the knitting together of opposites — which had been ordered by the Sultan's Minister several years before. The assistants called it algebra for convenience. Their duty was to copy out commentaries dictated by the master, to work out experimental calculations when he wished, and to search other books for such information as he required. In return Master Ali lectured them for three hours of the afternoon on mathematical science, and fed them.

He knew the names and the mental shortcomings of all eight of them, and being a conscientious man he endeavored to implant within their minds as much as possible of his wisdom, so that after his death mathematical science would not perish in that portion of Allah's world. Of the eight he felt most doubt as to the future of Omar of the Tentmakers who had joined his household only ten months before.

Omar, he believed, had a gift for solving knotty problems, and a dangerous quality of imagination.

"Mathematics," Master Ali had assured his disciples often enough, "is the bridge by which you may pass from the unknown to the known. There is no other bridge."

The pure speculation of the infidel Greeks he disliked as much as he admired the mathematics of the ancient Egyptians, who had first made numerals their servants. Their calculations had served to erect huge buildings.

"*Yah Khwaja Imam,*" one of his disciples asked, "O Master, of what use is it to trace the movements of the stars? The Moon gives us the measure of our months, as decreed by our Lord Muhammad, upon whom be peace! The Sun gives light. But what good would come of studying the stars?"

Master Ali nodded reflectively. He wore the green turban of one who has made the pilgrimage to Mecca; he clipped his white mustache neatly and his spare figure was as erect as a tent pole. He had no faith in astrological prediction, but since the Sultan and all the great nobles believed in it, he would not express an opinion against it.

"Yet, Master," persisted the disciple, "is it not true beyond doubt that the planet Mercury,* which is so named by the Greeks, influences the movements of quicksilver, while the

* In this book the customary English names for the planets and constellations are used.

34

Sun hath influence upon gold, as the Moon hath upon silver? I — I have heard it said."

Now it was always possible that the great Minister who was Master Ali's patron had placed a spy in his household, to make certain that he had no dealings with infidels or black magic. And he fancied that Omar might be the spy of the Minister. In the first place Omar had come to him alone, on foot, wandering out of Nisapur, saying that he desired to study under the great master of mathematics. Strangely, Omar had insisted that he had no patron. In the second place this youth with the body of a warrior and the restless energy of a lion on the prowl, was obviously not studying to be a teacher. Why then had he buried himself here in seclusion at the edge of the salt desert?

Having thought out his reply, Master Ali delivered it in his dry voice.

"The learned Abu Rayhan Biruni says in the first chapter of his treatise upon astrology that the knowledge of the stars is a science, and that prognostication of the cycle of events, politics, changes in fortune of cities, princes and men, is a special use of that science. So, you may become perfect in the knowledge of the stars without prognosticating, but you cannot prognosticate without a perfect knowledge of the stars."

The disciple received this wisdom with an inclination of the head. He was searching, so far without success, among the master's books for some hidden formula that would enable him to make gold.

"In the *al magest*," he observed timidly, "it is written that the influence of the Sun upon gold is self-evident, because fire is the essence of the Sun, and — and fire is the only means of approaching the nature of gold. If the essence of fire could be concentrated —"

"In a furnace," assented another.

"Of sufficient force," put in an elder sagely.

"That," said Master Ali, "is Cosmography, which deals with the natures of celestial and terrestrial bodies. It can never be an exact science like Mathematics. What believer could doubt that when Allah in his wisdom created the outer fire and the inner air which surrounds the water which in turn envelops this motionless sphere of our world, He also created the gold that is found within the earth? What true believer would be so devoid of wisdom as to endeavor to create what Allah had caused to be?"

"True — true," murmured the disciples.

Master Ali was quite confident in saying this. The Minister and even the Sultan himself had discovered that in spite of many charlatans who professed to have the secret, no one had yet been able to make gold out of baser bodies. Still, he glanced covertly at Omar who was listening with half an ear while he drew with a pen upon a sheet of paper on his lap-board. Alone among the disciples Omar sometimes worked at his papers during the Master's discussions.

At first Master Ali had assumed that Omar was making notes, to refresh his memory. Now he wondered if these notes might not be meant for the Minister's eye. Omar, it seemed, kept papers locked up in a sandalwood chest by his sleeping quilt.

Rising suddenly, the aged mathematician advanced to his pupil and peered at the paper. He saw a drawing of two cubes bisected by many lines, with numerals scattered about.

"What is this?" he asked in surprise.

"The problem in cube roots," Omar answered promptly.

Master Ali recalled that he had assigned to the scion of the Tentmakers that week a difficult equation in cube roots.

"How far hast thou progressed?" he asked.

"It is done."

To Master Ali this seemed doubtful. He knew that the Greeks had arrived at a solution, but he had been unable to work it out.

So he took the paper, requesting Omar to come with him to his room, and dismissing the others. When he was comfortably seated by his window Master Ali examined the paper, holding it close to his eyes.

"Well," he said at last, "my understanding fails to perceive the meaning of this. I see only that thou hast bisected the cubes to a minute degree, and here thou hast reached the solution of the Greeks."

"How did they reach it?" Omar asked eagerly.

"That," responded the master slowly, "is not revealed to me as yet."

He remembered that he had not given Omar the answer to the equation. Among his papers, however, he had a notation of the problem with its solution. These papers lay with the Koran upon the settee beside him. He had not taken them out of his room, and his pupils were not allowed to enter the room in his absence. So it appeared evident that Omar had either worked it out by this fantastic drawing, or had searched secretly among the master's papers.

"I see only," he added, "that thou hast traced cube roots through the dimensions of these solid squares. In what way didst thou arrive at a solution?"

"The answer is there." Omar bent over the drawing. "Subtract this segment, and this, and this. Add this —"

"I am not blind. But, by the Kiblah, this is geometry, after the fashion of the infidel Euclid. This is not algebra."

"Nay — yet it is the solution. I could not deal with the roots in an algebraic equation."

Master Ali smiled. "Was it not an algebraic equation?"

"Certainly. From this it can be cast in the symbols of algebra. In this manner." Kneeling beside the master, and studying the cubes, Omar wrote down line after line of familiar figures. Looking only at the figures Master Ali saw that his problem had been solved. Now it could be added to his treatise.

He felt a thrill of satisfaction. Kharesmi himself had not ventured to touch this problem in his book. How Master Ustad would grind his teeth in the Baghdad academy!

"Hast thou made attempt at other problems in this manner?" he asked quickly.

Omar hesitated. "Yes, often," he admitted.

"And reached solutions?"

"Usually — not always."

"May I see the demonstrations?" Strangely, Master Ali asked the question almost humbly.

For a moment Omar was silent. "I have eaten thy salt, O Master," he said, "I have sat at thy feet, learning much. What thou gavest to me to do, I have done. But these other problems are my own, and — I would keep them."

Master Ali's beard seemed to come to a sharper point, and his eyes to harden. "Keep them! For what purpose, O son of Ibrahim?"

Looking out of the window at the dried-up garden, Omar did not appear either ashamed or troubled. "I do not know yet," he answered.

Of all things, Master Ali had not anticipated this. Suspicion grew upon him, as he pondered. Omar had spoken much too casually.

"These demonstrations," the old mathematician persisted, "are kept in that chest of thine which is locked?"

"Yes."

"But I have not locked my door. There is naught in all my papers that may not be seen." He glanced up into the young man's face. "Even the answer of the Greeks in this equation lies — on the floor beside thee."

Omar did not turn his head toward the table with the Koran and the papers where the notation really was, nor did he show a trace of surprise. If he had ransacked Master Ali's room, he had the self-command of a diplomat, or a spy.

After Master Ali had dismissed his young assistant, he pored over the solution of the cubes for hours. To the amazement of his class, he forgot completely the afternoon lecture. He was trying to approach another problem, as Omar had done, without success. His well-schooled mind could not make geometry do the work of algebra — he could not think in terms of solid masses.

"Avicenna could not do it!" he thought, in exasperation. "And yet —"

It was a vague idea. His own lifework, algebra, had served to solve problems that mere arithmetic could not master. What if this preposterous geometry of the Greeks could solve, in similar fashion, problems beyond the scope of algebra? What if some yet-unguessed art could progress beyond the three dimensions of geometry, to deal with numbers to the point of infinity? Master Ali threw pen and paper from him in disgust.

He had wasted an afternoon. All this was ignoble imagination; it had nothing to do with the exact science of mathematics. Omar, he decided, had merely stolen into his room, discovered the solution to the problem, and by aid of the solution had concocted these deceptive cubes. Probably he had no others locked up in his chest. Probably he was a spy, and he kept his reports in the chest until he should be able to go to Nisapur with them or send them, somehow.

Master Ali, having reached this conclusion, put away Omar's solution of the problem, glanced out the window at the water clock, uttered an exclamation of dismay when he saw that he had only a moment before the time of evening prayer, and hastened to the pool to wash his feet and wrists.

A week later the old mathematician had reason to cogitate again about Omar of the Tentmakers.

That afternoon a horse drew up at his gate. The horse was escorted by a half-dozen staff bearers on foot. A carpet slave hastened to unroll a narrow strip of rug from the horse to the inner side of Master Ali's gate, while another slave ran in to announce that Tutush desired to visit Master Ali.

Tutush followed the announcement of his name. He had a round and rolling body clad in silk, a voluminous turban of sheer turquoise blue, and a voice of marvelous modulations. The instant he ceased ordering his own followers about, he was beseeching the slaves of Master Ali for assurance as to the health of their distinguished lord. When Master Ali appeared at last, in his best somber black, Tutush uttered an exclamation of joy and clasped him in his short arms.

"Praise and glory to the Lord of the Two Worlds that the health of the world-renowned Mirror of Wisdom is unfailing! May the Mirror be untarnished for uncounted years! May it continue to reflect the wisdom of the age — of the century — upon us poor slaves of ignorance!"

To this polite greeting, Master Ali objected with becoming humility. But Tutush waved aside all objection. "Nay, is it not well known in Nisapur that your Honor is the superior of Kharesmi, and the master of that stupid Ustad of Baghdad? Had Avicenna greater knowledge of the sciences? Nay, he had not!"

Master Ali fared badly in this exchange of compliments when they were seated on the guest carpet, with fruit and sherbet piled before them. For one thing, he could not check the flow of Tutush's voice; for another, he knew little about his visitor except that Tutush was the agent of the Minister, who in turn was Master Ali's patron. In Nisapur they said that he collected turquoises and delicate porcelain and old manuscripts. But he admitted to no title and no one seemed to remember where he lived.

When they had discussed the progress of Master Ali's book for an hour, Tutush asked to see a graduate student named Omar Khayyam. Master Ali pricked up his ears, and watched the two men covertly after Omar had appeared from the garden and had seated himself on a corner of the rug with his arms folded politely in his sleeves.

"In the last moon," observed Tutush casually, "we had tidings from the east. Romanus Diogenes, the Emperor of the Christians, was seized by his own people and blinded so savagely that he died of his hurt."

Omar looked up with a frown. It reminded him of the battle and his milk-brother.

"It is strange," added Tutush, glancing at him, "that this king was spared by our lord the Sultan — may he live forever — and then slain by his own people. Who could have foreseen that?" And he looked at Omar.

"No one," observed Omar, since an answer seemed to be expected of him.

After Omar had been dismissed from the presence of the elder men, Tutush sat in silence for the first time, playing with an ivory rosary at his throat as if musing upon something.

"Believest thou," he asked idly, "in the science of prognostication? Is it possible, O Master, to foretell what is to be?"

But Master Ali was not to be drawn into such an admission, least of all by the secret agent of his powerful patron.

"By my faith, all is possible with Allah. As for me, my poor knowledge is devoted to the perfection of my book."

Tutush murmured assent. "Suppose that a certain man should predict three things. Would it be possible — I seek the answer from thy wisdom — for all three to come to pass by accident?"

This touched the old teacher's instinct. "Two such happenings might transpire by chance, but never three. Yet where would a soothsayer be found foolish enough to make a three-fold prediction?"

"Where? Hast thou not among thy disciples at least one who is skilled in casting horoscopes? This young student to whom I spoke just now?"

"Omar?" Master Ali's beard quivered curiously, as if he had almost smiled. "That is the last thing I would expect him to do."

"My soul! Then what does he do?"

"He solves cubic equations as easily as thou, O my

40

guest, dost slip those ivory beads upon the silk string."

"Eh? Then he hath skill of a kind? What does he in his leisure?"

"He reads all my books; he wanders along the desert's edge alone; he eats pomegranates and plays at backgammon, and says little enough. And," Master Ali added, not without malice, "he makes calculations that he hides in a chest."

"Why should a young man walk about the desert? *Wallah* — our blood, O Mirror of Wisdom, is thin and cool after these many years, but the blood of a youngling is hot. Perhaps this student hath found him a comely maid in your wilderness."

"There is no woman about, other than the laundry hags who are full of fleas and warts."

Tutush grimaced. He seemed to be irresolute as a man who seeks a garden and finds himself in an empty courtyard, and still looks for the garden. The beads of the rosary clicked under his fingers and his brown eyes snapped. "Eh, eh. This is a strange student, with his skill and his silence. Perhaps his gift is of the Invisible — or, it may be, of a devil. Now it behooves One whom thou knowest to ascertain if any here makes secret practice of the arts of a devil. Wilt thou test this skill of the man of the Tentmakers to the utmost, and discover what he seeks to do with it? Write down his skill upon paper, seal it and put it in his hand to bring to me in one month, upon Friday-eve at the Takin gate of Nisapur. Now —" Tutush rose with a sigh and a smile "— I who gather knowledge must go from thy house where knowledge is. Alas, I have caused thee much trouble."

When his guest had departed, Master Ali spent some time in cogitation. It seemed strange that he had been asked to observe Omar, whom he had suspected of observing him. And stranger still that he should be asked to write down the result. He wondered if the two had not exchanged some hidden message under his very nose, and he wondered why Omar should have been summoned to Nisapur. Master Ali saw everything with the eyes of suspicion.

Yet at the end of the month Master Ali had not succeeded in ferreting out Omar's secret. He could not understand why his pupil was indifferent to routine algebra and still eager to solve new problems. Certainly he seemed to depend upon no occult aid. Omar worked things out by mathematical formulas of his own. That was all — but not enough to satisfy the master's jealous curiosity.

In the last evening he tried to surprise Omar into confession, as he had tried before in the matter of the cubes.

"When wilt thou return to the Arranger of the World?" he asked casually.

Nizam al Mulk, the Arranger of the World, was the great Minister of the Sultan Alp Arslan, a power in the land, and the patron of Master Ali as well as Tutush.

"Return? I have never seen him."

"Then in the name of Allah, why art thou here?"

Omar explained that he had come to study. After the death of his father, Omar had made his home at the house of his milk-brother Rahim. But when he had returned from the war, Rahim's family had treated the foster son as a person of ill-omen — as if by Rahim's death Omar had forfeited his right to be in their house. They had taken Zoë from him to sell as a slave in the bazaar.

After that it had been unbearable to wander in the streets of Nisapur where he had made merry with Rahim, so he had sought the house of the distinguished teacher, hoping to bury himself in fresh work.

"And what is that work to be?" Master Ali pursued. "By what gate wilt thou leave the academy to enter the work of the world?

"But first," he suggested, "consider how wisdom hath been brought into this small world. The great wisdom hath been revealed by Prophets, who were never taught, but who had natural insight into that other world, the Invisible.

"The Prophets are the first among bearers of wisdom. The second are the Philosophers, who from study of the revelations of the Prophets and from acquired mastery of the sciences may explain to common men what would be otherwise hidden from them.

"First in order of time among the supreme Prophets was Moses, second was Jesus the Nazarene, and third was our lord Muhammad. That is sure. As to the Philosophers, different opinions are held. Alas for my ignorance I can only say that Plato and Aristotle and then our master Avicenna have woven the

42

thread of wisdom into the warp of our poor minds.

"After the Philosophers come the Poets. Now the skill of a Poet is a dangerous skill, because his task is to excite the imagination, thereby making a great thing appear small, or a small thing great. By arousing anger of love, exultation or disgust, he causes the accomplishment of great things and petty things in this world.

"Since he stirs the imagination and cannot clarify the understanding, the art of a Poet is baser than the ability of a Philosopher. What poet's scribbling hath outlived the life of the singer?

"Whereas," Master Ali concluded, "the fruit of the labor of the mathematician never dies. He alone attains demonstrable truth, and he builds the solitary bridge from the unknown to the known. As algebra is the noblest branch of mathematics, I hope thou wilt devote thy skill to commenting upon the algebraic equations of the third degree."

Omar was stirred by the interest of the aged master. "I meant —" he searched for words to make clear his thoughts — "there are other problems, if only our wisdom could solve them. If we could measure the courses of the stars —"

"Of the *stars?* But that is Astrology, which seeketh to determine the influence of the planets upon human affairs."

"Yet the problems are the same."

"Sayest thou, O my pupil, that the problems of my book are like to the problems of the King's astrologer? That is folly — I regret to hear it spoken."

"Yet the truth of one differs not from the truth of the other, if it could be reached."

Master Ali sighed, and bethought him. "My son, thou art over young for such vain desires. In time thou wilt learn infallibly that what is demonstrated by one art is not the product of another. If the King's astrologer confined himself to the truth of mathematics —" Amazingly, Master Ali's beard quivered, a guttural sound emerged from his throat, and he laughed. Instantly ashamed of his lapse, he added gravely, "I think that our minds are divided. I wished — I would have given much to have you pursue your studies through the gate of Mathematics. That is the only bridge from the known to the unknown. Well, tomorrow I will give thee a letter to take to Nisapur where, it may be, thou wilt find a patron. May thy journey be pleasant!"

Omar lingered when he had risen. There was so much he wanted to confide in the aged master, and so little that he could say. He felt that another door had been closed to him.

When he had gone, Master Ali took up a pen and a sheet of rare, white paper.

> "It is apparent to me," he wrote, "that my pupil Omar Khayyam is already equal in ability to Master Ustad of Baghdad. He hath a secret by which he reaches the solution of all problems, but what it is I know not. It is impossible to say what he will do with it because he is as yet the slave of his imagination.
>
> "I pray that this knowledge of his, fostered in my house, may be acceptable to the Patron whom thou knowest, who hath no more devoted slave than the unworthy ALI"

After the ink dried, he folded the paper and sealed the folds carefully with melted wax upon which he pressed his seal. He addressed the missive to the Lord Tutush at the Takin gate of Nisapur.

The alley of the sweetmeat sellers, between the Takin gate and the mosque of the Sons of Hussayn at Friday-eve before the hour of prayer.

OMAR SAT ON HIS HEELS in the alley. In one hand he held a small iron spit, still hot from the fire. From the spit he drew pieces of crisp broiled mutton and bits of garlic. These he wrapped up in strips of bread torn from the slab on his knee, and ate with relish.

He was very hungry because he had come afoot since sunrise from the edge of the salt desert, without stopping. Most of the way he had sat on a donkey belonging to the men of a camel train bringing in baskets of salt. Talking with the camel men and listening to their songs, he had not minded the glare of the sun.

Such a day's journey, pressing against the wind, always

44

filled the son of Ibrahim with exultation. From his seat in the alley he could watch the last arrivals from the plain passing through the Takin archway — a trotting cavalcade of donkeys, two dervishes followed by a stray sheep, a creaking cart weighed down with wet clay for the potters' wheels, and a train of stately dromedaries, their heads swaying in unison with the massive bales they carried on either side.

"Eh," observed the keeper of the *kebab* shop, "from Samarkand. Every day now more and more come in from Samarkand road."

"And what," asked Omar, "do they bring?"

"Only Allah knoweth! Elephant ivory, silk for our looms, musk, ambergris, the new clear glass, fine bronze, rhubarb. There is nothing they do not bring."

"Except such *kebabs* as this." Omar smiled, handing back the empty spit. He felt in his girdle and brought out three copper coins.

"Mashallah! The praise to Allah, that our sheep are fat." The shopkeeper was pleased. "Hi, son of a worthless father — sleepy one, seest not that the young master is athirst? Bring water!"

A boy stood by them with a large brass urn strapped to his shoulder. He had been listening to the voice of a teller of tales seated in front of a fruit shop. Now he turned and drew a china cup from his girdle. Tilting the urn, he filled the cup and handed it to Omar who drank gratefully. When the cup had been filled a second time he poured water over his fingers and wiped them on a cloth the boy offered him.

"In the name of God," the boy muttered.

Omar gave him a small coin and the *kebab* seller exclaimed aloud upon the greed of the water sellers who would not quench a believer's thirst without money.

"And what of a believer's hunger?" asked Omar, amused.

"Oho, find me a man who will give me a sheep for alms — ay, and charcoal for the fire, and a boy to turn the irons, then could I give meat with an open hand." He wagged his head sagely. "But perhaps thou art a pilgrim, going to the shrine at Meshed?" Feeling for the three copper coins, he hesitated. The young student looked like an Arab of both pride and temper, but he wore a single camel-hair *abba* and he carried a small woven saddle bag. None the less, his words —

"I know not," said Omar, "whither I go."

He was content to feel himself part of the throng passing through the alley of the sweetmeat sellers to the entrance of the adjoining mosque. It being the eve of Friday, many were on their way to pray.

The heat of the sun had left the alley. Half-naked boys with waterskins sprinkled the dust. The voice of the blind teller of tales rose above the shuffling of slippered feet — something about lovers who sickened when they were snatched from their enchanted garden.

A slender figure paused before Omar, and moved on more slowly. He looked up into a girl's dark eyes, above the folds of a veil. There was something familiar about the slant of the eyes at the corners, and a brown curl that escaped the veil. Omar started, thinking of Zoë. Hastily he got to his feet with his package of papers and books, and followed the girl who had looked back.

The *kebab* seller loosed his coins with a sigh of relief. "He is no pilgrim," he muttered, and then aloud, *"Ahai*, who hungers? Who would have clean meat, no gristle or leavings? Here are *kebabs!"*

The distant voice of the caller-to-prayer floated down from the minaret. "Come to prayer. Come to prayer . . . to the house of praise . . . there is no God but God. . . ."

Kneeling and rising and kneeling again, Omar went through the familiar motions. Lights glimmered from the glass sconces just over his head, and a strange echo came down from the roof of the mosque. All about him garments rustled and voices murmured in unison.

When he rose to go out with the crowd, his eyes searched the group of women. The girl of the blue head veil was behind the others, walking beside the bulky figure of a servant. Out in the courtyard she put on her slippers carelessly, so that after a few paces one of them fell off.

She ran back and stooped to put the slipper on, within arm's reach of Omar. Above the shuffling of feet he heard her whisper.

"O son of Ibrahim, there were no roses on my birthday."

Before he could answer she had slipped away, to walk sedately by the servant again, her eyes on the ground. Then he remembered Yasmi the child who had given him a rose three years before.

When he left the alley of the sweetmeat sellers, he found the Takin gate closed and some Turkish spearmen standing guard. Dusk had settled down, and men were lighting the lamps in the shops.

"My soul! Khayyam, you make haste slowly."

The speaker, a round man in brilliant saffron silk, moved toward him on a sleek pony. Omar recognized Tutush, and drew out the letter Master Ali had given him to deliver. The plump stranger opened it at once, and leaned closer to a lamp to read it.

Tutush refolded the letter and tucked it into his girdle. He held out a silver *dirhem* to Omar. No one could have told if the missive pleased him or not. Yet Master Ali had hinted that this man who had visited the House of Wisdom might befriend Omar.

"Where is your home in Nisapur?" Tutush asked, fingering the beads of his rosary.

"I have no place, now, O friend of Khwaja Ali."

Tutush considered the youth's worn *abba* and the bag he carried. "Perhaps," he said as idly as if he were tossing a bit of bread to a dog, "I could find you protection in the house of a saddlemaker, if you could teach his eight children to read the Koran, that blessed book. Eh?"

The tone and the glance were sheer insolence, and Omar's temper rose.

"Give that protection to some *khoja's* lad who hath a bit of schooling, O Protector of the Poor. Have I leave to go?"

"Assuredly." Tutush reined his horse away indifferently, pausing presently to toss a coin into the bowl of a pock-marked beggar who stirred in his rags to croak *"Ya hu ya hak."*

"Follow that youth in the brown cloak," he whispered, so that none but the beggar could hear. "Watch what he does, and leave him not until thou knowest his abiding place."

"I obey," the answering whisper came. The beggar took up the coin, yawned noisily and shuffled off as if his day had ended with the largesse from the noble.

Omar, a shadow moving through loitering shadows, snuffed the odors of wood smoke and dung and wet cotton cloth and frying onions with a relish. What if that fat Tutush had looked down his nose at him? He had a couple of *dirhems* in his girdle, and for a while he would be his own master. He would go back to his old lodging and sleep in the roof shed with the sweet grass. Surely, if he told them some news of the world, the good people there would set food before him. If only Rahim were here!

In the Street of the Booksellers he stopped by the familiar fountain. The girl, who had been standing there idly with a water jar, bent over the basin holding the mouth of the jar under the trickle of water. Omar seated himself on the rock beside her, although now that he had come, she seemed to take no notice of him.

"Yasmi," he whispered.

In the near-darkness beneath the plane tree her eyes, from between the edges of the veil, sought his. Impatiently she brushed a wisp of hair from her forehead, and he heard her swift light breathing. Yasmi was there in the darkness, a new Yasmi, veiled and silent and scented with rose-water. The water ran from the jar's lip down the side, and she did not stir. She had grown taller and her bare arm gleamed white beside him.

"Yasmi," he whispered clumsily, "for whom art thou waiting here?"

She started as if he had struck her. "O fool," she cried, "great, ponderous fool — I wait for no one!"

Letting the jar slip from her fingers she turned and vanished up the street. She ran madly, because she had waited for every day of three years, watching and assuring herself that Omar would return.

From the trunk of the plane tree a figure in rags limped closer, peering into the face of the man on the rock.

"In the name of the Compassionate," the beggar whined, "give to the poor!"

Noon on the river by the cypresses of the burying place above Nisapur.

EVEN AMONG the tumbled graves of the cemetery the

flowers had pushed their way, making a magic carpet above the bones of the dead. And the sun, the warm sun, shone upon the yellow headstones leaning this way and that, some of them bearing the round turbans of men carved in the stone, others bearing a knot of flowers or nothing at all — these were the graves of women.

Under the dark cypress trees gathered the veiled women, their heads close together, their lips moving in talk. They sat about the graves in circles, only half-heeding the young children sprawled in the grass.

It was Friday, the day of peace, when the women came in long processions to the cemetery, to mourn. They found it more interesting to talk. Some of the older girls moved restlessly from circle to circle, and slipped away into the cypresses when they were not noticed. No men ventured within the cemetery during this time of the women's mourning. Still, there were paths near by along the river, and friendly clumps of willows where lovers awaited them.

Yasmi had wandered far off. She lay outstretched on a hillock, watching the pigeons that circled over her head. These pigeons had their home in the half-ruined wall that surrounded the girl. The wall had no roof, because it was only a barrier about the great tower that rose within it.

The tower had been built originally for a watch post to overlook the river and the plain beyond the cemetery; but in these last years of peace the tower had been abandoned to the pigeons and to chance wanderers like Omar who had frequented it at night to study the stars.

"*Ai-a*," Yasmi murmured, "why did I come?"

Her thoughts darted forth heedlessly as the pigeons that circled against the sun. She had planned very carefully what she would do at such a time, copying her sister in casting bewitching glances and speaking provocative words to the man at her side — until the man would lose his very senses in desire for her. But her hands trembled in the long sleeves of the Friday gown, and her words tumbled out without meaning.

And the man at her side had been silent such a long time. There was a hunger in his eyes.

"Eh, say," she insisted.

"What shall I say, little Yasmi?" Omar did not so much as

turn his head, but he was conscious of the girl's white throat, the darkness of her lips and shadowed eyes.

"Have you not been to the war and seen the Sultan? And — and many other girls in many towns? What else did you see? Tell me!"

Fleetingly Omar thought of Zoë and the long Khorasan road.

"It was nothing," he said suddenly. *"W'allah,* we moved about like pawns upon a chessboard, and then we were back in our boxes again. Who can tell anything about a battle?"

Yasmi remembered as if from a great age the conquering amir of the white horse with swordsmen at his tail who would take her away to the pleasure kiosk with its swans.

"What will you do in Nisapur?" she asked curiously.

"Who knows?"

"Are you going away again?"

Omar shook his head. He did not want to go away, or to think about anything except Yasmi who had changed in these years from a grave child to a lovely and disturbing woman. And yet she had not changed. With his chin on his arm, his dark face intent, he watched the tiny people moving back from the cypresses of the cemetery to the distant gates of the city.

"They say," persisted the girl, "you were the favored disciple of the Mirror of Wisdom, and now you are like to be a master."

It did not surprise Omar that she had heard such talk, for the Street of the Booksellers knew the gossip of the Academy.

"And I say," he smiled, "that I have no place to work, no protector, nor anything of my own. The dervish hath his tricks and the teacher hath his living, but what have I?"

Yasmi snuggled down into the grass pleasantly. If he were really a beggar, then he would not be taken away from her. So much the better. "Instead of being wise —" the words slipped from her lips — "thou art more foolish than Ahmed the soothsayer who gets much silver for reading the stars. He has an *abba* of silk and a black slave. . . . Look, the last of the women are turning back. Surely, I must go!"

But when he laid his hand upon her wrist she did not rise. The pigeons were perched in crannies of the tower, leaving the sky empty. "There is the moon," she said, pointing, "and now I must go."

"Soon there will be a star between the horns of that new moon."

"Nay, I shall not see it." A laugh rippled from her. "Thou alone, perched in this great tower of thine, wilt see it — and all the other stars. Are you not afraid of the ghosts that come up from the burying place, to sit in their shrouds?"

"Nay, they are friendly ghosts. They bring me astrolabes and star lanterns and teach me what the Chaldeans knew."

Her eyes widened in sudden fright. Men had said that Omar possessed a strange wisdom, by which mysteries were revealed to him, and perhaps he did talk with the spirits of the dead.

"But how dost thou speak — in the speech of the Chaldeans?"

"Nay, Yasmi, there is an angel of the Invisible who cometh to sit upon the wall. He explains all that is said, because the angels know all the tongues of the earth."

"That is a jest! It is wicked to jest about an angel. Do the ghosts really come?"

Closer to him she moved, staring down in fascination at the outlines of the cemetery, half hidden in the dusk. When Omar put his arm about her she trembled and tried to draw away. Her head sank lower and her eyes closed.

Against him he felt the throbbing of her heart, and he heard her breathless whisper. "I am afraid — I am afraid." The hunger that was in him found no words, but whisper answered whisper. Her hands stole up to his cheeks and pressed them. "Look at me!" But her eyes were closed.

The silver arc of the new moon grew light and a star winked within it. It looked as if it had been painted there on the curtain of the night sky. The strange hunger gnawed at Omar and thrills of pain ran through him — pain that ceased when he felt the quivering lips of the girl against his.

"Nay," she breathed, "it hurts — nay, I —"

Against the dark robe that he had taken from her, her shoulders gleamed white in the starlight. Her arms, clinging to his neck, drew him down to the warmth of her lips and the pulsing of her breast, and the white flame of her love that answered his hunger, until she cried out and lay still.

In the tide of his passion he held her, until they lay there breathing deep and little conscious.

Long after the night prayer they wandered back to the city gate, heedless of the earth under their feet and of the crescent moon poised like a scimitar in the sky. And when they reached the fountain beneath the plane tree in the Street of the Booksellers, Yasmi clung to him, the tears wetting the veil beneath her eyes. "O heart of my heart, how can I leave thee?"

For Yasmi there was only the one love and the one beloved, and the pain of parting racked her body, although her lips murmured that surely, surely the angel of the Invisible must have visited that ruined tower, touching her soul and taking the very blood from her body.

Omar did not want to eat, and he could not sleep. Drowsiness filled his body, but his senses yearned toward the magic of the night. He smiled down at the beggar he found curled up by the gate of his dwelling — a beggar whom he had noticed hobbling about the street of late. His wandering feet led him down the familiar way to the park, where the watchmen with their round lanterns cried out the hours in the name of God. The intoxication in him made him aware of strange sights in the night — a shadow that slipped through the trees behind him toward the great pool around which homeless men slept, breathing heavily, unconscious of the magic of the night.

A white donkey drowsed beside a crooked man who crouched at the edge of the pool, hugging a cloak about him. The twain seemed to Omar to be the figures of a remembered dream — somewhere before now he had seen them, but not thus.

When Omar seated himself beside them, the hunchback pointed down at the water. "Oh, brother, the moon hath drowned herself in a sea of tears."

Omar looked down at the silver scimitar reflected upon the pool's surface. Grief had no meaning for him this night, but he was aware that the crooked man grieved.

"What dost thou?" he asked gently.

"I keep watch. See how these others have fallen into

sleep. Verily I watch the moon that is drowned, for that is the true moon, and the other in the sky is unchanged, unheeding. Yea, it will set and rise again, as if this night were as other nights."

"True — true," Omar said.

"These others —" the hunchback waved at the sleepers — "have a master, a new master. But I am Jafarak, and I have lost my master. *Aiwallah* — he was the sun of kindliness. *Aiwallah* — he was the protector of unfortunates. *Aiwallah* — he loved Jafarak, the misshapen, the most ignoble of his slaves. Now the sun is gone from the Land of the Sun, and protection from the faithful, and his beloved from Jafarak. *Aiwallah*, the Sultan Alp Arslan is slain!"

Omar, watching the wavering light on the water, barely heard. "I knew it not," he said.

"When all Nisapur knows it this day that we returned, bearing his body from Samarkand? It was his kismet. Look ye, my brother, he was firm and strong in his power, with an army about him. But who can escape his fate? A dog of a captive was brought before my master at Samarkand. Two strong swordbearers held the captive by the arms when he came before my master's face. Then the dog cried out a foul word at my Lord, who grew hot with the flame of anger. He took his bow, he took an arrow, and he motioned the swordbearers to stand away so that he could end the life of that dog with his shaft — he, the skilled one who hath never missed with his bow."

Jafarak wiped at his cheeks and sighed. "Yet that one shaft sped amiss, and the dog who had two knives hidden upon him leaped and stabbed my master thrice in the bowels, and after four days he went to the mercy of Allah."

"*Aman,*" murmured Omar. "Peace."

"I sit," Jafarak rocked himself back and forth, "I sit by the moon of tears, and I weep."

From a great distance, Omar looked into a black night, with Rahim's grave at his feet, and Rahim's servant rocking at his side.

"What is i' the pot comes to the ladle," quoth the pock-marked beggar. "Nay, he is young yet and his blood does not sleep o' nights. *Ahai*, I am weary for sleep. Have I not followed at his heels since last Friday-eve? Nay, he suspects nothing. In his present state he could not tell a bull from an ass."

"Is the girl a slave?" asked Tutush. "Is she wed?"

The beggar blinked shrewdly. "At night a cat looks like a sable. But she is no slave, although the women of her house drive her to carry burdens enough. She hath no husband — that is sure."

"And her name?"

"Yasmi they call her. The bathkeeper of the Glory of Hussayn hummam sayeth that Abu'l Zaid the cloth-merchant of Meshed hath made an offer for her to the owl-blind bookseller."

"Abu'l Zaid the merchant?"

"Yes, lord."

"He hath a large tent and many camels." Tutush meditated a moment while the mendicant, not having been paid for anything as yet, waited respectfully. "At least our young Tentmaker will not stray from the booksellers' street. Go thou and watch, until a message comes."

"On my head. Yet how will I know the messenger, O lord?"

"When he stirs thee — thus — with his foot, saying 'Where wanders the Tentmaker?' Until then, do not sleep so much. Other men have eyes to see, and ears to hear thy snores."

"*Ai-a*, thy slave hath not —"

Tutush turned away, dropping a handful of coppers in the dust, and the beggar made haste to gather them up before the hovering urchins could snatch them away. As he did so his lips moved, counting their value. "No more than a Baghdad *dirhem* — black money for white labor. Eh, water would not run out of that lordling's fist."

Yet because he feared Tutush — the more since he did not know whom the plump man served — he hastened off to take his chosen place on the stone by the fountain beneath the plane tree.

From his post he beheld great activity around the gates of the academy. Long-beards came and went with their servants. Along the edge of the park below the street paused cavalcades of horsemen. All Nisapur was astir and speculating upon the

54

turn in the Wheel of Fortune. The Sultan was dead and even while the city mourned fittingly, preachers in the Friday mosque proclaimed the name of the new Sultan in their prayers — Malikshah, the young and comely, who had been known among the people as the Lion Cub.

Malikshah, whose beard scarcely covered his chin, who had hastened from his books and his tutors and his polo field, was now Protector of the Faith, King of the East and West, Lord of the World, and the amirs of the Land of the Sun* hastened to do him reverence.

All this the begger perceived with half an eye, because he was intent upon Omar and Yasmi. During the hours of daylight they were seldom visible, but after the curtain of dusk they met at the fountain — two shadows in the dusk, heedless of the hurrying footsteps around them.

Well for the girl, the beggar mused, that she was heavily veiled, a very twin to a half hundred others thronging the twilight to gossip and feast and watch the tumult of the Wheel of Fortune moving. Otherwise she would have been seen and known.

As to Omar, the beggar thought this tall scholar had lost both sight and hearing. Only at times did Omar remember to eat with the pilgrims, in the crowded courtyard of the Friday mosque. He drank at the fountain and he spoke to no one.

"Belike," the beggar thought enviously, "he is as drunk as if he emptied a whole wineskin down his gullet each evening. *Ai* — it costs him not one broken piaster."

It was the next day that a porter came and planted his slippered toes in the beggar's ribs.

"O Father of the lice," the porter muttered, "where wandereth this mad Tentmaker of thine?"

"*Ya,* father of nothing at all — windbladder!" The beggar, glancing up evilly, perceived that this was only an under-servant without a staff. "Sired by a scavenger on a woman without a nose! Ditch-born, and bred —"

A second kick jarred him into fuming silence. "Who sent thee?" he grumbled.

* Khorasan.

"One that could hang thy carcase on the Castle gate for the crows to peck."

"Omar, called the Tentmaker, is down yonder in the bath of the Glory of Hussayn. Allah be witness, I would be there if I had but one *dirhem* to pay the keeper —"

By way of rewarding him the porter spat into his bowl and swaggered off, leaving the pockmarked one nearly speechless with rage. "May dogs litter on thy grave — may vultures strip thy bones — may the fires of the seven hells scorch thy thick hide!" he groaned.

Omar followed the porter to the first courtyard of the Castle where the armed retinues of a half-dozen nobles waited beside saddled horses. Here they found Tutush who was in a fever of impatience, crying out at sight of Omar and grasping him by the sleeve, to hasten in past guards and servitors — all of whom seemed to know the voluminous blue turban and the swaying rosary — to a small chamber, empty of furniture.

"My soul," he whispered, "it is past the hour appointed. Yet *he* hath not sent for thee as yet." Curiously, he glanced at Omar. "Knowest thou who hath summoned thee into his presence? Nizam al Mulk."

Omar's pulse quickened, and he felt more than a little amazed. Nizam al Mulk — the Arranger of the World — was the title of the man who had been Alp Arslan's Minister and who still held authority now that Malikshah, the son of the slain Sultan, had come to the throne. More than that, Nizam al Mulk was virtually dictator under the Sultan's authority. A learned and brilliant Persian, he had gathered into his hands by degrees the administration of everything except the army. It was a mystery why he should have sent for a scholar of the academy.

Tutush cast no light on the mystery. "Once," he said reflectively, "I dug into thee at the Takin gate the spur of arrogance. It was a test. By command of Nizam al Mulk I have had thee watched —"

Omar glanced down at him swiftly.

"— and guarded. Thou art young, and without heed. But now, at this moment thy destiny is in the balance. Nizam

56

himself will test thee. So give heed."

Omar heard without comprehending. It seemed purposeless — unless that Lion Cub who was now Sultan had asked for him. But the Lion Cub was remote in the shadows of the highway and Yasmi's eyes looked up at him, unveiled.

Suddenly a slave drew back a heavy curtain. The empty chamber was in reality only an alcove of the long audience hall with its huge rose carpet. Against the mid-wall sat a man of some sixty years, erect and busied with the papers upon the low tables at his knees. His thin brown beard, carefully combed, lay against the gray silk of his tunic. He spoke briefly to a group of men — handed the papers to one who seemed to be a secretary, and acknowledged their salaams of farewell as they all backed, bowing, toward the far door.

Tutush advanced with Omar. They paused once to make salaam and then knelt on the carpet before Nizam al Mulk.

For some seconds the eyes of the Minister from beneath shaggy brows considered Omar. Then he glanced over the sheets of paper in his fingers. "You are the son of Ibrahim of the Tentmakers, student in mathematics, disciple of Master Ali? When you were a boy you studied philosophy under the Sufi Imam Muaffak?"

He spoke in the crisp modulated voice of one who talks in public for long hours and is listened to. Tutush, who sat apart from Omar, said nothing whatever.

"Master Ali writes that you have a strange power. There is no power save from Allah. I wish to know one thing. Tell me by what divination you predicted to our Lord the Sultan, who was then prince, the fate of the battle of Malasgird and the double death of the Christian Caesar and our own lord, upon whom be blessing!"

Omar felt the blood rush to his face. If only he could think of some plausible story. But he suspected that the man with the austere eyes and the cold voice would brush aside any pretense.

"The truth —" he gulped. "Highness, it was a jest."

Nizam stirred impatiently. "What words are these? Explain yourself. It could not have been a jest."

"But it was." Omar felt sure of himself now. He was telling the thing as it happened. "Highness, I wandered that night through the camps and came to the one guarded by Turks. I did not understand much of their speech — did not realize that the young lord was the prince. The professors about him made a foolish mistake in pointing out the star Suhail. The whim came to me to voice a prophecy in their solemn manner. That was all."

"You are abrupt to the point of discourtesy." The Minister leaned back against his cushions. "How do you account for the fact that this — jesting prediction — foretold three events. Ay, the battle, and the deaths of two kings?"

Omar thought for a moment. "Highness, how can I account for it? Nothing happens except by the will of Allah, yet this happened."

"Nothing happens except by Allah's will. I wish I knew what led you to say that." Nizam spoke as if Omar had been a lifeless thing under examination. "Certain it is that you could not have known the day and the hour of the birth of the Roumi king; you could not have calculated the sign ascendant at his birth. How did you cast the horoscope of the Sultan Alp Arslan?"

Tutush blinked involuntarily, perceiving the snare beneath the casual words.

"I did not cast it," responded Omar.

"But you have skill enough to make such calculations?"

"Certainly. So have five hundred others."

"Perhaps." Nizam's brows knit. "But I have yet to hear of a three-fold prediction made by any other. And Master Ali believes you are gifted with a strange power."

Tutush, who had been ordered by Nizam to find out all that was to be known about Omar Khayyam, made an imperceptible sign of confirmation.

"Son of Ibrahim," demanded the Minister suddenly, "hast thou not heard that Malikshah hath asked for thee many times since the death of his father?"

"I had not heard."

Both men glanced at him, and Nizam seemed satisfied, although he made no comment. "Thou art young to appear as yet in the Presence," he mused. "And since thy prophecy was but — a jest — thou hast need to tread with caution upon the carpet of audience. I do not hide from thee that Malikshah would receive thee with favor; yet a word such as thou hast spoken to me in this room would cast thee into disgrace, if not into the torturer's hands. . . . What reward wouldst thou ask of the Sultan for that strange prophecy of thine?"

At the swift probe of the question Omar flushed. It seemed to him that his whim of that night had become a millstone hanging upon his neck. "What have I to do with the Court?" he cried. "I seek no reward."

This Nizam could not quite believe — he was too well schooled in the way of that same Court. Yet he saw his opportunity to impress this headstrong youth.

"I, the Minister, am the servant of Malikshah, and I will befriend thee — since thou seekest no reward. Wilt thou have Nizam for protector of thy body and patron of thy studies, O son of Ibrahim the Tentmaker?"

Gratitude to the grave man with the clear eyes flooded upon Omar. The door of the House of Wisdom had been closed to him, and he had tasted beggar's fare for these last days, when he had longed for a roof to shelter Yasmi.

"Ay, indeed!" he cried, his eyes shining.

"Then say, of what hast thou need?"

"An observatory. An astrolabe of Baghdad make three cubits in diameter. The star tables of Ptolemy —"

"What more? Say on."

"If your Highness will! A celestial globe of polished bronze, with horizontal ring. And a star lantern. If it were possible, a water clock accurate to the two-minute space."

Tutush raised his brows at this marshalling of instruments both rare and costly. But Nizam signed to him to write down the list.

"And where," he smiled, "shall this observatory be? On some lofty roof?"

"By the wisdom of your Highness," besought Omar all in a breath, "Nisapur hath been guarded from war, and the ancient watch towers stand deserted along the roads. Beyond the wall, overlooking the cemetery and the river, there is such a tower — I have used it of nights, often. Could it be granted me, with a good lock for the door, and — and some fair Bokhara carpets, with pillows and a Chinese screen, and a water jar of silver?"

"*Wallahi,*" exclaimed Nizam, surprised. "Astronomy, it seems, hath many needs I had not guessed. Still —" the compliment had pleased him, and he caught the sincerity in Omar's entreaty — "all this shall be given thee, upon one condition."

Omar cast himself forward and pressed the Minister's thin hand to his forehead.

"Upon condition," added Nizam, "that never to any living being wilt thou say that the prophecy at Malasgird was a jest."

"I shall not speak of it, Highness."

"If you do," put in Tutush blandly, "say that it was an inspiration of the moment."

"Ay," cried Omar happily, "as you will."

"Although," remarked Nizam good-humoredly, "thou hast remembered a screen of Cathayan make and a silver water jar, thou hast taken no thought of food or service. Here is a small purse of silver for the one and Tutush shall find thee a pair of servants."

It was true that Omar had not heeded such things. He took the embroidered purse in his hand curiously. Never before had he possessed money by the fistful. A subtle intoxication warmed him.

"When shall I have the tower?" he asked anxiously.

Nizam glanced at Tutush who pursed his lips. "By the afternoon prayer, tomorrow," said that individual obligingly.

And Omar sensed the magic that authority can work.

"The praise to Allah the Compassionate!" he cried, bending his forehead to the carpet. When Nizam said that he had leave to go, he sprang up, forgetting the silver and then hurrying back for it at a whisper from Tutush, who reminded him to salaam again at the door.

As soon as they were alone, Tutush bent toward Nizam. "O Sun of Benevolence, said I not that this youth is the proper instrument, already shaped to thy hand? Where in all Nisapur would we have found such another? Is he not made for the part — with his strange wisdom, his stranger habit of speaking the truth, his naïve ignorance of all but his star gazing — and that incredible prophecy to bear witness to him? My soul, he even swore to Master Ali that the King's astrologer must determine the *truth*."

Nizam did not smile. "I wish I knew his secret. . . . Yet he hides nothing."

"Nothing!" echoed the chief of Nizam's spies with satisfaction. "Every other word from his lips is Proof, and every other word is Truth. My soul!" he flicked the rosary with abandon. "I shall call him *Hujjrat 'l haqq* — Proof of the Truth. Clothe him in a master's robe, teach him to be a trifle mysterious, and above all silent, then present him to Malikshah, saying 'Here is Omar the Tentmaker, who prophesied at Malasgird — I have found him for the Majesty of Allah upon earth.' My sinful soul, it fits like a dancing girl's slipper."

"At the end," mused Nizam, "he bore himself like an unbridled colt, yet once I had the feeling that he would have defied us."

"La — la! The stripling's in love — when he has not the girl in his arms, he is thinking of her in his arms —"

He stopped abruptly, for Nizam's eyes had grown cold, and Nizam was a fanatic of orthodox Islam.

"Perhaps," observed the Minister, "his secret may be a gift of the Invisible. Such men know, without knowing how knowledge comes to them."

"True — true. 'With Allah are the keys of the unseen.' "

"I cannot reason otherwise than that his prophecy was a miracle."

"True — most true." Tutush, who did not believe in miracles, had no intention of confessing as much to his distinguished patron. But he fell to wondering what might come to pass if Omar — if Proof of the Truth — should learn to prophesy again, and the prophecy should come true. "It can't be done," he assured himself. "Omar himself confessed that it can't be done. But now old Nizam hath half convinced himself that it can be. *Ma'shallah m'shallah* — my head was never made for these purely intellectual problems."

He determined to send the pockmarked beggar elsewhere and to select a discreet man and wife, confidential spies, to be the servants of Omar's tower.

By the fountain in the Street of the Booksellers, Omar was whispering eagerly into Yasmi's small ear, while the girl made

61

pretense of filling a water jar.

"Oh, heart of my heart, at last and at last I have a place to shelter thee and a door of which I alone shall have the key. I shall have grapes soaked in wine for thy lips that are more fragrant than wine, and sweet cakes for thy hunger, and — oh, glory to the Compassionate — thyself beside me."

"But," she whispered, "it is a ruin."

"And the bread is only a little bread. But with thou beside me in this ruin I shall have more joy than the Sultan in his castle there."

The tower that became the House of the Stars, above the burial place on the river.

TUTUSH HAD KEPT his promise, as far as the tower itself was concerned. By nightfall the next day he had handed Omar the key of his new observatory. And for several days thereafter woodworkers and brickmakers had labored to repair the tower and its outer wall — making bricks of clay down by the river's edge and letting the sun dry them after they were placed.

It pleased Omar, who wished to have no one else in the tower when Yasmi visited it for the first time. He ordered the workmen to whitewash the walls of the tower's ground floor, and there he spread a large woven ground cloth. This was to be the reception chamber of his observatory.

On the second floor he put the finest of the rugs, and the lacquered Chinese screen with a dragon in raised gilt coiling over it. Here stood his sleeping quilt and the chests for his belongings, of carved sandalwood.

The third floor he left bare except for the low work tables and the pigeonhole cabinet for manuscripts. This would be the place of labor when the instruments came. Tutush had brought many books, the gift of Nizam al Mulk; but he explained that the instruments Omar desired would have to be sought in Baghdad.

Omar, however, had no inclination to work. He spent hours in the Nisapur bazaar buying things with his new silver coins. He bought rolls of white floss silk for a dress — for Yasmi would wear white within doors when she was at last his wife —

and porcelain jars of sugared fruits; he bought incense powder to burn, and a bronze griffin to burn it in; he bought an armlet of thin silver set with turquoise, the color of the clear sky.

"*Ai!*" cried Yasmi when the gifts were laid before her, "this is surely magic."

"Then thou art the sorceress, O Disturber of Hearts."

Yasmi clapped her hands softly, and made him clasp the armlet above her elbow. She examined the great carpet with breathless interest — for such things were new in the Land of the Sun — and she studied the gilt dragon even while Omar was brushing the soft hair back from her throat where the pulse leaped under his fingers. Such happiness was almost pain to Yasmi.

"There are many books in the chamber above," she observed. "Dost thou read them, all of them, when I am not here?"

She was afraid every time she left Omar — afraid of the silence and the time that would pass until she could sit beside him again. She wanted to know all that he did in the interval.

"Nay," he responded carelessly, "yet there is one little book of verses by a man of the desert. I have read that."

"Verses!" Yasmi knew the rhymed tales that the poets sang about ancient kings and horses and battles. "Has it any love in it?"

"Not so much as I have in the smallest corner of my heart." And he bent back her head until she was forced to look into his eyes, which always disturbed her after their meeting.

"*Ai,*" she whispered, "I am ashamed."

"Thou art more lovely than Shirin whom the djinn-maidens adorned."

"Was that in the book?"

"*Wallahi,* ay, in the book of my heart."

"And what is in mine?" She smiled expectantly.

"In thine? Oh, cruelty and disdain that recks little of Omar's suffering!"

It seemed to Yasmi that her lover was gifted with unearthly powers. Surely he knew the wisdom of ancient men, and he could read the verses that poets sang — he could utter words more musical than any verses. Now he had made the ruined tower into a paradise for her and for her alone. But all that mattered little, so long as Omar was Omar, and loved her. She sighed with the sheer delight of it, and threw herself back on the cushions, her arms widespread, her dark eyes half closed seeking and holding his. "Say, am I cruel?" The whisper parted her lips. "Say, am I disdainful?"

And he threw himself down upon her, seizing her in the intoxication that was near to faintness.

For the blood in Omar was Arab blood, kindled through centuries of life in the dry, heat-ridden air of the wastes wherein the struggle against the barren land and the wolf-like enemies had created men sensitive to every mood and still implacable as steel. His passion for Yasmi gripped him with terrifying intensity.

It seemed to her very important that the beloved tower should have a name. After all, the people of Nisapur said that ghosts foregathered there from the graves below. With her lover, Yasmi cared not a snap of her little fingers for wandering ghosts; but an old superstition made her want to give the tower a name. Yet when Omar suggested some, she laughed, because she had learned when he was jesting.

"Nay, it is not the Abode of Blessedness, nor the Chamber of the Houri. I tell thee, it is not. It is — it is —"

"The Visitation of the Angel."

"Certainly not." Yasmi believed implicitly that a good angel had alighted there to bestow love upon them, yet she shrank from speaking of that. "It is the House of the Stars. Surely, my heart's heart, thou canst read the stars and tell other men what their fare is to be?"

Omar glanced at her curiously. "I? Who says that?"

"Oh, it is said in the street, in the bath — that thou didst prophesy the throne for our lord Malikshah. Thou knowest."

Yasmi felt proud that her lover should be able to read the fate even of kings. Moreover, that must be his work here in the tower. Yasmi considered that astronomy began and ended with casting horoscopes.

"I know," Omar acknowledged reluctantly.

"Then it is true. And soon — perhaps by the end of the next moon — thou wilt have here the tools to point at the stars, and more silver, and then thou mayest come to my father with a name that is known and the price in thy hand to pay for me, and we can stand before the witnesses."

Omar regretted that he had spent all his money upon the things for Yasmi. But at that time he had not thought of anything else.

"Soon," he nodded. "But how can I have a price that is worthy —"

"Foolish," she chided him. "If thou art the astronomer of the great lord Nizam al Mulk, the people of my house will not bargain much about payment. I wish — I wish it were done, and I could dwell behind the curtain of thy house without ever going forth again." Her eyes became fixed. "I could not live unless that happens."

"Then stay," he cried.

"How can I?" Her lip quivered. "They say that a woman who is not wed is stolen, and that is ill. Perhaps I have been too happy, and now I shall pray in the mosque for the mercy of Allah because I had thought for nothing but this joy."

Omar's thoughts, however, did not incline him toward the mosque. Sunrise was too fair upon the green plain, sloping down to the dark cypresses of the cemetery, and the very cushions of his chamber brought to him the scent of Yasmi's body. When she did not appear the next day, he browsed restlessly through his books, his attention caught by the refrain of the book of verses — solitary quatrains scattered among the pages like flowers in the grass. On a blank leaf he traced words out of his own mind.

> *When Spring's bright magic on the meadow lies,*
> *With wine beside me I sit, to devise*
> *A love song to my houri. Call me a dog*
> *If I can spare a thought to Paradise.*

He thought this would please Yasmi, to have a *rubai* written for herself alone. How contentedly she would laugh, and how her eyes would sparkle as she fixed it in her memory to repeat to herself afterward. Still, he knew it was a poor enough *rubai*; he had only put down in words what was in his head, instead of making beautiful phrases about love.

Yasmi did not come the next day, nor the next.

Omar had waited for long hours by the fountain under the plane tree. He had sat within the gate of the mosque looking at every veiled figure of a woman that came and went. And he had not seen Yasmi.

In the afternoons he hurried back to his tower, certain that she must be there waiting for him, only to find the rooms empty. Then he assured himself that she must be ill — perhaps too ill to send a message. He regretted now that he had not accepted the servants Tutush had offered him — he did not know one woman to send to the house of the bookseller to secure tidings of Yasmi and perhaps a message for him.

He was passing through the bazaar on his way to the mosque when he encountered a familiar pockmarked face, and remembered the beggar who had haunted the Street of the Booksellers. But this time the beggar turned away quickly as if to escape notice.

"Eh, say." Omar caught his shoulder. "Hast thou seen — the one who talked with me by the fountain?"

The red-rimmed eyes blinked at him shrewdly. "That one. By my head, young master, I have not seen her, because she is gone."

Omar's lips moved. "Gone?"

The beggar, who could read faces, saw his chance for even greater profit than he had made already out of his watching. "Hss!" he whispered, drawing at Omar's sleeve. "I have heard — but I am weak with hunger, and in need."

Mechanically Omar felt in his girdle and discovered that he had not a single coin left. Impatiently he motioned the beggar to follow, while he sought out the booth of a moneylender he had known in his student days. It was a silent Bokharan who squatted behind small piles of coins — Greek byzants, Baghdad dirhems, and copper pieces of every shape, some even square or pierced with holes and strung together.

"Give me a gold dinar, Nasir Beg," Omar demanded, "until the next moon."

The moneylender felt in a heavy wallet. "It will be a silver dirhem for each moon," he began.

"Be quick!" Omar caught the gold piece and handed it to the beggar, drawing him out of the crowd. "What is it thou knowest? The truth — tell only the truth."

"May the head fall from my shoulders if I lie! Three — four days ago they beat that one thou knowest for not keeping to the women's quarters. I heard the mothers-of-other-girls say it at the fountain. The brother of the father of that one is now master of the house. Eh, eh! One stone is enough for a house full of glass. Very angry was the uncle, and then, on the second day, by Allah's will, came a second offer for her from the clothmerchant Abu'l Zaid. The uncle did not stop to boil tea, not he."

Omar said nothing, but his eyes were bleak.

"*Wallahi,*" said the beggar, "they sent for Abu'l Zaid, they sent for the *kadi* and the witnesses. My eyes saw them all arrive, with friends to eat the saffron rice and sweet sherbet of the wedding. They gave me little enough."

"And she — what of her?"

The beggar considered. "I heard a carpet spreader say to another that *she* had been seen weeping the night before, led back to the house by two men. Perhaps she ran away, perhaps she was afraid — young girls are wayward and ignorant. But Abu'l Zaid paid a good price, having heard of her beauty. He is a merchant with many tents in his *kafila* —"

The beggar stared, because Omar had turned away and was pushing through the crowd like a man who cannot see. The pockmarked one felt of the gold dinar, and rang it anxiously against a stone. It was good, it chimed true and clear. With a sigh he stowed it away beside the pieces of silver that he had got three days before from Yasmi's uncle, for whispering to him that Yasmi was visiting a strange youth in the tower by the cemetery.

At that time it had seemed to the beggar that he could make more profit from the uncle than from either Omar or Abu'l Zaid. Of course after that the uncle had kept Yasmi under close guard, while he sent hastily to the cloth merchant.

But now Omar had enriched him, miraculously, with a gold coin. The beggar edged over to the moneylender's stall.

"Eh," he ventured, "what imp of folly led thee to lend to that masterless student who dawdles about the streets?"

The Bokharan thrust a stalwart arm before his piled-up

money, and fingered the knife at his girdle. "Stand back, father of thieves. There is no chaff here for thy beak to pluck. Knowest not that Nizam al Mulk hath bestowed his favor upon this same student?"

"On the Tentmaker? *Ai!*" The beggar moaned, as if flesh and blood had been plucked from him. If he had known, he could have gleaned twice the reward from Omar himself by merely threatening to tell his secret. If he had only known!

That day Omar was half blind and half deaf to everything except the tumult within him. Somehow he made his way to the street and the fountain, and called for Yasmi's uncle. A strange man came, who cried out upon him angrily, and Yasmi's aged father appeared pale and uncertain among the books of the well-known shop.

"Art mad," demanded the uncle, "to speak of what is behind the veil? Are the women of this house cattle that thou shouldst name them?"

"Let him beware of himself," a woman's voice railed from behind a screen, "this thief who hath no shame! By Allah, when did ever a thief dare come back to the scene of his theft, making outcry? Let him be beaten upon the soles of his feet! Let him be bound and beaten! O vulture! O son of a burnt father!"

But the men of the house were too prudent to lay hand upon the Tentmaker in his mood of madness. So the women railed unappeased, until Omar turned and ran from the lashing of their voices. . . . It was hours later, when he had found Tutush sitting looking at turquoises in the corner of a gem shop, that he became a little quieter. He told his story in broken sentences and the master of the spies listened intently while pretending to examine the stones in his hand.

While he listened, Tutush pondered. If this girl had been a common singer or slave, he would have exerted himself to find her and restore her to Omar.

But she had entered the harem of a Moslem; she was the property of her husband, and Tutush knew that Nizam would be reluctant to interfere in a matter behind the curtain — the Moslem law that isolated women behind the curtain was not to be broken openly. Besides, Yasmi had caught Omar in the net of infatuation, and Tutush did not care to have his protege under one woman's influence. Several women were safe, even desirable as sources of information and persuasion, but one — especially a young thing as obsessed with love as he suspected Yasmi to be — might be dangerous. So, having made up his mind not to interfere, he assumed a horrified and sympathetic manner.

"Alas, that this should have happened. Had you come to me earlier — but a marriage before witnesses is a steel chain. Who can sever it? Let us take thought upon it, and I will see —"

"But you can find her. Surely you can find her. In the next moon I could have asked for her. She — she was afraid."

Tutush nodded and shook his head and clicked his tongue and sighed. "It is incredible. Who can avert his fate?"

"Find out where she is. If I could know!"

"Certainly, at once. Tonight I shall send men to the *serais* of the bazaar. Tomorrow they will tell you where she is to be found. Meanwhile stay with me."

When Tutush's agents appeared the next day they assured Omar that the cloth-merchant Abu'l Zaid of Meshed was not with his *kafila*. The man was no longer in Nisapur. With his new wife and a few servants he had left the city, but whether to the east or west or north or south they could not discover. There were many roads and ten thousand merchants. Soon, no doubt, Abu'l Zaid would reappear. Meanwhile they would watch every gate.

Tutush hoped this would content Omar. But he was mistaken. The Tentmaker went off to the bazaar in his old brown *abba;* he was seen talking to the camelmen of all the serais, and then he disappeared so completely that Tutush's spies could get no trace of him, although they tried much more diligently than they had sought for Abu'l Zaid.

Omar was wandering with the camelmen. He was rising before the dawn from fitful sleep and seeking among the tents, looking into the hostelries where the merchants gathered when the camels were loaded, kneeling and grunting. He was asking them for tidings of an Abu'l Zaid, a cloth-merchant from Meshed. Through the dust and the outcry he hastened, to ask his questions.

Driven by a fever of the mind more insistent than a fever of the body, he searched the rest houses of Meshed and the great shrine of the Imam where the pilgrims gathered. Long he sat by the pillar of Sebsevar, and in the caravan-serai of Bustan. Once he followed an Abu'l Zaid to the northern mountains and found him to be only a rugseller of the Bokhara market.

The gnawing pain in his body would not let him sleep. When he hurried, beside the long-striding laden camels he felt easier. Yasmi would be in pain. Perhaps the sweat of fever clotted her dark hair. She had been sold like a slave, and taken off like a slave. They had beaten her and cried out upon her, and now she was somewhere in this ever-moving throng upon the roads.

As the weeks passed, the brief moisture of spring was drawn out of the plain by the heat of the sun. The baked clay became hard as iron, and the green growth turned brown except along a stream's edge.

In his agony, it seemed to the Tentmaker that he must not tread upon the last flowers by the water's edge. The jasmine and the lilies belonged, in his mind, with Yasmi and the fresh moist grass of the Nisapur River. . . .

"Verily," said a dervish, "here is one afflicted of Allah."

The increasing heat and the fatigue of continuous travel brought on a fever that laid Omar prostrate for two weeks, until the ache left his limbs and he rose, too weak to set out again upon his feet. A kindly Meshedi offered to take him on donkey-back to his home.

Omar's head had cleared after the fever and he understood now that it was useless to wander from place to place in this fashion. It seemed to him that he had been trying to run away from a torment within himself. And certainly by now some word from Yasmi would have reached the tower, or Tutush's spies would have tidings for him. It was foolish to have gone away; but then for a while he had been too ill to return.

Late one afternoon he descended from the donkey at the road to the cemetery and said farewell to the man of Meshed. He climbed the hill to his tower expecting to find no one there. Instead he found new buildings standing within the wall, and two servants tending a freshly dug garden. Over the

70

parapet of the summit bronze instruments gleamed.

On the hill beside the observatory a wooden pillar had been erected. Omar stopped to look at this shaft, with a circle traced on the hard clay about its base. A bearded servant came and stood by him respectfully.

"Happy be your coming, O master," he said. "We have labored to make the place ready. Will it please the master to enter?"

Only his eyes expressed a burning curiosity at the apparition of this gaunt and dust-caked youth in a tattered cloak.

"Yes," said Omar.

He went up to his own chamber. Nothing had been touched there; the dragon still coiled on its screen; the pillows lay neatly piled against the head of the bed quilt. "Say thou," he asked the servant, "was there a message — a token — that came?"

The man nodded, smiling. "*Ya khwaja* — O master, every day a message came from the lord Tutush, to know if your honor had been pleased to return. Even now I have sent the boy to Nisapur to say that the arrival hath come to pass."

"And no other messenger asked for me? No letter?"

Yasmi could not write; still, she might have sent something by a letter writer in some bazaar.

"Nay," the servant said, "no other messenger, or letter."

Omar seated himself on the divan by the window, while the servant brought clean water in the silver water jar to bathe his feet, and a white-bearded man entered with ornate greetings saying that he was Mai'mun ibn Najib al-Wasiti, a mathematician of the Baghdad Nizamiyah — the academy for research founded in that city by the benevolent Nizam. Mai'mun peered in surprise at the silent Omar, saying in brittle dry words that he had brought with him a revised Ptolemaic table of the stars, and at Nizam's behest the great bronze celestial globe that had been used by Avicenna himself.

"Good," Omar responded absently. After the glare and the fever of the sunbaked plain, here was quiet, except for that dry voice.

Khwaja Mai'mun snorted and withdrew as stiffly as a stork that has stepped unaware upon a tortoise. But long after dark, when Omar paced the tower summit, the elder mathematician could not resist going up to where his treasure stood. Without taking visible heed of the voiceless Omar, he lighted the four oil lamps fixed to the stand of the globe. Then he adjusted the shades so that a soft, clear glow covered the upper half of the great globe.

Omar ceased his pacing, his eyes fastened on the polished bronze. Drawing closer he peered at it. A whole network of tiny patterns covered the points of the stars. The lines were finely drawn, and only a word or two among the constellations with obscure clusters marred the gossamer of the tracery. Many hands had worked at it — he could see where fresh lines crossed older incisions. Yes, here was the last point of the Dragon's tail, turning away from the Pole star. . . . Glancing from right to left at the horizon, he laid his hands on the globe, turning it slowly until it coincided with the sky above him. His hands groped for the horizon ring.

"It is set so," Ishak's dry voice observed. "And it is locked in this manner."

"Yes," said Omar. "Yes." Here he stood at last with the noble work of the masters under his hands, and a Baghdad mathematician vigilant as a sentry at his side, and the fruit of Avicenna's observation under his eyes. But he felt no elation.

"My soul!" quoth Tutush the next morning, "you look like a hermit returned from the animal kingdom. How we searched for you! How will you cover the fire of Nizam's anger with the water of explanation? No matter — it is all one now that you are here."

"While I was gone," Omar asked, "did Yasmi send a message, a token?"

"Ah, that girl." The master of the spies blinked amiably. "Why, I think not — nay, I heard of nothing."

"But your men have tidings?"

Tutush pursed his lips and shook his head regretfully. His agents, he said, had watched like hawks; they had seen nothing. "After all," he observed brightly, "there are other girls in the market — little Persian bulbuls — Chinese slaves from Samarkand-way, very well trained, oh, most skillful. But Nizam is angry. We must have work to show him —

some plan to lay before him."

Omar was silent. He had not the ghost of a plan in his head.

"Think, O youthful khwaja. Think of the plan you brought from the House of Wisdom. What was then in thy mind to accomplish, for a patron."

"A new calendar."

"What?"

"A new measure of time that will be accurate, instead of losing hours."

Tutush glanced at Omar apprehensively. The servants had said that the new master behaved strangely. "Now," he suggested, smiling, "lay the hand of pity on the ache of my ignorance. We have the moon, created by Allah to tell us by its first light when a new month begins. Surely no mortal can fashion an instrument to do better what the moon does. Eh — eh?"

"The Egyptians have done it; the Christians have done it." Omar frowned impatiently. "But that small wooden gnomon you have planted here is fit for children to play with. Come, and see."

With Khwaja Mai'mun bringing up the rear they went out to the slender wooden staff. Tutush had taken great pains in superintending its erection by carpenters from the Castle. He thought it cast a beautiful shadow on the carefully smoothed clay. But Omar uprooted it with one heave of his shoulders and cast it down the slope. A deep anger seemed to be burning in this man from the desert roads.

"That thing would bend in the wind and warp in the sun," he cried. "Are we children playing makebelieve? We need what the infidels had, a marble column five times the height of a man, true to a fingernail upon all sides and at the point. Then a base of mortar, and marble slabs to make a triangle for its shadow. The slabs must be ground, polished, bound together with copper and laid with a water level. Oh — send me artisans, and I will tell them what is needed."

"First," muttered Tutush, "I must have the consent of Nizam al Mulk. This thing hath the sound of an infidel monument to me —"

"It is the only way to measure a hair's breadth change in the shadow each day."

"A hair's breadth!" Tutush seized his turban and drew the attentive Khwaja Mai'mun aside, to ask in a whisper if the mathematician did not believe Omar befuddled.

"Fuddled he may be," the old man announced. "As to that I know not. But this I know —" his beard twitched in a faint semblance of a smile — "he is not foolish in making calculations. Such a gnomon as he describes would be accurate. I will even admit that if truly placed it would be as accurate as the great globe of Avicenna yonder."

Tutush carried his perplexity to Nizam who listened coldly enough to his tale — Omar's disappearance had interfered with his own plans — until he admitted that Khwaja Mai'mun approved of the scheme to measure time.

"A calendar," the minister of the Court mused. "It would go against tradition — ay, the Ulema would oppose it. The Christians have one calendar from the days of Rome, the Cathayans have their cycles, and we Persians had the Yazdigird era before the Moslem conquest. I think — I think it would be dangerous."

Closing his eyes, Tutush sighed. "First Omar tells me Time is only one, and now the Arranger of the World doth declare that there are four different Times. Alas, for my understanding."

"Four calendars," corrected Nizam. "And, Malikshah still asks for Omar."

"And now Omar asks for a water clock to measure a single minute in a whole day. What would he do with such a contrivance — watch it every livelong moment of waking and sleeping?"

"With it he could select the day in spring and autumn when day and night are equal to the minute. With the great gnomon he could determine the instant when the sun's shadow at noon is longest in the winter and shortest in the summer. And with his observation of the star movements he could revise both calculations. Yes, I understand what he would do."

"Inshallah," murmured Tutush. "God willing."

"If God wills. We could present Malikshah with a new calendar for his reign."

Nizam suddenly felt that this would be an excellent plan. It would please the Sultan to have a new calendar devised for

74

him alone; being doubly pleased with Omar, he might name the Tentmaker — as Nizam had anticipated from the first — astronomer to the King.

"I will see that he has his new water clock," he decided. "But what made him wander in that fashion?"

Tutush blinked and smiled. "Only God knows — thy servant is ignorant."

"Make it thy task to see that he wanders not again. For I have need of him."

When he had left Nizam's presence Tutush hastened to his own quarters. At times he retired from sight to a certain nook in an old warehouse overlooking the bazaar and the mosque courtyard, where he kept such belongings as he did not wish to be known to any one else. His hiding hole was guarded by a dumb Egyptian who posed as the owner of the rooms. And here, rooting into a chest with triple locks, Tutush drew out a slender armlet of silver set with turquoises the color of the clear sky.

It had been brought to the tower by a hunchback who had been the favorite jester of the late Sultan. This hunchback had said it was a token from a woman named Yasmi who had said that her heart was sickening and she was being carried far along the western roads to Aleppo.

"Only in this one respect is Omar stubborn," Tutush reflected. "And by my soul I will not have him starting off into the western world, to Aleppo. Not with Nizam's anger hanging over my head."

He decided that he would rid himself of this silver token. Thrusting it into his girdle, he closed the chest and descended to the alleys. When he came to a bevy of half-grown girls playing around a fountain, he took out the silver armlet and dropped it. Nor did he turn his head at the click of the metal against pebbles. There was silence behind him, and then soft exclamations followed by a swift pattering of bare feet. Tutush glanced back.

The fountain was deserted, and the silver armlet had vanished.

"Hide a stone among stones," he quoted, smiling, "and a grain of sand in the desert."

Nizam al Mulk was pleased with events at the observatory. Before the end of the hot season the water clock stood in the workroom. It had a small wheel that revolved sixty times in the hour, and a large wheel that turned once in the hour. A silver point like a spear point moved along a graduated scale bar exactly once between noon and noon, and then started on its return journey during the next day. At least Tutush thought it to be marvelously exact, but Khwaja Mai'mun informed him that after a year or so they would be able to determine its variation from true time. Tutush rejoined that it lacked a miniature horseman, to mark the days with his spear like the one in the Castle. And Mai'mun merely glanced at him, pityingly. Mathematicians, it seemed, did not need any tell-tale to remind them of the days.

At last all the instruments were in place, and four more observers selected. The new marble gnomon reared skyward, and even Mai'mun admitted that they were ready to begin their great task of measuring time anew. Mai'mun believed it would take seven years, while Omar thought it could be done in four or five.

"My soul!" cried Tutush. "We could build a palace in four or five weeks."

"Yes," said Omar, his dark eyes kindling, "and when your palace is broken dust with lizards dwelling there, our calendar will be unchanged."

"If I had a palace," laughed the plump master of the spies, "I would not care a whit what came to pass after I was laid among the lizards."

But he reported to Nizam that the six astronomers were ready, with their loins girded up and their wits whetted down to a sword's edge. Nizam thereupon arranged a little drama for the benefit of his lord the Sultan, the week before the autumn equinox — when Omar had told him they planned to begin observations.

That day Malikshah the Sultan was persuaded to visit the tower after his return from a gazelle hunt. By mid-afternoon the observatory looked like a pleasure pavilion, with carpets spread throughout the new garden and trays of sweetmeats and sherbet set out beneath the trees.

Thither came a deputation of professors from the academy,

with Master Ali the Algebraist — all in court robes — and a group of silent mullahs from the mosque who kept apart from the others. Nizam welcomed these mullahs with all ceremony and seated them nearest the silk-covered dais reserved for Malikshah, because they were members of the all-powerful religious Council and they brought with them no sympathy for scientific innovations. He whispered to Omar to be careful to stand behind them, and not to speak before them.

Omar had no desire to say anything. He felt like a spectator at another's party, and he was glad when the salutations ceased and all eyes turned toward a cavalcade of horsemen coming up the slope from the river.

Malikshah handed his hunting spear to a slave and dismounted at the gate before the anxious servants could spread a carpet for him. He was dusty and in high good humor after his long ride, but Omar thought that the young Sultan felt no real pleasure in meeting Nizam and the oldest of the mullahs. Malikshah's pale face was poised upon a corded neck; he moved with an animal's grace. He did not lift his hands or raise his voice when he spoke.

When Nizam led Omar forward to kneel before him, he looked intently at the young astronomer. "That is the man," he said in his low voice.

"The servant," Omar murmured the expected phrase, "of the Lord of the World."

"At a serai on the Khorasan road thou didst come to me, prophesying what was to be — although those about me had filled my ears with lying words. I have not forgotten. I will not forget. What wilt thou have, now, from my hand?"

For a moment the two contemplated each other — the warrior still isolated in his thoughts from the crowded world of Islam, still the child of the remote Kha Khan who had ruled an empire of cattle and men up there beyond the Roof of the World — and the scholar who still lived in his imagination. Malikshah was twenty years of age, Omar twenty-two.

"I ask to be taken into the service of the King."

"It is done." Malikshah smiled. "Now show me what thou hast made, here."

He was pleased with the lofty gnomon, and he studied the other instruments curiously. When the aged Mai'mun, rendered awkward by the throng and the presence of his king, tried to explain the great celestial globe, Malikshah turned to Omar and bade him explain. He liked the clear words of the young astronomer.

The chief of the mullahs, exasperated by the attention shown to the scientific instruments, came forward to assert his dignity.

"Give heed!" he cried. "It is written, *'Bend not in adoration to the sun or the moon, but bend in adoration before God who created them both, if ye would serve Him!'*"

A murmur of assent from the mullahs greeted the words of the Koran.

"Also," said Omar at once, "it is written, *'Among his signs are the night and the day, and the sun and the moon. Unless the signs be made clear, how shall we receive them?'*"

Malikshah said nothing. His grandsires, pagan Turks and barbaric, had been converted to Islam, and Malikshah was as devout as the fanatical Nizam. He took farewell ceremoniously of the oldest mullah, but he summoned Omar to his stirrup when he had mounted his horse.

"The Minister hath besought me," he remarked, "to grant thee the post of astronomer to the King. It is done. At the Council tomorrow a robe of honor shall be given thee." He leaned down impulsively, "Come and sit beside me often. By my head, I have need many times of a true sign."

And with a twist of the rein, a thudding of flashing hoofs, he was off down the slope with a long queue of officers and huntsmen strung out in his dust.

"It was ill done," remarked Nizam when next they were alone, "to match words with the mullahs of the Ulema. Now, it may be, they will put obstacles in thy path."

"But why, O Father? I have naught to do with the Ulema."

"Then see to it, Omar, that thou keepest thy foot from the skirt of their garments. Now, give heed, for there are things to be learned that thou knowest not as yet. First, thine appointment is recorded in the Council, and a yearly sum of twelve hundred *miskals* shall be paid thee without deduction of any tax."

Omar uttered an exclamation of astonishment. He had never thought of such a sum as this.

"And it may be," Nizam resumed unconcernedly, "that Malikshah will make other gifts to thee. I think thou art firm in his favor, but forget not that he is harsh as edged steel to one whom he distrusts; his spies are like bees in the honeycomb of the palace. His favor is the very pole of thy tent — without it, thy house would fall."

It seemed strange to Omar that even while he was buried in his work he must contend for the favor of the young monarch whom he liked heartily. Nizam guessed his thought.

"Thou hast my support," he added calmly, "and at present, God willing, no one dares oppose me openly. Yet I also have my labor —"

Deftly he revealed to Omar how he was weaving together the fabric of a new empire.

Until the coming of the Seljuk Turks three generations before, the lands of Islam had been divided, in war, following different princes. The Kalif himself, at Baghdad, enjoyed only a shadow of the authority once held by the great Haroun ar Raschid — until the Seljuk Turks with their victorious clans had been enlisted to aid him. Alp Arslan, that Valiant Lion, had swept like a storm wind from east to west, clearing Khorasan of its enemies and entering Baghdad in triumph, as the Sultan acknowledged by the Kalif.

Then Aleppo had been conquered and the holy cities of Mecca and Medinah taken into the new kingdom. The Christian Byzantines had been first harassed and then overwhelmed at Malasgird — which Omar had seen with his own eyes. Now the growing empire extended from Samarkand to within sight of the walls of Constantinople, and the last descendants of the Romans paid tribute to Malikshah. In time Nizam planned to marry a daughter of Malikshah to the present Kalif — Malikshah had already taken to wife a daughter of the Byzantine Emperor of Constantinople. So, the young king would be united by blood to the lawful head of Islam, and to the Roman Caesars.

"This winter," Nizam added thoughtfully, "the Sultan will march with his army to Aleppo, on the way to take Jerusalem, the third of the holy cities, from the Egyptian kalif — an upstart and a troublemaker."

It appeared miraculous to Omar that any man could plan

out with certainty that this city was to be taken, and that riverland added to the empire. Nizam summoned him daily to long talks — explaining the details of law enforcing and tax gathering, the mobilization of an army, and the network of spies — the eyes and ears of the Sultan throughout the region. He explained carefully Malikshah's whims — a passion for hunting, a disposition to treat women as unthinking slaves, a superstitious reliance on omens.

"Remember always," Nizam concluded, "that his grandfather was a barbarian. If — if Malikshah had beside him an astrologer in the pay of his enemies, he could be ruined by this very superstition."

Omar nodded. He could very well understand how a charlatan could ruin any man.

"So is thy task a weighty one," Nizam said slowly. "I think thou hast little belief in horoscopes or omens. As for me, I know only that the regular courses of the stars reveal the power of God. When Malikshah consults thee as to a fortunate hour for an undertaking, or a sign as to whether success or failure shall follow it, make thy calculations truly, by his horoscope. See that no other influences him — and remember that many will be watching every act of thine with jealous eyes."

Omar assented readily. He had learned what it was to have his movements watched by spies. And if Malikshah asked him to calculate the meaning of celestial signs, it would be simple enough to do just that, by the rules of astrology as ancient as the towers of the Chaldeans. What if such signs had no meaning? If Malikshah asked, they should be rendered him without adding or taking away.

"At times," Nizam went on carelessly, "he may beseech thee for a portent as to matters of state such as I have in my hands. Then thou wilt send a message to me, to learn what is best to answer. For such matters must be planned, and I alone can arrange them."

Omar glanced up curiously.

"Two hands," Nizam smiled — his mind apparently far off — "rule the empire, under God's will. One the hand of the king who wears a crown, and the other the hand of the minister who wears a turban. From the hand of the king come

80

war and conquest, punishment and reward; from the hand of the minister — order and taxation and the policy to be followed toward other peoples. I serve Malikshah truly, yet in the end my task is to build the foundation of a new state. . . . So I ask only that thou wilt consult me as to matters of policy. That is understood?"

"Verily," Omar assented. He felt that he had been taken into the confidence of this austere man who was wiser than Malikshah, or himself, or the dogmatic Ulema. Nizam's integrity was as firm as the marble pillar of the new gnomon.

"I have thy promise," Nizam responded quietly.

He gave no sign of the exultation he felt. Ever since the sudden death of Alp Arslan two years before, he had planned to find Omar, to attach the young scientist to himself and to have Omar appointed astrologer to Malikshah.

"Now," he confided in Tutush, "we can use his influence to sway Malikshah."

But Nizam's satisfaction vanished at Omar's first request. For a year, the new King's astronomer explained, the day-to-day observations at the tower would be routine work which Mai'mun and the others could manage without him. Meanwhile he wished to journey with Malikshah into the west — in fact, the Sultan had requested him to come.

Omar did not explain to Nizam that he had put the idea into the Sultan's head. Or that he would search the roads of the west for Yasmi. Now he had wealth, authority, servants, and the favor of a mighty monarch, and he intended to find the girl he sought.

Tutush smiled when he heard the tidings. "Nizam old boy," he said to himself, "once you damned me because this same Tentmaker slipped away from me like a vagabond; but in the very first moon of your guidance he goes off to the road again with the Sultan for a cup companion."

Aloud, he only said piously, "It was written."

PART III

The camp of Malikshah in the ruins of Babylon by the swift waters of the Euphrates. Early spring of the year 1075 in the calendar of the Christians.

THE FIRST SIGN of danger came to Omar while the army waited to be ferried across the Euphrates.

The pavilions of the nobles — and Omar traveled with the personal following of the Sultan — had been pitched in the palm groves along the shore. Behind them stretched the huge mound of broken brick walls and heaped-up sand that had been Babylon. Omar had spent some time wandering curiously over these ruins. The Sultan, however, when he was not hunting, liked to sit and watch the antics of dancers and conjurers.

A courtyard of the ruins had been hung with tapestries, and a flight of marble steps had been covered with a rug, to furnish a stage for the King and his mountebanks, and in the cool of one evening Omar was summoned thither.

"Eh, thou watcher of the stars," Milikshah greeted him pleasantly, "sit, and watch with me these dogs of mine."

A place was made for Omar on the carpet. Below him the dance was in full swing. The leader of the mountebanks made his own music; bells upon his shoulders chimed in cadence, while his fingers thrummed on a saddledrum bound to his waist. His loose hair whirled about his head as he wheeled and stamped in his dance.

Suddenly stopping, the chief performer flung himself down before Omar and crooked his hands for a reward, bright eyes peering up through the tangle of hair. Omar tossed him a coin which he spun expertly upon a finger tip, leering the while.

"Ai jagudar," he cried boldly. "Ha, magician! I can summon hailstones down, or raise a sandstorm up. I can read thy thoughts."

"Then," Omar smiled, "thou art a true magician."

"That I am, by the stars of the She Goat line, by the lightning that strikes the star gazer! Thou art thinking that I am a foul rogue, yet thou art afraid of me."

His eyes glared fixedly, and Malikshah, who had been amused, looked at him curiously.

"Now read my thoughts, star gazer. Nay, tell me but one thing — if thou canst."

His shaggy head wagging, he peered up at Omar. "Tell me," he said quickly, "by which gate I shall leave this court. See, there be four gates — east, south, west, and north. Four gates, and by which one shall I go forth, O prophet of the stars?"

Omar would have laughed aloud. But a glance at Malikshah startled him. The Sultan was leaning forward intently, as if the *luti* and the astronomer had been two swordsmen matched against each other.

"That is but a little thing," said Omar slowly, "and —"

"Thou hast great skill, men say. Now name the gate by which I go."

The other mountebanks gathered behind the speaker, and the Sultan's attendants edged closer to hear the better. Malikshah waited expectantly. Omar started to explain that the observation of the stars had nothing to do with such trickery; yet the words did not leave his lips. He realized that the Sultan was convinced that he could read this man's mind. No reasoning would alter Malikshah's blind superstition.

Too late he understood that this strolling player meant to trap him, and that he must match the other's trickery with wit, if he could.

"Bring me a pen — paper," he said impatiently.

A secretary came forward and knelt, to offer him a small roll of paper and a quill pen. Omar took them, while he pondered. To match trickery with trickery. So this was to be the duty of the astronomer to the King! Malikshah would not forget his failure. If only he could guess aright! . . . Four doors the fellow had said, east, south, west, and north. By which of the four — they were clearly to be seen, with spearmen lounging in all of them . . . but why had not the *luti* said "By which gate?"

Omar wrote a few words on the paper, folded it, and stood up. If the player practised mummery, so could he. Asking Malikshah's consent, he went to the side of the steps and raised the edge of a marble block that had been the pedestal of some statue. Slipping the folded paper beneath it, he returned to his sitting place. "Now go," he bade the *luti*.

The eyes of the *luti* gleamed. He cavorted a few paces, and ran toward the east gate, his bells chiming. Then he whirled with a shout of triumph and darted at the wall. Clutching the embroidered hanging, he drew it aside, revealing a small postern door in the wall.

"By this," he shouted, "I go."

And the curtain fell behind him. A subdued exclamation of surprise came from the spectators, and Malikshah motioned the secretary to bring him the paper Omar had placed beneath the stone.

When he had it in his hand, the Sultan opened it slowly. He looked at the written words, and put his hand to his lips.

" 'By the fifth door,' " he read aloud. "*Y'allah!* Truly didst thou read that one's thoughts, O Master of the Invisible."

Omar had merely guessed that if the fellow were so insistent on the four doors — and a lucky choice might hit upon the one to be chosen of the four — he knew of yet another door from the court, although none was to be seen. But Malikshah leaned over to pat his astronomer on the shoulder, calling him a second Avicenna, and bidding the secretary fill his mouth with gold.

At once that official took up the tray of gold and silver pieces always kept at the Sultan's elbow, and began to stuff the coins into Omar's mouth.

"As for that dog of a *luti*," added the Sultan, "fill his mouth with sand, until he is full. By God, he was impudent to our lord of wisdom."

Some of the attendants ran from the court, to obey. When Omar had been given leave to depart, with the gold coins carried in triumph on a tray by a slave, he found a crowd collected by one of the gates of the audience court.

In the center of the throng two guards held the struggling

luti by the arms. While another pried the vagabond's mouth open with a knife blade, a fourth Turk poured sand from a sack between his bleeding lips. The man's face grew darker, and at times he groaned terribly.

Omar turned away, nauseated, to seek his tent among the palms. Behind him, the slave turned also, holding high the gold — although he lingered to cast an avid glance over his shoulder.

That night Omar worked late with his books. He noticed that the black slave who had carried the tray of gold did not go to sleep at the threshold of the tent as usual. The man crouched there, muttering: A second shadow hung about the opening, and finally their whispering made the Tentmaker give up his calculation.

"*Ya Khwaja*," cried the slave, seeing him rise, "this is verily a night of magic. The dog is afraid."

The other man muttered assent, salaaming. "Give leave that we may sit at the feet of the Lord of Wisdom. We are afraid of the night."

Edging toward the lighted lamp, the strange servant explained that he had been walking through the ruins after the last prayer, when he had seen a light upon one of the mounds. It was not moonlight, because there was no moon, as the Lord of Wisdom well knew, but in this circle of radiance appeared the white figure of a man. Going closer the servant had beheld two other things — the half-naked body of a man moving like a snake over the ground, and an eagle, a giant brown eagle, stalking about the circle of light.

"*Wah!*" cried the black slave who had seen nothing, but who was full of the tale, "it was on the highest mound, and the white devil talked to the eagle while the other one changed into a snake. There was also a knife. *Ai-ai* — that is a strange magic, and we fear."

"The body that crawled," added the other importantly, "was the dead *luti* with sand in his belly. I heard — I heard thy name spoken, O Master of Wisdom. It is a great magic they make."

"Where?"

"Yonder — up — on the high mound."

"Get a torch," Omar said impatiently; "show me the way."

Probably the servant had seen someone burying the *luti* among the mounds — still, Omar had no desire to have two frightened natives at his feet all night. The servant obeyed reluctantly, and the negro followed so close to Omar that he stepped on his heels. After they left the camp, the guide turned up a path that wound among broken walls, until he came to what had once been a broad street. Here he stopped, pretending to shake the torch to make it burn brighter.

"It is only a little way, master," he whispered, "there on the right. Thy slave — thy slave will await —"

Omar took the torch from him and strode on. Instantly he heard behind him a pattering and a sliding of gravel. The two servants were fleeing from the ruins with all the speed of their legs. He went on alone, looking from side to side, until he became aware of a faint glow above him.

It was on the huge ruin called The Temple — Omar had examined it by day and he knew where to search for a path leading up the sand heaps. When he came out on the height, he made his way toward the glow that seemed to come from a cleft in the brick wall. Yet it was brighter than the light of an ordinary oil lamp, and the man seated within the circle rose as if he had been waiting there for Omar's coming.

"One departs," he said, "and another comes."

He was shorter than the Tentmaker, with heavy eyebrows and a curling beard. He had thrown a white Arab burnous over his broad shoulders, but he did not seem to be an Arab.

Nodding toward the ground, he drew Omar's attention to the body that lay there, the body of the *luti* with the handle of a dagger projecting from its ribs. "I made an end of his agony," said the stranger.

Omar looked at the bird of prey that flapped about the ground. This he had expected to be a vulture or falcon; but he knew that it was an eagle. When he approached it, the great bird came to rest, its translucent eyes glaring at him.

"My companion," said the stranger. "Yea, he joins me upon the high places — he comes down out of the sky."

"Who art thou?"

"A man of the mountains." When the stranger spoke, his long chin jutted forward, his brilliant eyes flashed. "A man of Ray."

The ancient city of Ray lay almost within the shadow of the mountains that surrounded the snow summit of Demavend, loftiest of the peaks in Persia. Although this man might be a Persian, he had the accent of Egypt and the modulated voice of one who is at home in many languages.

"Thou —" his eyes held Omar's — "art the Tentmaker, the astronomer of the King. And thou art not at peace — hence thou art here, in the temple of Istar, speaking with a student whom many believe to be mad. I am Hassan the son of Sabah."

"It is a strange burial you make, Hassan ibn Sabah."

"It is no burial. By Allah, I leave that for the slaves. My work is done."

"You are a student — do you study the dying?"

Hassan pondered, as if considering something new in his mind. He was little older than Omar, and the vitality of his corded throat and muscular hands was that of an animal. "I am searching for the truth," he said at last, "of many things. This dancer I found where he had been thrown outside a gate of the camp, for the dogs to worry. So I had him carried hither, to a high place where the birds of the sky will pick his bones clean. I stabbed him to loose him from his pain — yea, all the camp feared to do that, because Malikshah had given command only to fill the gibbering fool with sand. . . . But most of all, I seek friends, true friends. So I waited long, in Babylon."

Hassan did not speak like an orthodox Moslem, or a courtier of the King. It crossed Omar's mind that he had the assurance of Malikshah himself.

"Have you ever waited for a sign?" Hassan asked suddenly.

"Did you find a sign, O son of Sabah" — Omar turned the question with another — "in Babylon?"

"Yes, when this *luti* died. For now, in this minute, I have met a man who knows his mind, and who seeks proof of the truth. By Allah, if I could have Omar of the Tentmakers for a friend! I think it was written that this should be. . . . But the stars are setting. It is late, and I go down."

As he spoke the light left the mound abruptly. Hassan appeared not at all disturbed. Saying that he knew the labyrinth of the ruins as well as a priest knows a wineshop, he took Omar by the hand and started down the narrow path.

Once below the summit, they could see nothing, yet Hassan pressed on with his long strides. Behind them, Omar heard the flapping of wings, as if the giant bird were following. Then without word of farewell, Hassan let go his hand and vanished into the night. The sound of the wings trailed away and ceased.

In his own tent, Omar found the slaves waiting, crouched by the lighted lamp. For a while before sleeping he pondered the meeting with Hassan, who had a gift of the grotesque. Omar was aware that Hassan had expected him to come — the strange servant who brought the tale having vanished — and that in some way unknown to himself he had been put to a test.

The light, no doubt, had been a cleverly concealed lamp. But who, except for hunting gazelles, had ever tamed an eagle?

Omar asked many times for tidings of a Hassan ibn Sabah who spoke like an Egyptian, but he could find no one in the army who knew him.

The mount above the valley of the damned,
opposite the east wall of Jerusalem.

BY LITTLE THINGS Omar understood that Nizam watched over him from a distance. No strolling players were allowed to confront him again. A smiling Hindu letter writer visited his tent at hours when he was alone, and gossiped about affairs in Balkh or Samarkand — and all Malikshah's actions.

Most helpful of all, weekly letters came from Nizam himself. Apparently these letters gave tidings of Nizam's works: actually they discussed policies to be followed, dangers to be avoided. Thus, Omar came to understand how important it was for Malikshah's army to take possession of Jerusalem — Al Kuds, the Holy, Nizam called it. Malikshah had become the recognized champion of the Kalif of Baghdad, who was looked upon by millions of believers as the head of Islam. Already the Seljuk Turks had won the overlordship of the two holy cities, Mecca and Medinah. It was important to add the third, Jerusalem, to the empire, taking it from the unlawful rule of the schismatic kalif of Cairo.

For a similar reason, Malikshah ought to press the campaign

against the infidel Byzantines in the north. So long as the champion of Islam pursued the path of the *jihad*, the holy war, he would never lack for men to follow his banners ... new clans of Turkish riders had drifted down from the steppes, and Nizam was sending them west to join the army.

Thus Omar could understand clearly how Nizam wove together his threads, as a rugmaker sitting before the loom knotted together tiny bits of wool, meaningless in themselves, but part of the pattern of the whole rug.

When he was asked by Malikshah if the time were favorable for an advance against Jerusalem, he did not need to hesitate.

"Verily," he said, "this month will be favorable. The planet Mars stands close to thy Sign."

This was true, as Malikshah well knew; yet if Omar had objected — so utterly did the Sultan rely on his astronomer — Malikshah would have changed his plans.

The army was encamped then in the red plain of Aleppo, and Omar decided to ride south with the cavalry of Amir Aziz who was to occupy Jerusalem. He wanted to see the western sea — he had never beheld the shore of an ocean — and make the pilgrimage to the Farthest Mosque, which was in Jerusalem. So he explained to Malikshah. But he had searched the marketplace of Aleppo and all the towns upon the way without news of a cloth-merchant of Meshed who traveled with a young wife.

From Aleppo, he knew that many caravans went south to Damascus, thence to cross the desert to Egypt. He might find some trace of Yasmi on this southern road. ... If only he had Tutush's means of gathering crumbs of information!

"So thou wilt make the pilgrimage," Malikshah assented. "Then make a prayer of nine bowings for me at the *mihrab* of the Farthest Mosque."

It seemed to the young Turk most fitting that the Tentmaker, whose wisdom was a gift from God, should complete a pilgrimage during the course of the campaign. But he was careful to have Omar leave him a chart of fortunate and unfortunate days for the term of his absence. The three planets, Mars, Saturn, and Jupiter, were in conjunction in the sign of the Dragon, which was the sign ascendant at Malikshah's birth, so momentous events might be looked for.

And he gave his astronomer a *bimbashi* with an imperial standard and a dozen horsemen of Black Cathay from his own guard for escort during the journey.

To the *bimbashi*, he gave command never to allow Omar, asleep or awake, out of sight of two of his men.

So, go where he would, Omar was always attended by a pair of silent bowmen. (The *bimbashi* had informed his followers that the one who lost sight of Omar would lose his head.)

And Omar led them into unexpected bypaths. From Damascus, where he had haunted the marketplace, he led them up over the pine-clad shoulders of Lebanon past the gray summit of mighty Hermon with its snow cap gleaming against the sky, down to the waters of the sea.

Omar spent hours wandering along the sandy beaches, sniffing the air, examining the strange debris cast up at the water's edge.

This was the edge of the Great Sea, over which the Greeks and Romans had come in their galleys, to build ports of marble, now half ruined. Here was Tyre, stretching far out into the sea, and Sidon with its foundations visible beneath the water. He climbed the round height of Mount Carmel where strange Christian saints had lived and died.

Then he rode inland, to descend the steep slope to the sunken lake of Galilee. It seemed to the Cathayans as if there must be devils in this valley lying down in the maw of the earth, with its sulphur springs and mosaic pavement of a forgotten palace, and its sad, bearded men called Jews.

But when they ascended toward Jerusalem they found themselves in familiar surroundings. The Sultan's army, after its capture of the holy city, had pillaged the infidels upon the countryside. They rode through fields of trampled grain, beneath the blackened walls of monasteries that had been sacked and given to the torch. At times they saw groups of strange people — men without turbans and women unveiled, with children in their arms — laboring to make graves for heaps of bodies.

On the highroad they passed chains of slaves, bought by traders from the Turkish soldiers, on their way north to be sold at Damascus. And Omar remembered his return along the great Khorasan road with Zoe and Yarmak.

He halted at the camp of Malikshah's commander, the Amir Aziz, because the *bimbashi* insisted it would not be safe to stay at night within the walls of Jerusalem. But he went by daylight to visit the Moslem sanctuary, where there had been no fighting.

This marble enclosure, the Haram, he found thronged with mullahs who had accompanied the army and who had now taken possession of the Aksa mosque — the *imam* pronouncing the prayers from the pulpit in the names of the Kalif of Baghdad and Sultan Malikshah. The Egyptian preachers had fled the city. To escape the crowd, Omar entered the Dome of the Rock, where in the half darkness of the painted glass windows there was silence.

Here he knelt to pray with his hands upon the gray rock that was only less sacred than the black stone within the sanctuary of Mecca. The half-pagan Cathayans who followed at his heels knelt also, peering curiously at the marble piers of the dome and the gold mosaics.

When Omar rose, a low voice greeted him respectfully.

"Peace, to the seeker of salvation."

"And upon thee, the peace," he responded.

Hassan ibn Sabah stood at his elbow with another man. This time Hassan wore pilgrim dress and he chose to speak in Arabic which seemed to be as familiar to him as Persian.

"To Allah the praise," he smiled, "that I have found my friend again. Wilt thou know what is in this Dome of the Rock, more than the Rock itself?"

When he spoke, heads turned toward him. Hassan had the gift of holding attention, and the listeners drew closer as he explained that a mark upon the gray stone had been made by the foot of Muhammad the Prophet, when he ascended into heaven from this spot — and the holes along its edge had been made by the hand of the angel Gabriel, restraining the rock from rising after Muhammad. (The Cathayans pressed near with exclamations of wonder at this evidence of a manifest miracle.)

"Below," Hassan explained, "is the cavern where the waiting souls will gather at the Judgment Day. Follow me!"

Lighting a candle — he seemed to know where to find everything — he persuaded a mullah to let them descend into the grotto beneath the rock, where he pointed out in whispers certain signs of the supernatural. The Cathayans, grim in their leather armor and bronze helmets, grew afraid, but Hassan's companion, a stout man in a velvet kaftan, whispered to Omar that there would hardly be room here for more than a score of souls — unless, indeed, souls should become smaller than atoms.

Going up to the rotunda of the shrine, Hassan held his candle close to one of the piers.

"Long ago, soon after the ascension of our lord Muhammad," he said, "a Kalif of Islam caused these words to be written in gold. Behold!"

Omar made out an inscription in rectangular Kufic, which he could barely interpret; yet Hassan read it with ease:

> " *There is no God but God alone; he hath no partner. . . . Verily Jesus, the son of Mary, is the messenger of God. Then believe in God and his messengers, and do not say there are three Gods; forbear, and it will be better for you.'* "

Hassan touched Omar upon the arm. "Few have beheld these words since they were placed there; fewer have read them — and who has understood them? But thou wilt remember, and thou wilt understand, perhaps."

Then, as if growing impatient of the crowd that gathered around him, Hassan led the Tentmaker through the narrow streets of the city, pointing out things that would have escaped another's notice. The other man followed them silently, buried in his own thoughts.

"Here," explained Hassan, "is the arch and the window from which a Roman governor, Pontius Pilate, spoke to the priests of the Jews, when that same Nazarene — upon whom be peace — was delivered to the soldiery to be slain on a cross. Now the rock upon which that cross stood has been forgotten by the Christians."

Pushing past groups of armed Turks, arguing over piles of spoil in the streets, he smiled. "Thus it has always been with Jerusalem — its walls broken down, its people slain by the soldiers of the kings. Yea, in one lifetime during the last years of our lord Muhammad — upon whom be peace — the Persian Chosroes, egged on by the Jews, laid it waste, and the swords of the Roman emperor, Heraclitus, took it again. Then the Christians made great slaughter of the Jews. Our Kalif, Omar, entered the city in truce and shed no blood; he cleared the dung and rubbish from the rock — thou hast seen it — of the Haram which is the true rock of the temple of Solomon and David. But now these Turks have shed blood, in ignorance. Their day will be short, for the city will be taken from them by new enemies."

"By whom?" asked the other man.

Impatiently Hassan shook his head. "That lies behind the curtain of the Invisible. I say only that the Moslems will lose Jerusalem — ay, at the hand of a new and terrible foe — because they could not dwell here in peace. *'Believe in God and his messengers, and do not say that there are three Gods; forbear, and it will be better for you.'* But who will heed the written word of truth?"

Omar thought of Nizam weaving his fabric of empire, and of Malikshah. Neither of them had seen the bare-headed people burying their dead, or the blackened walls of monasteries. He felt stirred by Hassan's passionate words.

"We know," said the other man calmly, "that there are three Gods in the minds of men. One is the Yahweh of the Jews, one is the God of the Christians, one is the Allah of the Koran."

"Thrice," replied Hassan, "thou hast said 'one.' What if there be but one? What if the Jews, the Christians, and the Moslems have each a little insight toward the truth, that there is One greater than Allah —"

He broke off, with a quick glance about him, and motioned them to follow.

This time he led them back toward the Haram, but turned aside to go out through the gate that opened to the east. They walked through the tombstones of the Moslem cemetery that pressed against the very wall of the city.

The path wound down into a ravine of clay and bare stones where along the dry bed of a stream mounted archers were driving sheep and black goats pillaged from the countryside. Seeing that Omar wished to pass through the sheep, the two

Cathayans opened up a way, the archers hastening to aid them, at sight of the uniforms of the Sultan's guard.

"It seems," observed Hassan's companion, smiling, "that the cohorts of war are your servants."

He was a heavy man, who moved slowly upon his feet. His eyes were veined, wearied, and always guarded. His words, few and penetrating, revealed nothing of himself. Hassan called him Akroenos and said that he was grandfather of all the merchants.

"And why not?" Hassan inquired, "when the soldiers obey the Sultan's will, and Master Omar shapes the Sultan's will? He is not only court astrologer, he is prophet-in-particular to the beardless Seljuk emperor."

Akroenos looked at Omar without expression, as if weighing him in the scales of his mind. They were climbing a gravel slope, past a grove of gnarled olive trees. Almost hidden in the trees lay the body of a monk in its black robe with its arms outstretched in the form of a cross. The shaven head made a white spot against the gray stones.

" 'Tis some sanctuary of the Christians," Hassan remarked. "This that we climb, they call the Mount of Olives."

The level sun of the late afternoon beat against the bare hill. On the summit the three men sat in silence, while miniature human beings pressed up and down the ravine below them, and the setting sun gilded the distant Dome of the Rock.

Omar knew the name of this valley, the Wadi Jehannem, the Valley of the Damned. Here, the mullahs of Islam taught, the souls of the condemned would pass at the Judgment day when all souls would be weighed in the balance. There were queer-looking tombs on the slope beneath him, already dark in shadow. The sun had become a ball of fire, deepening into red, suspended above the domes of the holy city.

Beside them a line of old men moved slowly down into the valley. Each one grasped the garment or the shoulder of the one before him, as they shuffled and stumbled along, some with faces upraised, some with drooping heads, for they were blind.

"Look," cried Hassan suddenly, "there go we. Ay, we peer at the sky, we search the earth with blind eyes. If we could know the truth!"

"We know," murmured Akroenos, "enough."

Hassan stretched out his arms toward the setting sun, his eyes kindling. "Nay, we are the blind. We know only what is behind us. What do we hold sacred, but old stones and buried bones? What if there be a higher God than the Allah of the Koran?"

Rubbing his fingers through his beard, Akroenos was silent. Omar watched the ball of the sun take shape in the sunset fire. But a passion of speech had come upon the son of Sabah.

He believed in a new God, inaccessible to human reason. All religions in the past, he said, had been successive steps toward this final understanding. All, to a certain extent, had enlightened men. So with the six prophets — Adam, Noah, Abraham and Moses, Jesus and Muhammad. In time — no one could say when — there would appear a seventh, to reveal the final truth.

"And how," asked Akroenos calmly, "will he be known?"

"He will be known, because he hath been among us in the past, when the time was not arrived. He was the seventh imam of the race of Ali, heritor of the soul of Ali. To some he is known as the seventh imam, to others as the Veiled One. What matter the name? He is the Mahdi, whom we await, unknowing."

Behind the gray wall and the domes of the holy city, the ball of the sun sank out of sight. Akroenos sighed gently.

"The Mahdi," Hassan repeated. "He was here when the white hand of Moses stretched from the bough, and again when the breath of Jesus passed over this land. But he will come again."

A step sounded behind them. One of the Cathayan archers who had been dozing while the wise men talked, said diffidently that it was time to return to the camp. Hassan smiled, his mood changing.

"The soldier always has the last word — whether Roman or Turk."

That twilight upon the Mount of Olives remained fixed in Omar's mind long after he had washed and supped in his own tent. While he was musing, the merchant Akroenos appeared, followed by a boy who laid a roll of white floss silk at the feet of the Tentmaker.

"A small gift," Akroenos said, "as remembrance of our meeting. If a merchant can aid your Excellency —"

"What think ye of Hassan?"

Akroenos rubbed his grizzled beard. "Eh, he may be mad, yet he knows more than any other man I have met. There be many who believe in his message. Now I have heard that your Excellency seeks tidings — some word of it came to me in the caravanserai."

"Yes."

"It was told me that several months ago Abu'l Zaid, the cloth-merchant of Meshed who took another wife in Nisapur —" he glanced inquiringly at Omar.

"What of him?"

"He abode a while in Aleppo, and then departed to the north. It was several months ago."

Omar drew a deep breath. At least Yasmi had been at Aleppo, and he might come upon some trace of her.

"Thou hast brought me two gifts," he said gravely. "What wilt thou have, from my hand?"

"For myself, nothing," Akroenos hesitated. "But think kindly of Hassan, who would be your friend. A time may come when he will lay the hand of supplication upon the skirt of your generosity."

When the merchant had made his salaam and departed, a vagrant memory tugged at Omar's mind. Going to the box of Nizam's letters, he drew out one and reread it carefully. It contained a warning against a new sect of *mulahid,* impious ones. "They preach," the Minister had written in his precise hand, "the coming of a new Mahdi who will overthrow the thrones and the laws of Islam, and they assert that their religion will be the seventh and last of the world. They have been making secret appeals to the followers of the accursed one who called himself the Veiled One of Khorasan. These heretics wear white when they preach their abominable falsehoods — may Allah send them to everlasting torment."

Omar glanced at the roll of white silk, and smiled. No doubt Nizam would have cast it on the fire in righteous wrath, but he intended to have a cloak made out of it.

The court of the dervishes beside the tank of the Jami mosque of Aleppo, toward the hour of evening prayer.

WRAPPED IN WOOL, they sat at the edge of the water, six dervishes and one hunchback in rags. Leaning on a staff, the hunchback held out crooked hands to the passersby coming with swishing robes, carrying filled saddlebags or boxes. Veiled women chattered, their heads close together as they passed on, discussing what they had bought. Girls, stumbling, lugged infant brothers on their slender backs. A rich Arab astride a belled mule counted coins from one hand to the other.

"Affliction," wailed the hunchback, "affliction cries to mercy. Give — give in the name of God."

"Weeper!" muttered the Arab, dropping the coins into a stout sack, and stowing the sack in his girdle.

"Ya hu ya hak! Oh, mercy! Give, in Allah's name, to the sick."

"Then get thee to the mosque," muttered a mullah, whose skirts swept the dirt.

" 'Tis for another, who must have bread."

The mullah passed on, but a woman stopped, fumbling at the bundle she carried. "Here," she whispered, pulling out a slab of bread, "is it for a holy dervish who weeps mightily?" (The woman knew that all dervishes mourned the sins of the world.)

"It is for one," the cripple assented, taking the bread, "who hath wept tears of blood."

Mounted on a thoroughbred horse, and wearing a robe of honor heavy with silver thread, Omar the Tentmaker came by, from his afternoon audience with the Sultan.

"O Master!" cried the hunchback, running forward. His fingers trembled as they caught at the stirrup. "Stop. For two years and ten moons I sought your Excellency."

Looking down into the anxious face, Omar remembered the King's fool who had wept over the reflection of another moon, drowned in another pool. "Jafarak!" he cried, wondering at the rags of the man and the absence of the white donkey.

"Ay, Jafarak, who holds court with beggars and dervishes now. Why didst thou delay to send for me?"

"To send?"

"Verily, after I brought the silver armlet to thy house — I came back to Aleppo and I waited while moon followed moon. At first she grew stronger and at times she laughed. I would have taken her to thy house, but how can a fool travel with a beautiful girl upon the road? We had no money, and she said surely, surely you would come. Hast thou forgotten Yasmi?"

Omar caught his thin arm. "Is she here — now?"

"I beg for her." Jafarak held up the slab of bread. "Every evening she asks if perhaps there was some word of your Excellency's coming."

"Take me to her."

Tugging at the rein, Jafarak led the horse out of the throng into an alley. He hobbled along, still clutching the bread. "*Ai*, the demon of sickness hath gnawed at her," he said over his shoulder. "Will your nobility wait, just a little, while I tell her what Allah hath brought to pass?"

When Jafarak vanished into a doorway beside a coppersmith's forge, Omar dismounted, leaning his head against the shoulder of the horse, saying to himself that Yasmi was here in a room above this street. When Jafarak came down at last, the jester brushed a hand across his eyes, smiling and grimacing.

"Eh, eh, what a tempest. All this time she hath been like a dove, and now she flutters and cries for incense and henna stain and kohl blacking for her eyes, and bids me warn your Excellency that she hath no silk to wear —"

"Is she ready to see me? Can I go up?"

Feeling his way up dark stone stairs, he passed landings where dim figures peered at him and reached the roof where oranges and wet garments were piled. Beneath a shelter in one corner Yasmi lay on a stained quilt. He saw only her eyes.

"O heart of my heart," he whispered, kneeling beside her.

"How magnificent my lord — *ai*, I have not even a rug to offer —" her breath caught in her throat, until she threw her arms about his neck. He felt tears upon her hot cheeks.

When she grew quiet, pressed close to him, he saw how her face had thinned and paled. Only the scent of her hair and the dark eyes aswoon with love remained the same.

98

"I watched the stars come up and go down, when I was ill," she whispered, "because they were the same that stood over the House of the Stars. . . . Is the dragon still on the screen? Nay, life of my life, I can see all that is in the room — is it still the same?"

"It is the same. It is waiting."

Yasmi stirred and sighed contentedly. "I thought so. But I could not remember the names of the stars, except for Orion and Aldebaran. Jafarak told me some more; he said thou hast become great in the council of our lord the Sultan . . . how pretty the silver is on thy sleeve."

"I will find thee a robe of Cathayan silk, and embroidered slippers."

"And sugared ginger," she laughed. "Nay, we must have a feast, with sherbet to drink."

"The wine of thy lips!"

She touched his cheek shyly, and looked eagerly at his fine shagreen riding boots. "If only I were strong. My heart hurts when it pounds so. *Aiwallah*, thy slave hath lost her beauty!"

"Thou are more lovely, beloved."

Suddenly she laid her fingers on his lips, and heeded not that he kissed them. "Tell me — nay, look at me, do not speak — is there another wife who sleeps in my room in the House of the Stars?"

Omar shook his head and she relaxed. "I wondered many times. When my marriage was made a fire came into my brain and I tried to run away. When — when Abu'l Zaid took me in his arms, I grew sick. And then the fever came. . . . They made me travel in closed camel hampers, and sometimes I did not know where I went. It was in a serai among the mountains that I saw the cripple Jafarak, who pitied me. Then quickly I gave him the silver armlet with the turquoises, and bade him take the message to thee at Nisapur whither he was going. But here, in Aleppo my husband grew angry, saying that I mocked him. He went out and cried to witnesses that he divorced me, because I was ill, and evil minded. Then he went away —"

"I knew nothing of the armlet and the message," Omar whispered.

"But now I am a wife outcast —"

"Nay," Omar laughed, "thou art a wife to be. Shall I wait

another hour before making thee mine, O houri?"

"This houri hath neither beauty nor dowry."

Still, the warm blood flooded her cheeks, and her eyes brightened. Not until Omar had departed did she lie back upon the quilt, curled up to ease the pain that gnawed at her.

In the street below Omar took the rein from Jafarak. "I go to fetch a *kadi* and witnesses," he said, "for I take Yasmi to wife now, this evening. Go thou to the confectioners — take this purse — bring trays of sweet cakes and rice paste, bring sugared jellies, and sherbet and red wine. Call out to the people in this street to share in the festival. Fetch a lute player — find candles. Light up the roof, and by Allah stint not!"

He swung himself into the saddle and rode away, hardly seeing the curious faces and the outstretched hands of beggars.

"O believers!" cried Jafarak, lifting high the wallet. "O believers, the door of festivity is open. Come ye!"

Aware only of Yasmi in her veil, Omar heard the dry voice of the kadi who sat beside him on the carpet. ". . . daughter of a bookseller. And what is agreed as to her dowry? I said, what property doth she put into your hands?"

Behind the judge, a scribe wrote down the terms of the marriage.

"Property?" Omar smiled. "Hair dark as the storm wind, a waist slender as a young cypress, and a heart that knoweth naught but love. She needs no more. Make haste!"

"Write, 'Nothing of tangible value,'" the kadi instructed the scribe. "And now, what property doth your Excellency bestow upon her?"

"Everything — all that I have."

The kadi folded his arms doggedly. "Will your Excellency please consider that we must place reasonable terms on record? 'Everything' will not stand before the law. We must have itemization: how much land and where situated, what dwellings upon it, and water rights, rights of fishery, and assessed valuation. Then, furthermore, must we have some account of goods, whether rolls of cloth, kantaras of musk, white falcons, black fur, fish teeth suitable for ivory carving, how many camels and where, how many slaves and their approximate value —"

"Write 'Everything of tangible value,' " Omar instructed the scribe, over his shoulder.

The kadi lifted indignant hands. "By the beard of my father, and the holy Kiblah, who ever heard such words as these in a marriage contract? First, and before all, such a declaration infringes upon the dower rights of other wives, of whom it is written in the Book-to-be-read that the first four shall —"

Reaching behind him, Omar took a fistful of gold from the tray brought hither by one of his slaves. A coin at a time, he stuffed it between the bearded lips of the judge, then tossed a double handful of silver into the laps of the attentive witnesses. Taking the roll of paper from the scribe, he bade the witnesses sign, while Jafarak poured out a goblet of wine for the scribe. Into the wine Omar dropped a ring from his fingers, amid exclamations from the crowd watching the scene upon the carpet.

"Thy words are golden," he said to the kadi, who was coughing and bowing like a puppet in a show. "Never were such words. Now is the marriage finished. Let the lute be heard, ay, and the harp. And ye, watchers of blessedness, forget not Omar the Tentmaker who took his bride this night."

Rising, he strode to the parapet of the roof and looked down into the lighted street where the beggars, the dervishes and the children of the quarter had gathered. The lutist wailed a song of love, and the harp twanged.

"O men," he cried, "eat and be full! If the cakes fail, eat the confectioner! Is there one among ye who is not merry?"

"Nay, Master Omar. Merry we be."

"Is there one who is not full of rice and sweetmeats and sherbet?"

"By Allah, not one."

"Yet are ye ragged and woeful. This night ye may not be rich as the Tentmaker, for he is rich beyond all counting — nor intoxicated as the Tentmaker, for he hath tasted the wine of Paradise. Still, ye shall not want. Throw out the tray," he ordered his money bearer.

"Master — the tray?"

Taking the great brass salver from him, Omar emptied it into the alley. A roar of satisfaction rose from the crowd, while boys scrambled in the dust and women knelt down to clutch the bright coins.

Omar picked up Yasmi in his arms. She held to his neck, trembling. He carried her down to the street where a palanquin stood — borrowed in haste with two eunuchs to lend it prestige from his friend the Amir Aziz — and lowered her gently to the cushions.

"O my bride," he whispered, "never wilt thou know other arms than mine."

The eunuchs closed the lattice doors, and the crowd which had rubbed elbows with Yasmi for months when she had been an outcast among them, seeking food like themselves, fell back from the guarded chair of the bride of a great noble.

"*Ilhamdillah!*" they cried. "The praise be to God! . . . Praise for the Lord of Wisdom, who giveth gold! Praise for the Tentmaker!"

"Is there," cried a dervish, "a lord to the Lord Omar, from the Gates to Cathay?"

"Not one!" shouted another. "Peace be upon him."

"May his road be smooth!"

A little girl darted out from the crowd with a basket of rose petals which she strewed about the hoofs of Omar's charger.

"Whither," asked one of the eunuchs, "will the Favored of the Throne direct his steps?"

"To the bazaar."

"But the bazaar is closed. Since the late afternoon prayer, it hath been closed."

"Good," assented Omar. "Now, make haste."

Trotting beside the palanquin, which was borne on swiftly by the stalwart black slaves, the eunuch whispered to Jafarak that the Lord appeared to be drunk.

"Thou," grinned the jester, "wilt never be drunk with such wine."

At the closed gate of the nearest bazaar street they found a Turkish *onbashi* with a half-dozen spearmen and a round Chinese lantern. The officer stared at the imposing sedan and the robed eunuchs, and saluted Omar respectfully.

"Nay, lord," he objected, "this entrance is closed during

the hours of darkness by order of the Sultan."

"By favor of the Sultan," Omar smiled, "nothing is closed to me this night. Take this ring as token that I grant thee permission to open. Be quick!"

"Wilt thou keep the royal astrologer waiting?" cried Jafarak.

The commander-of-ten took the ring and shook his head dubiously. Still muttering, he swung open one half of the double gate, bidding his men stand back. As he did so, a bearded form topped by a black skull cap sidled forward and entered the vaulted bazaar street behind the palanquin.

Once inside, the man with a beard ran forward eagerly to grasp Omar's stirrup. *"Ya khwaja,"* he said softly, "this way, this way. Come to Zurrak's shop, to behold silks of Khoten and jade pendants from the temple troves. Zurrak hath Balas rubies set in pure gold, to match the hue of a houri's lips. Or will the Lord of Wisdom have lapis lazuli set in silver gilt? Alabaster cups, or crystal basins —"

A second bearded form hastened up, panting with hard running. "O Protector of the Poor, not that way! Zurrak's wares are made here, in the back shops of Aleppo. He knoweth not jade from soapstone. Come this way to the place of thy slave, Sholem of Antioch. This very week I have had a caravan of silks woven with gold thread, and damask sewn with pearls —"

Omar's stirrup was shaken by a third panting merchant. "What words are these, O infidel dogs? O dung from a dunghill, see'st not that the noble lord desires precious stones for the white throat of his bride? This way, Master, to the shop of thy slave Bastam the true-believer, the grandson of a Sayyid —"

"O ye thieves of the night," cried Omar, "I will buy everything, and the Sultan himself shall pay, for this night will never come again."

The hours of that night had passed like minutes. Lying near the entrance of his tent — for the midsummer heat was upon them — Omar played with Yasmi's hair, winding it about his fingers. Now, at last, he felt alive again. The sounds of the night had meaning. All the long hours of the last three years had vanished, like a vision rising from the sea and sinking into the sea.

The glimmer of starlight outlined Yasmi's white arm beneath him. He could see the coverlet rise and fall as she breathed. The dry scent of sage came from the sand outside.

"Thou hast not slept, my heart," he whispered.

He had waited long, but now that the cool breath of coming day was in the tent, he thought that she would not sleep.

Her dark head turned toward him. "I am too happy," she said faintly, "and it hurts. . . . I have been counting my happiness. Is it wrong to do that?"

"If it is wrong, then am I a sinner foredoomed."

"*Hssh.*" She laid her fingers on his lips. "I feel afraid. So many times have I waked when the stars were sinking, to long for thee, beloved. It — it is cruel, at such a time, to be alone in love. . . . Now am I afraid that something may take thee away."

"Nay, we will both go to Nisapur and the House of the Stars. I will ask the Sultan for leave to go."

"Canst thou do that?" She laughed a little. "I had forgotten — thou hast power. Alas, how many garments and precious things thou hast brought from the bazaar! I am no longer a beggar woman, it seems."

"Thou art my life. For three years my soul was sick."

"It is a very vigorous soul, meseems." She was silent, pondering. "How strange it is. I — I know not how such things be. But I have loved thee ever since thou camest to the Street of the Booksellers. At first — nay, I have wondered about this for many moons, my lover — I was afraid, and then I was frightened because I desired thee so. Didst thou know how much a word punished me, then? Of course not. . . . And after that I cared for nothing but thee. Thou wert with me, and I was enmeshed in magic of the djinn; thou wert absent, and my whole body ached."

The sky had turned from dark to gray, and the white side of a tent took shape.

"That is finished," Omar said.

He could see her eyes, the pallor of her skin. "All but the pain."

"What?" He lifted his head. "What saidest thou, my heart? Look, the sword of dawn rends the robe of night, and we have not slept. O sweetheart, grieve not. This is our dawn — quaff thou of it. It is ours, and all the dawns that come after will not be like this."

"Never like this," she smiled.

"And all who sleep, they know naught. See, the first shaft hath struck the Sultan's pavilion. Now I must bathe and wait upon him, so that we may depart from the camp."

"In just a little. Nay, life of my life, I must have yet another moment to count — and see the light fall upon thy face."

Omar was filled with a passion to be gone. Once Malikshah had given consent to his departure, he selected guards for the journey, and pack camels. While his slaves stowed his property in sacks, he found a closed litter that could be slung between two horses, for Yasmi. He even bought another white donkey for Jafarak.

"Thou shalt never beg again, Jafarak," he laughed.

The jester looked at him timidly. "Master, I beg thy remembrance of one thing. Thou art strong as Rustam, but Yasmi is weak. She is too weak for joy."

"Thou art a wise fool."

"Nay, I am a cripple. Only one who hath tasted anguish can know what a woman feels."

But at the setting forth, in the cool of that afternoon, when the great amirs came mounted, to escort Omar Khayyam a little upon his way, Jafarak pranced about on his donkey, leading the way.

"*Ahai*, lords," he cried back at them, "only a fool will ride before men of the sword."

That night Yasmi had a chill, and after it came the heat of fever. She would not touch food, but she smiled when Omar became anxious.

"I have had too much happiness, and surely it will pass."

On the second night they halted at the edge of the river Euphrates, their tents on the high bank in a fringe of tamarisk. In the morning, they could cross the river on the ferry barge that served the caravans. Yasmi lay under many covers, her cheeks flushed. Her eyes followed Omar when he moved about the tent, but it hurt her to turn her head.

"See how poor a wife I am," she whispered, "to lie at rest while my lord serves me. Show me some of the precious things for my wedding."

To amuse her, he took embroidered shawls and pearl-sewn veils to her couch, and she fingered them absently. He showed her a silver tiara with a single glittering sapphire.

"It is beautiful," she said, caressing it. "Tomorrow I will comb my hair and put it on.... Some time, will we have a kiosk on our river — not this one but our own — with white swans to swim around it?"

And then, in a moment, she was delirious. The sickness gripped her swiftly, darkening her eyes. Omar summoned Jafarak, who turned his head away after one glance.

"The plague," whispered the jester.

"Nay, not that," cried Omar. "See, it is a fever. Pray God that it will break before morning."

"There is nothing to do," Jafarak said, "but to pray."

Fires were lighted about the tent, to drive off the night chill. Their red reflection covered the cloth walls, while Yasmi tossed from side to side, moaning, heedless of Omar kneeling beside her or of the hunchback crouched in a corner murmuring without cessation the holy names of God. The fires sank to embers, and the shadows no longer danced on the walls.

Jafarak heard Omar's voice. "Light the lamp. She hath spoken, she hath touched me. The fever hath left her."

When he stood by them, shading the flame of the lamp with his hand, Yasmi lay still, her eyes closed. One hand was touching Omar's throat, and her lips were moving.

"My life . . . my life."

Then she turned her head away, and Jafarak waited, shading the light. He thought that Omar was listening, and this seemed strange to him, because Yasmi was not breathing. So he put the lamp down and touched Omar upon the shoulder.

The caravan men sat around the tent, by the ashes of the night's fires. A wind from the desert lifted the dust into a veil, through which shone the red ball of the sun. At times Jafarak came from the tent and sat with the men.

"Still, he speaks not," the jester said. "Still he bathes her closed eyes with rose-water."

"Barakullah," muttered a soldier, "and she dead of the plague."

"He knows that she is dead, because he is putting the bridal jewels upon her, and wrapping the veil about her breast."

"Better that he bellowed his grief and tore his garments as a man should in mourning."

"Ay, that he wept. But he will not. *Ai,* so white she lies upon the ground. So young she was — like the desert flower that blooms after the rain and withers i' the wind the next day."

The men moved uncomfortably. It seemed to them unwonted, to have dug so large a grave on the knoll under the wild pear tree, and to have carried the closed litter into the tent of death. Young girls died easily, in childbirth or sickness, and it was to be expected. It was written and who could alter what was written? They looked uneasily at the ferry waiting upon the shore.

"Belike," ventured one, "he is mad. Allah shields those who are afflicted."

"There are many girls," spoke up the communicative soldier. "Now for eighty pieces of silver at Baghdad —"

"Dog!" cried Jafarak, springing up. "What knowest thou, in thy kennel run, of love that burns and slays?"

He went back to the tent and disappeared within it. When he returned, it was to summon slaves to carry the litter to the grave at the hilltop.

"Be quick," he ordered. "For the master hath placed her in the litter, and the gifts beside her, with his own hands. He believes it is time for her to depart upon a journey. Be quick — for he lieth upon the ground —"

"We be no bearers of the dead!" cried the *chavadar* of the camels. "Allah — they will not take a corpse on that ferry —"

"Nay, to the grave. The grave is dug. Be quick!"

Driving the frightened men before him, Jafarak flung back the entrance flap of the tent. "O Master," he said, "we are ready to set out. Abide thou here for a little, until all is ready." And, whispering to the men, "Fools, make haste — he knows, he knows. Gently, or he will rouse and speak!"

Stumbling in their fear and haste, they carried the heavy litter out of the tent and up the wind-swept knoll. There they lowered it into the grave, and began with their hands and feet to thrust the dirt back upon it. The stones they saved to pile upon the mound. Then they ran down, to cluster about the tent, while the camel men got the bales upon their beasts, and the soldiers saddled their horses.

"Master," cried Jafarak, "we are ready. It is time."

When Omar stepped from the entrance, the end of his turban was drawn across his lips. For a while he looked curiously at the whirling dust and the gray river. Then he turned to the waiting men who huddled together. "Burn this tent," he ordered, "and get ye gone. Take the goods ye carry, and go. I know your faces. I will remember them. Let not one of ye come before my eyes again."

"Master," protested Jafarak.

"Get thee gone. See'st not that the plague is here?"

When the barge had poled its way across the river, and the men and beasts had disappeared over the far bank, Omar watched the smoke rising from the blackened débris of the tent. Rising in swirls, it darkened the dust veil until the red ball of the sun looked like a lantern hung in the sky.

The lantern hung over his head, and all the sky was draped with banners. And the gray earth was empty. As far as he could see, it was empty. The caravan had departed into nothingness, and the fire that had eaten up the tent was eating into his heart. Burning, burning, into his body. . . .

"Master," said the voice of Jafarak, "that is the river. That is death."

The water was a flood, rushing past his feet. Bits of clay slipped into it and vanished. Jafarak's arm pulled at Omar's shoulder, and after a while he sat down to look at the flood that eddied by.

The *clong-clong-clong* of camel bells came to his ears. A chain rattled and the line of a new caravan stalked down to the waiting place. The ferry barge poled back across the water. Strange men led down horses to drink.

"Nay, it is not the plague," Jafarak's voice went on. "H

hath no fever. It is in his mind — I did not know he would suffer so. Something to give him, lord? Hast thou the gift of tears?"

Another man moved and spoke. A heavy goblet touched Omar's hand, and he looked at it. It was filled with red wine.

"The river water," said the voice of Akroenos the merchant, "is not good to drink. But this is good."

The hands of Akroenos held the goblet to Omar's lips, and he drank a little. When the goblet was empty, Akroenos filled it again. The wine was heavy with spice. It cooled the fire in his brain. So he drank until the curtains in the sky descended upon him and the lantern of the sun vanished behind them.

The Pass of the Pilgrim Stones, in the mountains of the Kurds upon the road to Khorasan.

CAMEL BELLS CLONGED in his ears. A shaggy pony jogged under him, and Omar dozed, nodding in the saddle, because the heat of the earth rose like a living thing to meet him.

At night, when he could not sleep, he drank the wine of Akroenos, and he talked with the watchers of the beasts, who answered gently, believing him mad. When words failed, and the vision of Yasmi lying in her veil beneath the ground far back by the river's bank came into his mind, and the fire in his body began to burn again, he sought the wine jar and drank a little at a time until the stars wheeled across the sky.

"He is weak," Jafarak said to the merchant Akroenos.

"It is better to drink," responded Akroenos calmly, "than to thirst."

"But what of tomorrow, and the morrows to come?"

"When they come, we shall see."

Hearing this, Omar lifted himself on his pallet and looked at them. "If it were not for yesterday and tomorrow, how easy it would be to live." For a moment he pondered this. "If we could hold the veil of oblivion over yesterday, and if we would never draw the curtain from what is to be! If today never changed into something else!"

"Peace," murmured Jafarak. "The peace be upon thee."

They were climbing up from the desert floor into the red ravines of the Kurds, up the ancient road that the pilgrims had worn smooth. Late one afternoon the merchants of the caravan halted beside a cluster of gray stones, half the size of a man.

Some of these stones had the trace of a human face upon them, and all had the corners worn round by rolling. The merchants of the caravan dismounted and went to the stones. Pushing and tugging, they rolled the stones a short way down the road.

"Ekh," said Akroenos, "they aid the stones toward Mecca. For these are the pilgrim stones that have come from the mountains. Every Moslem helps them upon their journey. I remember, when I was a boy, that they stood in the marketplace of Shirin's Castle."

Jafarak went to look at the great stones. They were ordinary enough; still, it was strange to find them standing patiently on end along the road. He wondered how long it would take them to reach Baghdad and if they would ever find the way across the desert to Mecca. But the merchants prayed loud and long that evening, and those who had performed the great pilgrimage displayed talismans that they wore to guard them against the knives and arrows of robbers.

For in these hills the Kurds descended from their camps to raid the camel trains.

When the night had passed without disturbance, the merchants gave thanks to Allah and pushed the pilgrim stones again a little way. Then they demanded that the one who had wine in his camel bales remain behind the train that day.

"Let him follow, out of sight and hearing, for his trade is accursed and will bring evil upon us. Let him follow behind our dust."

In their zeal they sought out Akroenos. "Thou art a Greek, an unbeliever. Stay thou with the wine merchant."

"There is danger upon the road this day," the grizzled Akroenos protested, "and two men apart from the train may be set upon and slain for their horses. Besides, I am an Armenian and not a Greek."

"It is all the same. *Wallahi*, hast thou no shame — eater of pig's flesh? Wilt bring calamity upon us?"

Akroenos went off without another word — for the merchants of Baghdad were armed and they had their guards.

When they mounted, and the camel strings started up the road, Omar remained seated on one of the pilgrim stones by his pony.

"Come, Khwaja Omar," they called to him.

"Nay, ye go without the wine. But I will not."

" 'Tis folly," added Jafarak, "to linger behind. So that is the place for a fool. Ride on, ye of the pilgrimage performed!"

The wine merchant, a sallow man who complained much, did not protest when the caravan left him. He bade his men wait until it was out of sight. "What will befall this day is written," he said dully, "and what is written will come to pass. It hath come upon my head that I shall travel with a fool, a drunkard, and an Armenian."

When the last of the main caravan had disappeared over the head of the gorge, the wine merchant got his camels up, his servants picked up their staffs, and Jafarak mounted his donkey. They toiled up to the pass under a glaring sun.

While they were winding through the slopes on the summit, the camel men stopped the beasts. "Listen!" they exclaimed.

Echoes of clattering hoofs filled the gully. Somewhere men shouted, and the wine merchant cried that now the Kurds would come and slay them.

"Let us hide the beasts," said Akroenos. "We cannot escape by fleeing."

"No man," groaned the merchant, "can escape his kismet."

The herders, babbling with fright, forced the laden camels into a small gully, up the dry bed of a stream. The riders took shelter behind a growth of tamarisk.

On the skyline above them they beheld horsemen with lances moving at a trot. Shouting came from near at hand, with a scattering of gravel and a clatter of falling stones.

"Verily," whispered Jafarak, "these hills have given birth to men."

The Kurds seemed to be surrounding them, and exulting at the prospect of spoil. Akroenos shrugged his shoulders and waited impassively, until silence fell.

"They did not see us," cried the jester.

When quiet prevailed for another hour, the merchant consented to return to the trail. Apparently the Kurds had departed.

But at the first turning they reined in, amazed. Before them in a level space, lay the remnants of the main caravan. Ropes sacks and torn bales littered the ground. Except for a lame donkey and a few dogs all the animals of the Baghdad merchant had vanished, with the merchants themselves. A handful of camel men squatted disconsolately in the debris. That was all.

Not a weapon remained, and the armed guards had vanished into the air.

Akroenos, who had seen more than one raid of the hill tribes shook his head moodily. "Eh," he said, "the Kurds have attacked our brothers of Baghdad, and the caravan hath been plucked away like a plucked bird leaving these feathers behind Perhaps a few of our friends escaped by the speed of their horses but the rest are being taken for ransom — we heard the Kurds taking them away. Ay, and their guards served not to guard them — now they are slaves of the Kurds."

He had lost a valuable load of cloth in the raid, but at least he was free.

"Verily," said the wine merchant, sighing, "it was written."

But Omar laughed. "We have the wine. What did the merchants lose one half so precious as the stuff we bear?"

With the survivors of the caravan, and the dogs trailing behind, they hastened across the uplands. The fear of the Kurds drove them on, and they did not stop to make camp that night Under the scimitar of a tired old moon they pressed along the shoulders of the mountains, and Jafarak said to Akroenos that they looked like dead men seeking their graves.

"Yet is the Tentmaker pleased with this windy wasteland."

"Tell me," answered the Armenian, "one thing. Thou hast said that at his house, three years ago, thou didst seek him with tidings of this girl Yasmi. Yet Omar saith that he heard naught of her until he found thee among the dervishes at Aleppo."

"Allah be my witness, I sought him at the House of the Stars as thou sayest. He was gone from there. I left a token and a message."

"But it seems he had no message. How is that? Come, and tell him."

"Nay he broods upon the girl, and I am afraid."

"Of what? Come thou!" Akroenos urged his pony forward.

pulling at the halter of the jester's donkey until they were beside Omar. "Jafarak saith," he observed, "that three years ago he left a token and a message from Yasmi at your house. Hast thou forgotten?"

Omar reined in his horse and looked at them.

"I wondered, master," cried Jafarak, "why thou didst delay to send or seek, for month after month."

"What token was it? What message?"

"A silver armlet, set with turquoises. And the message was that Yasmi sickened; she was being carried to the west, to Aleppo."

The day that he had clasped that armlet on Yasmi's arm was clear in Omar's mind, and his hands clenched upon the reins. "I knew it not. To whom didst thou speak — to the servant? To the Khwaja Mai'mun?"

Jafarak shook his head. "It was a stout man; he wore a turban of sky-blue silk — a little man with a voice like a bell. He asked me if Yasmi were afflicted with a great sickness, and I said, yea — *Allah kerim* — that she wasted —"

"Be silent!" Omar turned his head away. "It was Tutush, and he lied to me. He lied."

When he said nothing more, Jafarak dropped back, and when they were out of hearing, he turned to the Armenian. "What was the worth of that? What gain to thee, master? Now he is like one with a blood feud."

"And that is worth a few camel loads of cloth."

Akroenos smiled but he would not explain his words, and Jafarak wondered in vain why the merchant should wish to have Omar at dagger's point with Tutush, the chief of Nizam's spies.

The House of the Stars by the river of Nisapur.

KHWAJA MAI'MUN IBN NAJIB AL-WASITI sat with his hands tucked in his sleeves in the audience room of the tower. Beside him sat Muzafar al Isfizari, from the observatory of Urghand. And along the wall sat their six assistants who had labored with them for a year.

On low tables before them lay sheets of paper with columns of figures, the fruit of their labor. In his dry voice Khwaja Mai'mun was explaining what they had accomplished, while he

113

wrestled with inward misgivings. Certainly, the sunburned young King's astronomer who had just returned from the west and who lay outstretched on cushions appeared to be drunk. At least his eyes wandered and he hummed gently to himself a song.

Moreover, behind Omar reclined a tattered jester and a dour graybeard in a black skullcap. Khwaja Mai'mun felt that he was losing dignity before his fellow mathematicians. A jester among scientists!

So he broke off his ceremonious report and observed with cold disapproval, "The sunrise of the vernal equinox failed to meet our established time by three hours and nine minutes."

"Three hours," responded Omar, "and nine minutes."

Mai'mun lowered his eyes. Secretly, he had hoped to strike so close to the sun's time in Omar's absence that credit for the calculation would be given him.

"Take a hammer," said Omar, "and break up the water clock."

"Nay, Excellency," put in Isfizari who had the observation of the clock in his hands, "it varies no more than seventeen minutes from the sun. Perhaps a little more, but —"

"O God," cried Omar, sitting up, "the clock is as true as that?"

"*Inshallah.*"

"And still, you are out with the sun six hours and eighteen minutes in the full year?"

"It was our fate —"

"Go! Find me boys from the bazaar to watch the instruments, and fair dancing girls of Isfahan to set down the hours! And ye were masters of mathematics! Oh, get ye gone, and teach school."

The assistants rose and left the chamber with Isfizari, only the aged Mai'mun remaining motionless.

"Master," observed Jafarak timidly, "six hours is little enough. Why, I would doze that long after eating a melon, and never think of it again."

"Then you should be an astronomer." Omar clapped his hands. "Bring wine — the dark wine of Shiraz from the sealed jar."

When the frightened servant had filled his goblet, he drank slowly. It seemed to Mai'mun that a devil had entered the

Tentmaker. But he would not leave his place without justifying himself. Akroenos looked on impassively. Omar sighed and took up one of the papers.

"Who made these records?"

"Excellency," said Mai'mun grimly, "I myself verified them. You will find no error."

Omar ran his eye down the figures and took up another sheet at random. Thoughtfully he studied it. "Thou dost swear the calculations are true, and Isfizari swears his clock is unvarying. One of ye hath failed — but which?"

"As for the clock, it serves well enough. Ay, after the first month we knew its variation." Mai'mun lifted his head stubbornly. " 'Tis easy to cry 'Be gone' yet I swear by the Kaaba and by my faith that my hand verified those findings."

"Using the Ptolemaic star tables?"

"Ay, surely."

"Corrected for the latitude of Nisapur? Ptolemy made his observations in Alexandria."

"As I have known. Will your Excellency see for himself? Here is the table of the last month."

Taking up a pen, Omar made a brief calculation and compared it with one of Mai'mun's. Then he frowned. "What is this? The correction is truly made. The stars do not vary, and the clock is known. Yet here one lags six hours behind the other. Hast thou an explanation, O man of Baghdad?"

Slowly Mai'mun shook his head. "It is hidden from me."

"Bring me the Ptolemaic tables."

When the great manuscript was spread before him, Omar took up the first sheet of Mai'mun's records. With bent head he set to work. Akroenos departed to his bed, and Jafarak curled up on a rug to sleep, but the old Mai'mun, watchful as an owl, waited silently. When the flame in the lamp flickered and sank, Mai'mun poured in more oil.

"It cannot be," Omar muttered once, and turned to a new sheet.

When the morning light came through the embrasure, and the lamp dimmed, he reached the end, and Mai'mun stirred expectantly.

"My figures are correct?" he croaked.

For a space Omar studied the first and last pages of the

Ptolemy manuscript. "Thy calculations are without error," he murmured. "And so the error of the six hours and eighteen minutes is constant. Thy first entry — there — is like the last, six hours and eighteen minutes away from the sun."

Mai'mun blinked, and assented. It must be so.

"The error is here." Omar laid his hand on the worn manuscript of Ptolemy.

"God forbid! What sayest thou? An error — after all these ages —" Mai'mun choked in his astonishment.

"A constant error, yes."

"But how — such an observer — and no one knew!"

"If we knew how, we could correct it." Omar smiled, his tired eyes thoughtful. "But the great Alexandrine hath been a long time in his grave."

Incredulity struggled with interest in the old man's face, for these star tables had been in use by the scientists of Islam for centuries. He would have expected to see the pillars of the great mosque of Nisapur sway as soon as suspect Ptolemy to be in error.

"*Ahai!*" he moaned, as the full significance of their discovery dawned on him. "Then is our work vain. Vain, the labor of Kharesmi, and all the others. Our tables of the fixed stars are false — false." Utterly confounded, he looked about the room. If the floor had risen to stand on end, he would not have felt surprise. But Omar's dark eyes were intent.

"Wait, Mai'mun — wait. The error is slight, it is constant. 'Tis here in the first column, as in the last. These observations were truly made, yet ever false, by so little." He sprang up, to stride across the room and stare out into the blinding sun. "False and true — it cannot be, but it is. If we could tear the veil from the mystery!"

Mai'mun could only shake his head. "With Allah are the keys of the unseen."

"If we could find the key — the key." Omar turned suddenly. "Tell me, are not Ptolemy's longitude and latitude correct?"

"Ay, verily — else we had not followed him these thirty generations."

"Then must he have known the key to his tables of the fixed stars. He could use the tables, but another — not knowing the key — would always fail, as we have failed." He struck his hand

116

upon the open manuscript. "With the key, we can use these tables, Mai'mun — we alone."

"If a hair divide the false from the true, still the false is not the true."

Omar stared at the scientist, and his face relaxed. "Mai'mun, old master, forgive me that I cried out upon thee. Thou hast shown me the key by which the false becomes the true. I see — I see."

"*Y'allah,* no man can see."

" 'Tis such a little key. Why didst thou correct these tables for the latitude of Nisapur?"

"Because —" the astronomer was past wondering — "the fixed stars as seen from Nisapur are seen from another angle at Alexandria, where Ptolemy worked."

"And what," asked Omar gently, "if they were not seen at Alexandria?"

"*Y'allah.* Was not Ptolemy's observatory at Alexandria?"

"Yes, and there is our error."

Mai'mun looked up wearily, without comprehension. "Art mad?" he muttered.

"Nay, for Ptolemy, working at Alexandria, did not make these tables. They were made by another, before his time, at another place. He used them, as we have used them — thinking them his — yet he knew this unknown master of the stars who made the tables. He knew! And so his calculations were true."

Mai'mun's eyes flashed, and then he shrank back. He saw the truth instantly, but it seemed to him as if Omar must have occult power, to discover what had been hidden for nine centuries. Had not Nizam himself said that Omar possessed a strange power?

"It must be so," he sighed. "Yet we will never know who made these tables, or where. Perhaps it was a Chaldean of Babylon, or a Hindu of India, or a Greek in the far west. Who knows?"

Unless they could discover where the observations had been made, the tables would be useless for exact work. Ptolemy had known, but that great Egyptian had kept the position of the unknown observer a secret.

"In a few days," said Omar quietly, "I will tell you the place of the observations. But now I will sleep."

As he limped from the tower to his own quarters, Mai'mun

had one hope. A man who could accomplish one miracle might effect another — although he had never known a miracle to happen in mathematics before. But when he found his assistants gathered disconsolately at his threshold, awaiting him after the morning prayer, the old astronomer lifted his head and thrust out his chin. It might even be said that he swaggered.

"O ye of the classrooms," he said proudly, "Khwaja Omar and I have found the error. After nine hundred years, I have discovered an error in the star tables of Ptolemy the Geographer. In a little while we will correct the error, but now I am weary and would sleep."

Gathering his *abba* about him, he passed into his chamber, having asserted his dignity, and for a moment there was stunned silence among the assistants.

"*La Allah il allah,*" whispered one, "Old Fusty hath become drunk also on that wine of Shiraz."

Except for the routine recording of the gnomon's shadow and the minutes of the sunrise and sunset by the water clock, no work was done in the House of the Stars for the following days, save by Omar, who never ceased his labor. He acted, the assistants decided, like one possessed — first calling for a copy of Ptolemy's geography from the library, then for a list of all the Greek astronomers of ancient days.

For the most part he worked in silence, covering sheet after sheet with figures that he passed on to Mai'mun to verify. Mai'mun, helpless when dealing with the unknown, looked on with the fascination of one observing an operation which he does not expect to be successful. He understood readily enough that Omar was seeking the proportion of the error, and using this proportion to calculate the probable distance of the unknown observatory north or south of Alexandria. This, however, could only be approximated — it finally proved to be about five degrees of latitude.

"The observatory of the unknown," Omar said at last, "lies close to five degrees north of Alexandria."

"But why not to the south?"

True, there seemed to be only deserts and unknown mountain ranges on the map south of that point, but Omar was not trusting to the map. He explained that many of the stars in the tables could not be seen from the earth's surface south of Alexandria.

"Nisapur itself lies along that line, to the north," Mai'mun observed, "Ay, and Aleppo, and Balkh and many others."

They decided the point they sought could not be in India; it must lie west of Nisapur. Omar believed it to be west of Aleppo, which made their search more difficult because they did not know so much about the ancient cities in the far west.

One evening when they were deep in their tests, a jovial voice saluted them from the entrance.

"Health to the two pillars of wisdom. May your labors be fruitful!"

Omar turned as if pricked by steel, but Mai'mun beheld only Tutush, smiling beneath his blue turban.

"What is this talk," Tutush observed, "in the bazaar of a great discovery made in the House of the Stars?"

Omar dropped his pen and stood up. "It was upon the road I made the discovery," he said calmly, "and it is thou who wilt enlighten me."

"Thy slave to command!" Tutush salaamed, "Thy friend of years — thou hast need only to ask of me."

"I ask in what place thou hast hidden the silver armlet with turquoise inlay. Ay, and the words that were spoken with it?"

The master of the spies had a quick mind, and he recalled the armlet that he had thrown to the girls by the fountain. For an instant he blinked, wondering by what magic the King's astronomer had found out anything about it.

"Ah, there are a million armlets with turquoises! The Khwaja is pleased to jest."

"There was one, given to thee by a jester with a message, in this room. The message thou didst hide from me, and now the death of a girl lieth upon my soul, never to be lifted." Omar's cheeks whitened, and his hands clenched at his girdle. "Now say to me again, Tutush, there are many girls. I loved only one, and *that* thou knewest. And hast lied to me."

He was moving toward the plump master of the spies, and suddenly Tutush became afraid of the eyes that searched his soul. Omar had read his thoughts, and had seen his fear.

"By the Ninety and Nine Names," he cried, "I know naught of this, and I have never set eyes upon any girl of thine. *Hai,* what — Mai'mun — aid!"

Omar's hand gripped his throat and shook him, and Tutush

choked like a beast in a snare. The fingers sank into his soft flesh like steel, and his eyes burned in his head. He heard Mai'mun shouting for help, and then, in overmastering fear he snatched a knife from his girdle and struck blindly. The edge of the blade slashed cloth and flesh, grating against bone. Then his wrist was caught and he was flung to the floor.

There he sprawled, sobbing for breath. Looking up through a red mist he beheld Omar fast in the arms of a half-dozen servants and scholars. The cloak was torn over one shoulder, and a dark stain spreading down his breast.

"There is blood between us, dog," said Omar in the same quiet voice, "but it is not this blood. It drips within me a drop at a time, and it is not to be staunched like this. Go, or thou wilt die."

They took Tutush away, and Jafarak who heard the tale from the servants confided to the merchant Akroenos that night by the Takin gate that Omar had been wounded when he set upon the master of the spies in a blind rage. And Akroenos thought so much of this, that after Jafarak had departed, he summoned a runner from the bazaar. He wrote two words on a square of paper and gave it to the man without sealing it.

"Take this," he ordered, "to Ray. Go to the khan of the travelers and cry aloud in the courtyard that thou hast a missive for the Lord of Seven. When he approaches thee, give this to him."

"But how, O master," objected the slave, "will I know if it be truly the Lord of Seven? 'Tis a strange name."

"He will tell thee whence thou comest."

"*Wah!* That is magic."

The slave felt curious about his message, and he opened the paper often to look at the two words. Since they appeared very much like any other two words, he was reassured; still he took some pains to find a mullah who could read, in order to make certain there was no curse attached to the words.

"*Sa'at shud,*" the mullah read aloud, "The hour hath come. Or, the time of commencement hath arrived. What is there to fear in this?"

After his shoulder was bandaged, Omar kept to his room. Isfizari, who looked in at his door once, reported that he seemed to be writing on small slips of paper. Some of the papers lay on the floor.

In the observatory, Mai'mun labored upon the unfinished calculation. Without Omar, he could get nothing done. The map was inaccurate and the list of Greek astronomers meant nothing to him. After trying some experiments of his own without result, he abandoned the observatory.

He did not return until the night when Isfizari told him that the lamp in the workroom was lighted, although none of the assistants was in the tower. Hastening thither, the old astronomer found Omar kneeling at the low table, engrossed in the manuscript of Ptolemy.

"The point we seek is west of Asia Minor," he said. "I am sure of that, now."

Mai'mun's heart sank. "But west of there is only the sea."

Omar nodded.

"Alas, our search is useless."

"Nay, 'tis near the end. For on the land there were many cities in the ancient days. On the sea there were few." Omar was studying the list of the astronomers, crossing out one name after the other. Finally his pen paused.

"The island of Rhodes," he murmured. "Hipparchus of Rhodes fixed the position of a thousand stars."

The lips of the old astonomer moved soundlessly. Through his thin veins ran a fever hotter than the lust of a miser or the hunger of an explorer. They were on the verge of discovering a secret of science hidden for nine centuries.

"Ay," he cried, "and Ptolemy wrote down those thousand and eighty stars of Hipparchus in his *al magest*. If it be true — if it be true!"

"I think it is," said Omar carelessly. "Now we must verify these tables for Rhodes, the city of Rhodes, and the year one hundred and thirty-four before the birth of Jesus of Nazareth."

"Let each of us do it — working apart." Mai'mun was fearful and yet eager for a share of the glory of discovery.

For three days they labored, sleeping little, the savant of Baghdad scarcely taking his tired eyes from the pages before him, while Omar worked swiftly between long spells of musing. They ate sparingly, late at night and in the morning. Until Omar stretched his uninjured arm and laughed.

"Enough. It is enough."

"Nay, it is little," objected Mai'mun, because it appeared to him that he had only made a beginning of the task. But when their calculations were compared, he flushed and made strange sounds in his throat.

"By the Kaaba, by the waters of Zem-zem — it is so. Avicenna himself would declare it so — and he never suspected. Oh, Khwaja Omar!" He seized the Tentmaker in his arms and caressed him. "Now we have accurate tables, Khwaja Omar. As Ptolemy himself used these tables of Hipparchus of Rhodes, we can use them."

Mai'mun wished to go and sit in the courtyard; he longed to expound the momentous discovery to his disciples, to taste again the delight of the moment — even to visit his colleagues of the academy in Nisapur and to gossip about it with them. But to this Omar would not consent.

"Already," he explained, "the masters of the Ulema say it is forbidden to measure time, and we are aided by evil spirits here in the House of the Stars. What would they say if they knew we were using the tables of an infidel Greek? Wait until our work is done and presented to the Sultan."

"True, Khwaja Omar. Once a Hanbalite threw a blazing torch into the tower, crying out upon us. And of nights we watch the gnomon, for a crowd from the mosque stoned it while you were in Aleppo. We must put the seal of discretion upon the lips of confidence."

He did not understand how Omar could turn at once to new labor. He did not know that when Omar's mind wandered from the tables, it passed into a distant region where a girl lay dying, moaning and clinging to his arms.

It was a shadowy limbo, that, by the rushing river under the burning sun. At times he could dwell in imagination with Yasmi when her eyes were bright, and she smiled, tossing back the flood of her dark hair. But more often there was the river and the pain.

"He labors," said Isfizari once, "as if he wished never to cease. And then he sits alone with his wine."

"He has a strange power," answered Mai'mun with the importance of one who knows whereof he speaks, "and that is his way. If he fail not in strength of mind, he will outdo the labor of Ptolemy."

But Jafarak, having the pitilessly clear understanding of a cripple, went to sit of nights with the Tentmaker. Crouching down by his friend, he watched the shadows cast by the lamp flame flickering upon the wall. He made no jests at such a time. "When Alp Arslan, my master, went out of this world," he ventured, "I wept an ocean of tears and was comforted. Yet the wine in that cup doth not make thee weep, O Tentmaker."

Omar stared at the cup within his hand. It was old silver, inlaid with lapis lazuli. "When you can't sleep, you can be drunk. It is better than searching yourself to find out what you are and why you are — you."

"Yet it brings no contentment."

"It brings forgetfulness. See, Jafarak, how this cup holds the secret of alchemy. For one measure of it will trounce a thousand cares. Drink of it and you will reign upon a golden throne like Mahmoud's, and you will hear music sweeter than that which came from David's lips. . . . Tell me, would the man who made this cup fling it down to shatter it to bits?"

"Nay — God forbid."

"Then what love fashions a fair human body, and what wrath destroys it?"

From the floor Omar picked up a crumpled sheet of paper, and tossed it to Jafarak. The jester smoothed it out, and, turning it to the light, saw that it was a *rubai* of four lines written in Persian in the astronomer's clear hand.

> *This caravan of life in mystery*
> *Moves on. O Saki, bring the cup to me —*
> *The cup of laughter while the night goes by —*
> *And look not for the dawn that is to be.*

"Alas," Jafarak sighed. Suddenly his wizened face brightened. "But write — write more verses. This is thy gift of years!"

A year passed. When the astronomers of the House of the Stars compared their findings anew, Mai'mun and Isfizari were pleased. Their timing of the sun agreed with their star time to an hour, as measured by the water clock.

They were certain, then, that the year had 365 days, and also five or six hours. This was infinitely better than the moon calendar of Islam which made a year of 354 days. Astronomers in ancient Egypt, they knew, had devised a calendar of twelve months of thirty days each, with an additional five days of festival at the end of the year — 365 days in all.

" 'Tis another quarter of a day we must add to the days," Isfizari suggested. "What if we added a whole day every fourth year?"

But Omar and Mai'mun reminded him that they were preparing a calendar not for four years or forty but for centuries. So they made observations for another year, to compare with the first. Tidings of their success drifted in to the mullahs of Nisapur, who preached against the star gazers who used infidel machines and talked with the spirits of the dead coming out of the graves of the cemetery.

To this outcry Mai'mun paid little heed and Omar less. But the old astronomer knew that the Tentmaker was engrossed in a new calculation the nature of which Mai'mun could not guess — except for one thing. Having discovered that Ptolemy had relied on the wisdom of Hipparchus, Omar likewise had turned to the manuscripts of the savant of Rhodes. Now he was buried in study of a new kind.

"It hath to do with the shadow shape of an eclipse. That is clear," Mai'mun confided to Isfizari. "Moreover, he is solving problems by hyperbolas which deal with infinite numbers."

"May Allah the Compassionate befriend him." Isfizari, who was younger and bolder than Mai'mun, laughed. "Ordinary numbers twist my brain enough."

"He is using the *sifr** circle."

"The 'Emptiness'?"

"Ay, the circle beyond which is emptiness — the Greek zero. Yet that is not all. He said that beyond the *sifr* — beyond this emptiness — lie myriads of ghost numbers."

Isfizari pondered, and shook his head blankly. "It sounds like the dream of some Greek. They were always dreaming of perfection and wrangling among themselves as to how it was to be had. And what good did it do them in the end? One of their *khwajas,* Ar-km — something or other they called him — he invented a way to move the earth, if he could find something to stand on outside the earth. And while he was dreaming he was

* Zero: the Islamic mathematicians of the eleventh century understood and used the "sifr," zero, some centuries before medieval Europeans; but only a few of them had a vague conception that numbers could be negative as well as positive.

slain by a common soldier during a battle. Then again in ancient time their greatest sultan, Iskander* conquered most of Asia. Ay, he planned to extend his dominion over the whole world; yet he died of drunkenness when he was little older than our Master Omar. His great amirs divided up the fragments of his empire, fighting among themselves. Now the champions of Islam have overthrown the Greeks. Nay, the dreaming of the Greeks did them little good."

"Master Omar saith that the ghost numbers exist. When he bringeth one in from beyond Emptiness, he taketh away the same from the positive numbers on this side the *sifr.*"

"Allah grant the mullahs do not hear of it."

When Isfizari was alone with the younger assistants, he confided in them: "Proof of the Truth was drunk again. Ay, he rode an hyperbola up among the stars, and marshaled the ghosts of dead numbers."

"Well, once at night he went down and sat among the graves. He had the keeper of the garden plant tulips by the deserted graves."

The year passed to its end, the last records were made, and Omar and Mai'mun set themselves to the final task of selecting a proper fraction for the final day of their calendar. They had fixed the surplus interval as 5 hours 48 minutes and 45 seconds.

This was a trifle less than one quarter of a day, and Mai'mun ventured the opinion that it was seven twenty-ninths. It was Omar who hit upon eight thirty-thirds.**

"So," he said, "we shall add eight days during thirty-three years."

Together they drew up a table of the years to present to Nizam al Mulk, who was waiting impatiently for their solution. Mai'mun and Isfizari in their robes of ceremony carried it to the Arranger of the World in Nisapur castle.

And Nizam had a copy illuminated in gold and bound in a cover of scarlet silk embroidered with the likeness of a dragon. This he took himself to Malikshah.

---

* Alexander the Great.
** The estimate of the year accredited to Omar Khayyam by scholars is very nearly exact. It has an excess of only 19.45 seconds in the year, whereas the calendar we use today has an excess of 26 seconds.

"O Lord of the East and the West," he vouchsafed, "by thy command thy servants have measured time anew, discovering all other measures to be false. Here, at thy wish, is the true tabulation of all future time. Here — I place it in the hand of authority — is the record of all the years to be while Allah permits men to endure upon the earth."

Curiously, Malikshah scanned it. The embroidered dragon pleased him as much as the calendar, which he could not quite understand. But the Dragon was his sign, in the heavens, and the wise Omar Khayyam could interpret the omens of the heavens so that his rule would continue to be fortunate.

"Good!" he announced. "Give robes of honor and chests of gold to the learned men who have labored in the House of the Stars. But to my astronomer give the small palace of Kasr Kuchik, in the hills."

Nizam bowed, exclaiming under his breath — taking care that Malikshah should hear — upon the generosity of the Son of the Dragon. "Now it remains only to command that the evening before this vernal equinox the old calendar of the moon shall cease in all the lands of the Empire. That evening will begin the year One of the new era — thine era, which shall be called the Jallalian in accordance with thy name."

The evening of that day, in the next Spring, when the hours of light and darkness were exactly equal, Malikshah ascended to the pavilion on the summit of the Castle tower, attended by his nobles.

At the edge of the great plain the red sun was setting. On the flat house tops below them the people of Nisapur had spread carpets and hung lanterns, because that night was to be one of festival. The tinkling of guitars and the laughter of women rose out of the dusk — with the wailing of the criers who were proclaiming in the streets that the first hour of the new day approached.

In a robe stiff with gold embroidery, Omar stood at the shoulder of the youthful sultan, who watched the sun dip into the dark line of the land. The sky was clear, except for a cloud bank high above the sun upon which the red glow turned to scarlet.

"See," murmured a bearded mullah, "how Allah hath hung the banners of death in the sky."

Heads turned toward him, but the Amir of Amirs cried out in a loud voice, "Behold, O Lord of the Universe, great King and Conqueror — behold, thy day begins."

The last of the sun's rim sank out of sight, leaving the blood-stained sky empty and the earth dark beneath. A chorus of voices welled up from the streets and drums sounded in the courtyard beneath. Omar went to the parapet and looked down. Half visible in the dusk a water clock dripped unheeded. The falling drops marked the new time — but had time ever changed? The sun had been the same in the day of Jamshid and Kaikhosru.

"Will the morning be favorable," Malikshah asked in his ear, "for gazelle hunting?"

Omar repressed a smile. "I will examine the signs," he responded, "if your Majesty will give me leave to depart."

He was glad to escape from the palace. When Jafarak searched for him late that night, he was sitting by the lighted lamp of the workroom in the House of the Stars — although every one else was at the festival in Nisapur. Omar still wore his heavy robe of honor.

"Our Lord," the jester observed, "desires word about the omens for the hunt."

Omar glanced up impatiently. "How is the wind?"

"It is mild, from the south."

"Then tell him that I have observed — nay, tell him to hunt where he will and fear not."

"But the mullahs say the banners of death are hung i' the sky."

"The priests! They prophesy evil because they are angered by the new calendar. Yet Malikshah will be as far from harm as he was yesterday."

"Art certain, Master?"

"Yes," said Omar with conviction.

Still Jafarak hesitated. "I go. But wilt thou not come also to the palace where laughter and song go round. They are happy, in the palace."

"And I — here." Omar looked up at him gravely: "Wilt see, O companion of my joy, what never man like to thee hath seen before?"

Jafarak murmured assent, troubled and yet trusting. In loneliness and silence he had never been able to find joy. Omar rose, heedless of his stiff robe, and led the way to the tower stair.

Through the darkness they climbed to the roof beside the great bronze globe.

"Look up — what see'st thou, Jafarak?"

"The stars. The stars in a clear sky."

"Are they moving?"

His head on one side, the jester considered. True, he could not see the star groups move, but he had not dwelt at the House of the Stars so long without learning that they rose and set like the sun and the moon. He could even tell by the bright point of Orion that the night was nearly half gone. "Verily, they move. Slowly, they circle the earth each day. I have seen that before."

"And this earth of ours, what is it?"

"A round ball, Master, like to this globe. 'Tis the center of all things, as Allah hath ordained, and it alone moves not. Mai'mun told me that."

For a moment Omar waited. Down by the river night birds fluttered. An owl passed silently by them, and the cool wind stirred their faces.

"Two years I have labored to see," Omar mused aloud, "and now I see. Look up, Jafarak, again. These myriad points of light, these everlasting stars, move not. Long before the ages of men, they were there, afar. Nay, beloved fool, it is this earth we stand on that moves. This round ball of ours turns upon itself once in a day and night. . . . Look up, and see the stars as they are."

Suddenly Jafarak bent his head and shivered. "Master, I fear."

"What is there to fear?"

"The night changes. Thou hast spoken words of power. Me-seems this tower moves." His trembling increased, and he clung to the parapet. "O Master, unsay the words! Or — or we will fall. I feel the tower moving, and we will fall."

Omar cried out with exultation. "Nay, we will not fall. The earth turns and we are safe. We fly through space among those other worlds which may be other, mightier suns, remote and unchanging. Dost thou see, and feel, Jafarak?"

"Allah protect me!"

His head hidden in his hands, Jafarak sobbed. Now he was sure that the master he loved had become mad. "I must go," he choked. "I must tell the sultan of his hunting."

And he crept to the dark well of the stairs, blinded by his fear.

PART IV

The selling pillar in the alley of the slave sellers within the great bazaar of Nisapur, the seventh year of the new calendar of Sultan Malikshah.

THE CRIER STOOD UP and beat upon a brass basin.

"Bism'allah ar-rahman ar-rahim," he called, "In the name of God the Kind, the Compassionate, the door of bidding is opened. Give heed, ye buyers!"

They sat crowded together, nobles, merchants, gentlemen farmers seeking stalwart plowmen, and pious Nisapuris who desired new handmaidens. For word had got about that new caravans of slave-stuff had come in from Syria where the glorious Sultan Malikshah had made fresh conquests.

So large was the crowd that the *dallal* had to clear a space about the stone pillar, to place his first offering on the slab before the pillar.

"Behold, O educated lords," he announced, "here is a Greek boy of some fourteen years, strong and with all his teeth, without sores or sickness of any nature, trained to play the lute and already circumcised as a Musliman. Who will say thirty dinars?" He looked about him. "Five and twenty dinars? Then make haste and say twenty, for that is less than the price of a Kurdish horse."

Lifting an arm of the motionless boy, who had been stripped to the waist, the *dallal* turned him about slowly, to show his fair skin unblemished. But the vast quantities of young slaves brought into the markets recently had forced down prices. These captives must be sold to make way for others now on the road. The ribs of the Greek showed through his skin. He was half-starved, and wished only for food.

"Verily," cried a stout Persian, "a horse is worth more. His strength is as water, he understands no word, and he will not serve at his age for a eunuch. Eleven dinars I will pay."

"Eleven! By Allah, this infid — this young Moslem hath gentle blood in him. Say, is his price no more than the price of a cow? No more than eleven?"

"Such a Greek as this will never bear spear-and-shield," cried another merchant. "Twelve."

"Twelve and two dirhems."

"Is this bidding or alms-giving?" shouted the *dallal,* who did not want the first offering to go at such prices.

"Yes, it is charity," responded the stout Persian, "for these boys are selling in the Baghdad *souk* at less than ten. I say twelve and four."

The boy was bought by a merchant for thirteen dinars and three silver dirhems. And an Abyssinian woman covered with bangles whispered to the girl who sat by her that they would go cheap.

"*Ai,*" she mourned, "and once a Sayyid bid three hundred gold for me."

"O many-times-a-mother," the girl whispered back, "that must have been long ago."

"The Turks are better than these," the Abyssinian went on, "who are merchants and palm lickers. *Thou* wilt never hear a hundred bid for thee, Ayesha."

The girl Ayesha hugged her knees and considered. She had good teeth and a fine body, a bit too thin for the Persians' liking — she was an Arab of the *banu's Safa* from the black tents of the Hauran — and her skin was not as light as that of the Persian women, although not as dark as the Abyssinian's. If the merchants had only kept her for the private auction, some young noble might have fancied her.

Unlike the experienced Abyssinian, Ayesha was not reconciled to her fate. The thought of being sold to a shopkeeper who would expect her to bake his bread and caress him at the same time filled her with silent fury. "O God," she prayed half-aloud, "may it not come upon my head!"

"What? Well, you'll be sold for what you are. You don't get fruit from a willow tree." The Abyssinian combed the short hair over her forehead and smirked into a hand-mirror. "Listen now! Those two pockmarked Yamenites sold to a Jew for twenty dinars. What times — what times!"

Ayesha had been sold once in Baghdad, and the fierce independence of the desert-born tormented her. From the edge of her veil she scanned the faces of the buyers and inwardly cursed them for street-born hagglers. Then she became utterly still.

A horseman had drawn rein at the edge of the crowd — a man indifferent to the crowd. In the clasp of his turban's plume a great emerald gleamed. Evidently he was well-known, because heads craned toward him, and a guard muttered to another that here was the King's star gazer wandering after his wont.

So, Ayesha thought, the newcomer must be an officer, a man of authority. True, he had a stern face with eyes like an eagle's under tufted brows; but he could not be much over thirty. Ayesha drew a long breath and rose to her knees.

"Sit, woman," muttered the guard. "Thy turn is not yet."

Instead Ayesha darted under his arm, and thrust her way through the nearest men. Swiftly as a frightened gazelle, she ran to the horseman and clutched his stirrup.

"Protector of the Poor," she gasped, "give aid. I am from the high tent of a shaikh — my father was chieftain of the *banu's Safa* —" this was a lie — "and now, behold, O Amir of Amirs, they sell me with boys and drabs at the public post."

Omar glanced down into dark eyes passionate with entreaty. He noticed the strength in her slim young shoulders, the curve of a fair throat. Ayesha had let her veil fall, and her lips moved imploringly. Inwardly she was praying that he understood her Arabic.

Omar understood, but he was looking into eyes that made him think of Yasmi, after ten years.

The *dallal,* pushing through the throng, caught her shoulder angrily. "Cease thy clamor — back to thy place, she-panther." To Omar he salaamed profoundly. "Do not take it ill, Khwaja. 'Tis a girl with the temper of one possessed."

Ayesha still held fast to the stirrup, her cheek against his knee.

"What is her price?" asked Omar. "No matter — I will pay a hundred gold."

Scenting a good profit, the *dallal* turned to the crowd that had forsaken the dais to gather about them. "O believers, a hundred dinars is bid for this matchless girl with a waist slender as a cypress and a temper as gentle as a fawn's, who sings like a bulbul and banishes care from troubled minds." He caught the eye of a helper who had been placed among the merchants for just such a cue. "Who will bid more?"

"A hundred and ten," cried the disguised helper.

"Two hundred," said Omar. "I will take her with me now, *dallal*, and the money will be paid thee at my house."

"The praise be to Allah," cried the startled auctioneer, who had not expected to get more than seventy pieces for a girl like this Arab. "O believers, what an open hand hath this *chelabi*, our revered master! What splendid taste! What munificence! Now is the singing slave Ayesha sold to Khwaja Omar for two hundred, and —" he decided that, the attention of the crowd being focussed on Omar, a little more gain could be had — "a poor twenty dinars, my commission, with only five for the mosque of the market. What generosity! Wilt have a litter, to carry hence this lovely singer? Wilt buy an African eunuch to guard her, for such a little price?"

But Omar signed to the servant who followed him to dismount. Ayesha scrambled up into the vacated saddle with a gasp of relief — she had feared that something might make this lord repent of his bargain at the final moment. Obediently she bent her head, for Omar to draw the veil across her face. Now she was his.

As the horses moved away she cast one triumphant glance over her shoulder at the Abyssinian slave with the bangles.

"*Yah bint,*" Omar addressed her. "O girl, art thou truly the daughter of the shaikh of the *banu's Safa?*"

Instinctive cunning checked the response on her lips. She glanced at Omar, as a dog looks up into the face of its master to understand what lies behind his words. "Nay, not of the chieftain," she admitted boldly. "That was a lie. But I can really sing."

Omar smiled. And Ayesha wondered what manner of lord this could be, who desired to hear truth spoken by a fair woman.

*The garden of Kasr Kuchik, in the foothills two
days' ride east of Nisapur.*

ALTHOUGH AYESHA WAS SURPRISED, naturally, when
the King's star gazer did not yield at once to her charm and
solace himself by sleeping with her, she understood that he
might want to wait a month. That was customary. Often in the
desert raids, warriors would enjoy the captive women before
the heat of battle had cooled in their veins; otherwise they
would wait for the month ordained by custom and religious
law. When Ayesha was sent away under guard to the summer
place of her new owner, she did not feel slighted. She wasted
no time, however, in satisfying her curiosity about Omar.

Her first discovery amazed her, almost beyond belief. The
palace was, as its name implied, a little one — a dwelling lovely
with blue tiles, standing at the back of a hill garden
overlooking the gray plain. Ayesha was given a chamber
opening into a roof terrace, and in an hour she had satisfied
herself that no other woman of her class resided there.

"Nay, the master hath no wives," old Zuleika admitted.
" 'Tis said that once he married one who died of the plague
before her homecoming."

Being mistress of the kitchen, old Zuleika had the gossip of
the place at her tongue's end.

"Sometimes," she added, "he brings hither dancing girls for
a little while, but they weary him and he sends them away
with a gift."

Inwardly Ayesha resolved that he would not send her away
so speedily, with or without a gift. True, he had bought her
and he was responsible for her, but Ayesha had no illusions
about the fate of young slave girls who did not please their
masters. Moreover, she found Kasr Kuchik delightful.

The garden had a stream coming out of a grotto and
winding between cool cypresses down to the pool where the
rugs were spread. White roses climbed everywhere, even against
the high walls of dried mud. In one corner stood a fairy-like
kiosk. Here Ayesha was privileged to lie on heaped-up cushions

and nibble at sugar paste, while she watched the spray of a fountain and stained her nails with henna. Ayesha thought life would be very pleasant in Kasr Kuchik.

"This place," Zuleika informed her proudly, "is only one of many. Our lord hath a palace in Nisapur and another in Merv, by the great palace of the Sultan. He hath besides a house of science which is called the House of the Stars. Wise men with long beards work there making books at his command."

"*Wah!* Making books?"

"Yes, books are as common as dates with our mast... he made for the Sultan was an algebra."

"A — what?"

"An algebra. It hath to do with magical numbers. Our master in his wisdom knoweth all that has ever been, and all that will be — God willing. That is why the Sultan will do nothing without his advice, so he is as great-in-power as the aged Arranger of the World. Ay, at the royal banquets he sits above the Amir of all the armies, and our Sultan loveth nothing more than an army, unless it be his hunting."

This Ayesha understood readily enough. War, raid, and hunt were the occupations of strong men, who looked to women for their diversion, and to bear their children. The more powerful the men, the fairer and more numerous their women.

"And the banquets he gives!" Zuleika rambled on — having perceived from the first day that Ayesha would never interfere with her domestic supremacy, she allowed herself to gossip freely — "In an ants' house a dewdrop is a flood, but here wine flows as if for the giants. *Hai* the jars they empty in the garden — the roast pheasants, the gazelle steaks, the mounds of rice-and-saffron, the platters of Shah's-delight, and the camel-loads of melons cooled with snow from the upper hills! They eat and they sit and they talk until the stars fade."

"*Wah!* Thy cooking is fragrant as a garden in Nejd. But what do they talk about, if they have no girls?"

"Oh, about Cos-reagraphy and Pre-isms and such-like. My soul, they use mighty words of power and it fair blisters my brain to understand them."

Ayesha thought it must blister one's brain. She herself could never arrive at Zuleika's comprehension of the mysteries.

In fact, she felt the difference between herself and those Persians. All of them — from the half-blind gatekeeper, to the hunchback who came and went on a white donkey — lived on the bounty of their lord. They talked more than they slept and they slept more than they worked. There was no *makaddam* with a whip to see that they labored.

The garden had twenty gardeners, from the planter-in-chief to the lowest sweeper. Yet seldom did they do more than sit and discuss the affairs of the garden and themselves. From her roof terrace the she-panther — the servant who had escorted her from the street of the slave sellers had brought that nick-name back with him — listened to them. "O Ali, the last rain washed stones into the lily beds. It is time that the bed should be dug." . . . "Knowest not, Hussayn, that the proper time is in the moon before the equinox? Besides, it is Ahmed's work, and by God's will he lieth sick." . . . "The master will be angry if the bed is not dug." . . . "That is true. Well, I will make haste and remove the stones, and rake the leaves and dig it deep, tomorrow."

But tomorrow Ali would wait for Ahmed's son to repair the hoe that had been broken last autumn. "It is important. O Hussayn, to fill up the holes in the gravel walk by the kiosk. Our master might stumble in those holes and then would be calamity." . . . "How can I fill the holes when I am pruning the rose vines?"

Hussayn, however, was not actually pruning the roses. He had cut some to take to the daughter of the miller in the village, and he meant with all his heart to clip and trim and tie up all the vines — he would certainly do something about it tomorrow.

Then if they worked a little in the morning, they would sleep in the shade of the cypresses through the noonday heat, leaving the flies to buzz about the tools in the sun. When they woke they would be too drowsy and the sun would be too hot to resume work — it could be done tomorrow.

Still, in spite of this neglect, the garden was heavy with fragrance of roses, and its canopy of foliage made a sanctuary of shadow. Ayesha liked to drowse in it while she waited for Omar's coming.

But when her new master at last rode into the gate — and the gatekeeper put on his best garment, and all the gardeners even Ahmed who had complained of sickness, scurried about with their tools as if interrupted in diligent toil, while Zuleika stirred the kitchen into pandemonium — Ayesha could no longer go into the garden. A half dozen visitors accompanied Omar, and for weeks the Lord of Kasr Kuchik did nothing but entertain his guests. Some went away, but others came, and Ayesha perforce kept to her rooms and roof-top, wearing her heaviest veil the while, and wondering as the days passed if Omar had forgotten her.

She could not speak to him while the other men filled the place, outside her harem. And, after all, she was only a new-bought slave; she did not dare send a message to him by Zuleika. He must have seen her from a distance on her roof, and perhaps he regretted buying her and meant to sell her again. Ayesha pondered the question for long hours, while she bathed and anointed herself and colored her nails carefully. She was a little afraid of Omar, but she did not want to be sold again, and she determined that if he came face to face with her only for a moment without her veil, he should not neglect her again.

Meanwhile she listened to all the talk in the garden below, as had been a woman's privilege since Allah created Eve of blessed memory.

When the men feasted after the hour of candle-lighting, she could stretch out in her eyrie and hear — she had the ears of a panther — all that was said, and wonder about the characters of the visitors.

There was a grizzled Armenian merchant, Akroenos by name, of whom she approved decidedly. He conversed, with Omar apart, of turquoises from the mines, of caravan-loads of elephants' teeth, and profits of thousands of dinars. Ayesha understood such matters very well; she realized that Akroenos was Omar's man of business and that Omar had great wealth to dispose of. The price he had paid for her had been no more than beggar's pence to him. So much the better. . . .

Of a certain poet with oiled hair named Mu'izzi, the Glorifier, she did not approve. True, he praised Omar without stint, saying that the King's astronomer had reached threefold perfection, in a thing called mathematics and in knowledge-of-the-stars, and also — as he, Mu'izzi had heard —

in the art of music. Were not the very children of Islam reading Omar's books in the schools? But Ayesha thought to herself that words were cheap.

Once Mu'izzi was prevailed upon to recite an ode of his own:

"Picture fair, by whose beloved presence by me here
Seems my chamber now like Farkhar, now like far Cashmere,
If thy darkling tresses have not sinned against thy face
Wherefore hang they, head-dependent, downward in disgrace?
Yet, if sin be theirs, then why do they in heaven dwell,
*Since the sinner's portions is not Paradise, but Hell?"**

Ayesha thought this pretty enough. When Mu'izzi asked anxiously for Omar's opinion, the lord of Kasr Kuchik said:

"I see now why thou art the King's poet."

Mu'izzi drank too much that night, and disputed with a Sufi whether he should have said "curling" instead of "darkling" in his ode. The Sufi was full of strange words like Being and Not-being, and universal love. Ayesha paid little attention to him, but she listened readily enough when Mu'izzi cried out that he would tell a secret of a party of his own.

" 'Twas a jest, O my cup companions, and such a jest! To my house and my poor garden — only the shadow of this moon-adorned paradise — I summoned young nobles from the polo field. When we had eaten and drank a little — not such spirit-exalting wine as this — I clapped my hands to fetch in the dancing girls. But they were not girls. I had hired boys fair as the new moon and dressed them in the garments of dancing girls, even to the anklets and veils. So, behold, they danced, and then ran away, while I whispered to my guests to catch them if they could. They all vanished into the darkness, and I waited for my guests to run back crying out at the jest I had devised for them. Behold they did not come — it was an hour ere the first one came!"

And Mu'izzi laughed, throwing back his head. Ayesha looked at Omar who gave no sign, either of amusement or dislike.

* From the translation of Edward G. Browne.

The Arab girl grew hot with indignation. So many Moslems, amusing themselves with boys, lost all desire for women. She remembered that she had found this harem of Kasr Kuchik deserted, and Zuleika had assured her that its master soon tired of singing girls from the city. But there was no trace anywhere of a beardless boy. Still, she hated Mu'izzi and devised names for him that would have startled the King's poet.

There was a Hindu, silent as a shadow, who whispered to a companion that Omar's secret knowledge was remembered from a previous life, without Omar's knowing that he remembered.

Ayesha could make nothing of that, but she understood vaguely that this Hindu was kindred in spirit to a youth with fearless eyes who wore only a camelhair *abba* and who came to the palace alone and barefoot. They called him Ghazali, the mystic.

When Ghazali talked with Omar, they paced the garden together, so that the girl could not catch all they said, and she understood even less. Odd snatches of words about the veil of the Invisible that men could not draw aside. *Omar:* "If we could see the heavens as they are, we would behold a new universe. Ah, we would do away with the old and find our heart's desire in the new." *Ghazali:* "That veil may not be lifted until we have perfected ourselves in love of God. . . ."

Once when Omar raised a goblet of wine to his lips, the mystic cried:

"That is accursed."

Omar drank, and set the goblet down empty, smiling a little. "Do not blaspheme wine. It is bitter only because it is my life."

His life! Ayesha, who was already jealous of Ghazali, wondered what would come next. But Ghazali merely argued that while there were many religions, there was but one God.

"Islam itself is a house divided, for we have the orthodox believers, and the Sufis who rebel against orthodoxy, and the Alyites who follow the tradition of Ali, and also those who await the coming of the Mahdi. All believe, and yet they follow different paths. Listen now to the story of the Elephant. . . . In Hind it was that the keepers of the Elephant desired to show the Elephant to curious ones. Yet it was in a dark room. The seekers came and felt of it, since they could not see. One, laying his hand on its trunk, said, 'This creature is like a water-pipe.' Another, feeling its ear, said, 'Verily, it is a fan.' A third came upon its leg, and he said, 'Nay, beyond doubt it is a pillar.' Had any one brought a candle to the room, all would have seen the same."

"And where," Omar asked, "will you find a candle to enlighten the world?"

"In the dreams of the mystics," cried Ghazali. "For they can see what lieth behind darkness."

"And who are they?" Omar shook his head. "I have sought them, but where are they? They have not taken a step from their couches into the darkness of the Universe. They have told an old tale, and have gone back to sleep again."

For one thing Ayesha was grateful to Ghazali. After the mystic had departed on his wanderings, Omar wearied of Mu'izzi and the other cup companions. One evening when they were in deepest dispute, he led in Jafarak's white donkey, and when at length the guests fell silent, he assured them gravely that the donkey bade them take warning by its example — in a former life it had been a professor of an academy.

All the guests left after that, and Omar was pacing the starlit garden when Ayesha at last dared to approach him. She knelt beside him, pressing his hand to her forehead.

"Upon my lord be the peace."

"And upon thee, the peace."

"My lord, I watched. There was one who came creeping, and spied upon you. He hid there, behind the roses, and crept away again. I saw his face."

"Was it Ahmed, the gardener?"

"Ay, Ahmed. Let him be scourged!"

To the girl who had been weaned among the desert clans a spy was an enemy, to be struck down as one would strike a snake.

Omar was silent a moment. "Nay, let him go to those who sent him and tell of the donkey. If I beat him and cast him out they might send one more dangerous than Ahmed."

Ayesha wondered at this. Her master, then, had been aware

of Ahmed's spying, even as he had known when he saw her first that she was not the daughter of the chief of the Safa clan. How great was his magic! Surely, he could read her thoughts, as she knelt beside him, while he stroked her tresses.

But Omar was following his own thoughts. "They talk of paradise, yet what is paradise but a moment's peace?"

Ayesha did not know, so she was silent.

"Here is a garden, and quiet. Yet even here the seekers come, and the talkers, and the watchers intrude. . . . Are my servants kind to thee, Ayesha?"

"Verily, they are. Will — will my lord be pleased to have me take my lute and sing?"

"It is late — in an hour it will be the light before the dawn. Go thou and sleep, Ayesha."

The girl returned to her quarters, obedient but resentful. With all these goings-on, how would the master ever notice her? He had stroked her head as if she had been one of the horses of the stable, and had sent her off to sleep like a child.

Omar sat by the pool, musing. Ghazali was no older than he had been when he rode to the war with Rahim, and Yasmi gave him a rose. In Ghazali was the unreasoning sureness of youth. Why must the book of youth be closed? He himself was no more than thirty-four, but he felt that youth had deserted him. Who knew how, or whence? The book was closed, a new book opened.

Life, that was so assured to Ghazali, had become uncertain to Omar. To the ascetic, it lay open like a map, awaiting his coming. To the astronomer, it offered barriers within barriers.

"He will be a fine teacher," he thought. "And I could not teach."

Upon an impulse he clapped his hands. A servant came running from the house and paused respectfully at a little distance. "Bring me," Omar requested, "the case of my cameos and older coins. It is in the blue tiled chamber beside the pile of Chinese rugs —" he glanced up at the man's face for the first time — "Ahmed."

When the case lay upon his knees, he unlocked it with a key taken from the wallet in his girdle. It was necessary to keep this case locked because, while his servants would never steal the box itself, Zuleika or the maids would be tempted to pilfer

140

the gold coins if it were open for their curiosity to pry into. Their fingers could never resist the soft touch of gold, although they would weep their hearts out if the master ever dared scold them for thieving.

"Is there something more, O master?"

"Nothing — thou hast leave to go, Ahmed."

For a few moments he took up the rare coins and inspected them. Here was a Byzantine piece, with the image of an emperor and his wife seated beneath a cross. Omar could make out the Greek letters — it was Justinian, in the sixth year of his reign, but the name of the woman was not there. And here lay a clay stamp, with the hollowed image of a flying bird, that he had picked up in the ruins of the desert city of Palmyra, where Zenobia had defied Rome not so long ago. What stories of human ambition these tokens had to tell!

Justinian had restored much of the power of Rome, but he had died upon a fruitless quest into Asia. Zenobia — Omar remembered that this queen of a caravan empire had been forced to yield at last to a Roman army and had been carried off captive to grace with her beauty a Roman triumph.

It was strange to hold in his hands the clear-cut heads of these long buried Caesars. Only the other day Nizam had announced that the latest Caesar of Constantinople had sent tribute to Malikshah. So the wheel of fortune had turned, until the west lay in chains before the triumphant march of Islam. . . . Ghazali thought that he, Omar, sought his ease. Yet for seventeen years he had not ceased doing the labor of three men, and now Nizam made greater demands upon him than before. . . . He wished that somebody else had brought him his coin case. Ahmed's impassive face reminded him of the secret supervision from which he could not free himself because it was carried out by Nizam's officers, and by Nizam's enemies. If he rid himself of the one, he would still have the other, and, after all, he had nothing to conceal. Still, they might have left him his rose garden with its solitude undisturbed.

Another servant appeared, and murmured a request.

"Nay, I will look at no letter! I will hear no message. And I do not wish a supper to be brought into the garden. Go thou, Ishak, and see to it that no one enters this garden. Take this accursed case and go!"

"But —"

"If even a jackal enters the wall, thy feet will be beaten."

The gatekeeper took the coin case and stood shuffling his feet uneasily. "But, master, there is one —"

"O God!" cried Omar, so vehemently that the servant fled.

The sun had set and twilight crept through the trees. A last breath of air stirred the surface of the pool and vanished. . . . Ghazali, walking alone down the hill paths toward the city, had found happiness in solitude. Yet Omar wondered if he himself, working among crowds, were not more alone than the mystic. Ghazali shared his thoughts with his fellow disciples; Omar had no one with whom to share his thoughts.

Out of the twilight came the low note of a lute, and a woman's song. The song was of men who came in from war to the well on the desert road, their camels laden with spoil — of the camels kneeling by the thorn bush, while the captives of the warriors wailed a lamentation. It was an Arab song, and presently Omar realized that the singer was near at hand, stroking the lute gently.

"What is this?" he demanded.

Out of the dimness Ayesha appeared. She walked with the grace of a gazelle, and she had taken the veil from her head. Kneeling close to him she bent over the lute again. "A song of the *banu's Safa*," she answered. "There is more — much more — of it. Will my lord hear?"

"I mean, why art thou here, Ayesha? I gave an order."

"But at the time of the order I was in the garden."

"Well, be quiet."

Obediently Ayesha put aside the lute, and curled her legs beneath her. She seemed perfectly satisfied not to make a sound. Still, she was not motionless by any means. First she thrust back the mass of dark hair, that smelled faintly of musk, from her shoulders. Then for a while she turned her face up as if contemplating the stars. After that she began to take the silver bangles from her bare arms. Whenever she moved, she turned fleetingly toward Omar.

He could not recapture the thread of his meditation. Instead he watched Ayesha's graceful hands, piling the armlets in her lap. She made the pile too high, and it fell over with a chiming of silver, and she caught her breath, like a child surprised in mischief. Her shoulder touched his lip, and he felt its warmth beneath the sheer silk covering. By now it was too dark to see anything very well.

Ayesha was concerned with her hair again, her arms raised to her head, bringing the faint scent of her body to him. Although she had said nothing at all, she had become part of the night that surrounded Omar, shutting him in from all that was outside. A few moments ago his words and his thoughts had been all-important, now only the girl's slight movements mattered.

His hand touched her knee, and a shiver ran across his flesh. Without lowering her arms, she turned her head toward him, her lips smiling. He bent down to kiss her, and suddenly she slipped away from him.

"Ayesha!" he whispered.

But this voiceless girl had altered in magical wise. She was no longer the submissive slave, fearful of his displeasure. She was a thing of the night, elusive and defiant. When he followed her she turned and fled back into the depths of the plane trees where even the stars were blind.

By chance his arm caught her shoulder and his hand fell upon the softness of her breast. Ayesha freed herself and vanished, her bare feet making no sound. All thought of kissing her had left Omar; his body was tensed in the pursuit of her, his blood quickening as they ran through the night.

Losing trace of her, he paused to listen — hearing only the throbbing in his ears, until her low laugh sounded beside him. He sprang toward it, only to stumble into a tree trunk. Again Ayesha's laugh mocked him, and this time he went toward her slowly, making no sound. She was poised to flee away when his arms caught her fast.

For a moment she struggled against him, but he was the stronger and his lips sought hers until she relaxed in his arms and her warm mouth pressed against his. Her loosened hair caressed his throat.

When he lifted her from her feet, and laid her on the ground she did not resist. Her arms closed about him and she was breathless, sobbing as the fire within her overmastered her.

A half hour later as they lay silent, relaxed and content, Omar could still feel the quick pulsing of her heart. The dancing girls he had known did not lie thus, half-unconscious. After her fashion the wild Arab girl loved him.

As for Ayesha, she had become by the night's magic a

different being. All of a sudden, she ceased to be quiet and remote. Like a child she patted her hands together and began to sing softly. She laughed over her torn dress, and took his hand, begging him to come with her to swim in the pool.

Out in the starlight he could discern the slender shape of the girl, as she coiled her heavy hair hastily about her head. When she stepped into the warm water she splashed him gleefully. The very pool became aroused and animate when Ayesha cast herself into it. The night and the water and the scent of the sun-warmed roses — all this belonged to her.

"It is good," she said softly, "oh, Allah, it is good to be with my lord."

But when they had dried themselves and put on their garments, Ayesha changed into something else. She uttered an exclamation of warning, and sat listening.

"Men are coming," she whispered after a moment — Omar had heard nothing. "Yonder — look! *Ai*, they hold bare swords."

Looking where she pointed, Omar saw the flicker of torch-light in the mesh of the trees. It glittered on bright steel, and the brush crackled as the bearers of the torches moved toward them.

"Thou hast no weapon," cried the girl. "Quick, to thy house, to rouse the men-at-arms!"

Omar, however, was in no fear of a night attack. He waited until the men came out into the open, when he recognized Ishak, his gate-keeper, and four of his own armed followers. Still distrustful, Ayesha veiled herself and slipped back into the rose bushes.

Ishak advanced to the pool, until he saw Omar, when he gave a cry of relief.

"Ya Khwaja!" We heard sounds of moving within the trees. We thought that thieves had beset thee. Then a body was thrown into the water, and I said to these ignorant ones, 'Come, we must look into this. God forbid that our master be slain!'"

Omar flushed with anger. "Has it come to this, that I cannot enjoy a girl in the garden without the whole of the household coming forth like bees from a hive?"

Snatching a scimitar from the nearest man he beat the terrified Ishak about the shoulders with the flat of the blade until blood ran. Groaning loudly, Ishak submitted patiently. He had intruded upon a woman's seclusion, and fully deserved a beating. He was glad to be beaten now, because Omar would forgive him later instead of ordering the soles threshed from his feet. The other men, sheathing their weapons covertly, were also glad, because in beating Ishak the master might forget them. Still, Ishak believed and they believed that they had done right in coming.

After a moment Omar lowered his arm and laughed. "Go, now, O ones without sense. But remember that henceforth this garden is *haram* — forbidden, to men."

"On my head," responded Ishak, wiping the blood from his lips. "Yet, O master, what of the gardeners; what of Hussayn and Ali and Ahmed —"

"Let them kill flies in the stable. The garden is better without them."

When the servants had departed hastily, Ayesha came forth from her hiding place. She was laughing. "Good it is that thy servants are sluggards. I would not have welcomed them a little earlier."

Omar did not think of his letters for several weeks. He did not, in fact, think of anything except Ayesha. She could go unveiled in the garden now, and she found something new to delight in every evening.

She could not share Omar's thoughts, and that became a curious tie between them. For the Tentmaker longed to escape from his own thoughts, and Ayesha understood this. In certain things she was wiser than he — and wisest of all in her silence.

There was something of mothering in her love and something more that was fierce and unbridled. In no time the rest of the household was made aware that the Arab girl had become the master's favorite.

Ayesha would go herself to prepare the trays of his food in the kitchen. Only once did Zuleika challenge her right to do this.

"Thou hast enough," said Ayesha calmly, "to feed — all thy brats and thy low-born cousins who go away from the storehouse with meat under their coats, ay, and the pockmarked lover of thine eldest girl who should be married instead of hanging about the road. I will see to the master's dishes and try to forget what slips from thy hand."

After that Zuleika contented herself with muttered remarks about the temper of desert-born waifs.

This very remoteness of the girl from the people he had known pleased Omar. Only in his presence did she become altogether human and alive. While he knew every curve of her slim throat and every hollow of her body, he never knew what was in her mind. Lying beside him, her breath mingling with his, her eyes half closed, she seemed to be listening to something far off that he could not hear.

Then she was always surprising him. Once she asked calmly if he meant to have a eunuch to guard her apartment.

"Certainly not," he denied.

"Well, there is one now, sitting in the corridor." Ayesha felt rather pleased by the importance of a guardian eunuch. It was customary, she knew, among the gentlefolk of Islam. Still, it would not be altogether agreeable to have a creature attendant upon her all her days.

When he inspected the outer corridor Omar noticed a strange figure sitting against the wall within summons of the door. The figure — a thin black man in a red khalat — rose and crossed its hands respectfully at his approach.

"What art thou?"

"May it please the Protector of the Poor, my name is Zambal Agha, and Ishak sent for me to serve this house."

The high-pitched voice and lacklustre eyes convinced Omar of what Ayesha had perceived at a glance. "Come with me," he said.

At the gate he called forth Ishak, whose head was still bandaged.

"When did I give thee command to employ a eunuch for the *hanim's* chambers?"

Reproachfully, Ishak glanced at his master. "I knew that my lord's attention was bestowed elsewhere, so I applied the whip of expedition to the rump of necessity, and brought hither this one."

"Well, send him hence again."

"I hear — but, master, the garden is large and all of it cannot be seen from the house."

"Send him away."

The thought of Zambal Agha mounting guard in his garden

displeased Omar. Besides, Ayesha had not been brought up among eunuchs, and he had no wish to set a spy upon her.

Ishak was offended, and asserted his dignity before Zambal Agha by changing the subject. "It is now twenty days that the letter from his Highness Nizam al Mulk waits unanswered, although I told thee it was pressing. A post rider brought it in haste. I have watched it carefully, for Nizam al Mulk writes only upon great matters of state. Shall I bring it forth?"

Omar had forgotten the letter. When he ripped it open and read it, he bit his lip.

"Bismallah ar rahman ar rahim," the message ran. "In the name of Allah the Compassionate the Merciful, write thou at once without an hour's delay to Malikshah, assuring him that the portents of the stars are unfavorable for his return to Nisapur. Imperatively I desire that he continue the war north of Samarkand. I have word from his camp that he is thinking of returning to Khorasan and dismissing half the forces under arms for the winter."

Again Omar read the letter through, and then tore it into shreds. It was hazardous to put a message like that in writing — Nizam should have known better. Also the astronomer had had more than he wanted of false prognostication, at Nizam's dictation. Granting that the Minister was working only in the interest of the state, still Malikshah was King. The Sultan had spent most of the last years in the saddle of war. If he wished a winter's peace, why should he be opposed?

In Nisapur Omar might have reasoned differently. But he had talked with Ghazali, he had tasted of happiness with Ayesha, and — bidding Ishak fetch him paper and sealing-wax — he wrote in answer to Nizam only one word: "No." Below this he traced his signature — Khayyam. Folding the paper, he sealed it with his signet. "Send this by a galloper to his Highness at Nisapur."

"By now," put in Zambal Agha, "the Minister is at Ray, to suppress a religious rising."

Ray was far to the west of Nisapur, more than a week's fast ride.

"Find out where he is, and send it to him."

"On my eyes." Ishak turned the missive curiously in his gnarled hands. "Yet is it a marvelous short letter, O my master, and —"

"Since thou must know, it is but one word and that is 'No.' Below that is the *takallus* of Khayyam. Don't send Ahmed," he added as an afterthought. When he walked back to the house, he stopped beside a fire on the driveway. It was a little fire, but the three chief gardeners, Hussayn, Ali and Ahmed, were all tending it. They were squatted beside it talking, and they rose at his coming, respectfully crossing their hands.

"May thy day be happy, O master," Hussayn said.

Upon the fire Omar dropped the fragments of Nizam's letter, waiting until every particle of paper had charred before he went on. The three gardeners watched with great interest, and when they sat down again they had a new topic of conversation.

"Beyond doubt," Hussayn maintained, "this was a communication of vast importance. What fine handwriting!"

"And the seal," put in Ali sagely, "was red. Such a red as we see in the seals of Nizam al Mulk. Look how it makes drops like blood i' the fire."

They stared at the crimson drops that vanished into the ashes. After a while Ahmed rose and sought through the grounds until he came upon Zambal Agha making up a bundle of his clothing in readiness to take to the road.

Nothing seemed to trouble Ayesha. When Omar asked her if she did not want something, she considered for a while and admitted that she would like some new silk for a dress and thread-of-silver to embroider a pattern on it, and a jar of musk with a little ambergris and oil of poppy seed. That was all. When he gave her a headband of polished gold she cried out with delight. Then for hours she experimented, arranging her hair within the new band and studying the effect in a silver mirror. At times she would stretch out on the carpet beside him, and breathing deep, would fall asleep as easily as a drowsy animal. For the good-natured and procrastinating Persians of the household she had only mild scorn.

"Tomorrow," she exclaimed. "It is always tomorrow with them. They talk about yesterday, and they do things tomorrow."

"But they are happy."

Ayesha had not thought about that. They had different feelings in them: they laughed and cried easily.

"And thou, Ayesha," he persisted, "thou livest only in today."

"Only in thy presence," she said, looking full into his eyes.

At such moments the memory of Yasmi stirred in Omar. Something in Ayesha's eyes, and in her way of turning her head swiftly, was the same. Omar understood that during these years he had been seeking Yasmi, unreasoning. She had died so suddenly, and the agony of her death — of which he never spoke, even to Jafarak — had seared him like a flame. It was all distant now, as if he recalled a dream that had no reality in his waking moments.

With Ayesha he could not feel the happiness that had been almost pain in Yasmi's arms. With Ayesha he was at peace; her love was like the walled garden with its roses that bloomed and scattered their petals on the ground, heedless of the hours or the tumult of men. Still the memory of Yasmi crept into the garden.

Once when Ayesha had been playing in the sun with her cherished headband, he cried out in anger: "Oh beloved fool, thou art not made of gold, that men will dig thee up after thou art buried!"

Surprised, she burst out laughing. She looked at her slim arms with great amusement. "Of *course* I am not made of gold." For a while she cogitated, wondering more at Omar's outburst than at the meaning of his words. "The dead," she said gravely, "are the dead. They do not change."

"They do not change," he repeated.

For years he had been struggling against the conviction that the desert-born girl expressed so simply. The dead did not walk again in life upon this earth. They were dust and drying bones, buried in the earth — and still the memory of Yasmi would not die. At times when he was very tired he thought that if he raised his head he could see her coming along the path to the House of the Stars, her veil billowing in the wind.

Two weeks later a courier on a staggering lathered horse beat with his stirrup on the gate of Kasr Kuchik bringing a summons from Nizam. The Minister asked Omar to leave at once for Ray and to make all possible haste.

When Omar said farewell to Ayesha the next morning, there

were tears in the girl's eyes. She had teased him for hours to take her with him. "May Allah watch over thee," she whispered. "Do not wander among strangers without a weapon."

At the gate Ishak came forth to make his salaam, and Omar fancied that he had seen disappearing around the corner the white turban and the red khalat of the long-dismissed Zambal Agha. He reined in sharply.

"What is this, Ishak? Is that castrated black hanging about the place?"

Ishak crossed his hands submissively. "After the late prayer last night, I heard that the Protector of the Poor would journey to Ray. Only Allah knows when he will return. Is not the honor of his house in my keeping?"

"Well?"

"All women are the better for watching. Surely no one would dream of letting so young a woman wander in so large a garden. Since Zambal Agha was not far off, I thought —"

"One of you," Omar directed the troopers behind him, "find that eunuch. Take a horse from the stable and escort him in to Nisapur. Turn him loose in the bazaar, and then see that he never sets foot within this gate again."

He did not wish to go away leaving Ayesha under the eyes of a jailer in her garden.

For three days he pushed steadily west along the caravan road, stopping to sleep at the serais. To avoid losing time, he did not enter Nisapur, where crowds would have gathered to greet the King's astronomer. Since Malikshah spent most of his time at the frontiers, and the aged Nizam was closeted with his papers, the people of Khorasan had come to look upon the splendid figure of the astronomer royal as the representative of power.

When they halted for the third night, a rider with a hawk on his wrist approached Omar and salaamed respectfully.

"May thy journey be pleasant, Khwaja! Behold, here is an omen." The stranger drew a small silver tube from his girdle — a tube no larger than a penpoint. "An hour ago I loosed my falcon in the plain yonder. I meant to fly him at a heron going toward the river, but he chose instead a pigeon flying west. Behold — I meant no harm — it was a messenger pigeon and upon its leg I found this tube with the paper that is in it. Read!"

The paper was no larger than a man's thumb, with a single line of writing upon it.

"Omar the Tentmaker is upon the road to Ray."

Instead of a signature there was a number.

"There is no harm," Omar assured the anxious falconer. "The pigeon was flying west?"

"Like an arrow, into the setting sun. And then I heard of the Khwaja's arrival here, in this very spot, and I said to my companions, 'Verily, nothing happens save by Allah's will.'"

Turning the slender tube in his fingers Omar reflected that he could not know who had sent this message, or for whom it was meant. The pigeon had known whence it came and whither it was bound, but the pigeon could not tell. The tube smelled faintly of musk. Only the people of Kasr Kuchik had been aware of his departure for Ray, and he had taken some pains not to be seen near Nisapur.

Perhaps one of Nizam's spies had sent the pigeon. Either the sender expected the writing to be recognized, or the number beneath it identified him. There was not one chance in a hundred that Omar could discover the truth.

But on an impulse he tucked the tube and paper away in his wallet. It had been only one chance in a hundred that the falcon had brought down this message to him.

The Place of the Books in the ancient city of Ray.

ACROSS THE CARPET Nizam al Mulk and Omar Khayyam faced each other. For the first time the Arranger of the World found himself opposed by the King's astronomer, and he had not yet recovered from his surprise.

"But why?" he repeated. "Why should you throw the stone of refusal into the path of our progress?"

Nizam was quite calm, even curious. For nearly two generations he had administered the affairs of the growing Seljuk Empire. Now the empire stretched from the desert by the great Wall of China to within sight of the walls of Constantinople across the narrow strait that divided Asia from Europe. It extended up to the northern snows and down to

151

the barren heart of Arabia. Nizam turned the signet ring upon his thin finger. The King, he said, was the father of a universal family; his deeds should be equal to his exalted rank. His skill in waging war had brought pagan lands and peoples under the rule of Islam. His victories had enhanced his prestige at home. Still, Malikshah was the grandson of a barbarian Turk. If he returned with his four hundred thousand horsemen and dwelt in the peaceful cities of Khorasan, the people would see only a warrior taking his ease among them, and besides, his soldiery, accustomed to the battlefield, would make trouble in the villages.

"What is this army?" Nizam demanded. "As you know well, Khwaja Omar, it is made up of Turks from the north, of *ghoulams* who are the children of Turks trained as slaves to war, of Georgians, Turkomans, Arab tribesmen. Few are Khorasanis, and fewer Persians or Arabs of Baghdad. We should not make grants of land to such unruly spirits, prone to cause civil war. Nay, when the war in the east is finished, we will turn to the west to take two rich prizes — if God wills it — Constantinople itself, and Egypt."

For a moment the idea startled Omar with its brilliance. A holy war, to sweep over the land of the schismatic kalif and the last stronghold of the Caesars. Had he not seen Jerusalem fall, in just this fashion? Nizam, withered as a figure of dried parchment, appeared to be invincible — an alchemist of power, a magician controlling the fortunes of men.

Then the illusion vanished. Each new campaign could be paid for in lives and wealth only by another invasion. There was no place within Nizam's new state for the victorious machine it had built up, the Seljuk army. What would they do with the war elephants, brought up from India? Or the thousands of Turkish officers accustomed to a life of plundering?

"By the army," he said, "you have built up a great empire, which in turn hath need of a greater army to defend it. Then, what can you do but make new conquests, to pay for the new army? What will be the end of this?"

Fleetingly Nizam glanced at the astronomer. He had believed that Omar had thought for nothing except his science, his occasional dancing girl, and his wine. So long as Omar and

Malikshah were compliant, his — Nizam's — plans could go forward without interference. But if Malikshah returned to Khorasan, and dismounted from the saddle of war, he would soon take the reins of administration into his own hands.

And this was the last thing Nizam desired. Firmly he believed that Malikshah's conquests had been preordained, as well as his own administration of the empire.

"It was ordained," he said, "by God's will that our Sultan should make these conquests, and that we should rule over them."

Omar studied the pattern of the carpet before his knees. "And was it ordained that I should lie to the Sultan about the portents of the stars?"

"Believest thou that a man's fate is to be read in the stars?"

"Nay."

"Nor do I." Nizam smiled, and decided that Omar at last would see reason. "So, if the portents read in the stars be lies, how can you refuse any longer to write to Malikshah the portent that will best guide him along the road to victory?"

Abruptly he bethought him of something that had puzzled him for days. "A man calling himself Hassan ibn Sabah came to this room four days before thy letter from Kasr Kuchik reached my hand. He claimed to be able to read the future, and he said to me 'Soon, in a few days, your Highness will have a message from the King's astronomer of only one word — No.' Who is this Hassan that he should be told thy secrets?"

"He is the preacher of a new faith. At Jerusalem he spoke with me." Omar frowned. "But I told no one of that message, before it was sent."

"That cannot be! Thy courier who brought it was eight days from Kasr Kuchik to my presence. Yet Hassan knew of it four days before the courier came."

No rider, Omar reflected, even a king's messenger, changing horses at every stop could make the journey in four days. It was impossible that any one in Ray could have known of his message much before the arrival of his own courier, unless — it had come on the wings of the air. He felt the little silver tube in his girdle. A messenger pigeon had been carrying this warning that he was on the road toward Ray, and a messenger pigeon could have carried the tidings of his letter to Nizam from Kasr Kuchik to Ray in four days.

Then someone in his household had spied upon him and had sent tidings twice by pigeon to Ray. Was it Ayesha, or Ishak the keeper of his gate? Both of them denied that they could read or write.

"A pigeon might fly the distance in three days," he said aloud.

"The praise be to God!" Nizam, misunderstanding, leaned forward to pat his shoulder. "I knew that thou wouldst see the right path to follow. Write then, now, at once, to the Sultan, and we will send thy word by pigeon to Samarkand. Only be sure to say there is danger, if the Sultan turns back from the war."

"There is no danger." Omar smiled. "Would you have me write that Nizam hath decided the war is to go on?"

"God forbid. What child's talk is this?"

"Then I will write neither the one nor the other. I will write neither the lie nor the truth. I will write nothing."

Nizam started as if the last word had been a bell struck in his ear. His eyes peered from a network of wrinkles, and his hands clenched upon his knees. "You dare say that to me!"

"It is said," Omar nodded quietly, "and will not be unsaid."

For a moment Nizam was silent. "I raised you from a ragged student to the third dignity of the Empire; when the mullahs would have stoned you, at the making of the calendar, I guarded you from harm. I gave you masters for assistants. How many palaces have you now — how much wealth in goods and gold? Men say that you speak the truth, but I have heard you lie often enough to Malikshah before now. I ask that you answer me with the truth — what is your reason for seeking to ruin my plans?"

"The truth? I think you are mistaken, in forcing Malikshah into a new campaign. You would like to keep him at a distance, serving as commander of the army, while you govern the Empire."

Nizam took up a cloth and wiped his lips. His fingers trembled. "Do you deny that for nearly twice your life-time I have served only Islam, and never myself?"

"I know that." Omar did not add that at seventy-five

Nizam was not the man he had been at thirty-five.

"I think I understand," Nizam nodded. "I will give you an order on the treasury for ten thousand gold dinars. Will that suffice?"

"It is not enough, nor will Mahmoud's golden throne be enough."

"Ten, and five thousand, gold?"

Omar looked at the aged man across the carpet. These were large sums. "Thou hast aided me, O Nizam, but I do not remember that thou hast bought me. I do not think that I will sell myself."

"Then go to Akroenos, and the unbelievers! Go where thou wilt, Omar Khayyam, and look not to me for protection, for they who eat of my salt serve only Islam. As I have done."

His thin arm motioned toward the door. Omar rose and turned away. When he reached the door he heard the murmur of Nizam's voice. But the Minister of the throne had not called him back. Kneeling on his prayer rug the aged Nizam was bowing toward Mecca, repeating unsteadily the ninety and nine holy names of Allah.

"Peace," Omar said under his breath, "be upon thee."

Across from the Place of the Books rose the scaffolding of a new mosque with blue tiles gleaming from the moist clay. These mosques and academies stretching over desert lands — these rest houses for travelers, and giant market places, were part of the glory of Islam, and the aged Nizam had built them. Over nearly half the surface of the known world men were kneeling and praying in the same speech as Nizam.

Now Omar felt that another door had closed upon him, never to be opened again.

He was striding across the square, heedless of his surroundings, when a man cried out beside him. Bodies swirled in a sudden struggle and curved steel flashed in the sun.

"Mulahid!" other voices yelled. "Heretics! Strike — slay!"

Omar could see the first man, who wore a white robe and red sash, on his knees in a knot of soldiers. Blood was streaming from his throat and he gasped like an animal caught in a net. A hand closed over his face, the fingers catching in the nostrils and jerking it back. Then a scimitar was pushed across the man's throat and his severed head was lifted for all to see.

Another white figure ran desperately across the square. It stumbled, and pursuers closed about it. Sword blades slashed as it, and the man's white garment became red of a sudden.

"Death to the heretics." A bearded mullah raised his arms, invoking the wrath of the crowd that gathered as if by magic to join in the slaying. Hearing him, a ten-year-old boy began to weep, and the priest of Islam noticed the child. "O believers, here is a brat of the Seveners."

Frightened, the boy cried out and fled. Seeing Omar he flung himself down, catching the astronomer's robe. "O Khwaja — O prince, do not let them hurt me."

A youth with half a beard, a knife in his hand, clutched at the sobbing boy. Omar thrust him aside. "What is this? Do you hunt children in Ray? Stand back."

Beside the stripling with the knife appeared the mullah, red with fury.

"Khwaja Omar ibn Ibrahim," he shouted, "it is by command of the Nizam al Mulk that these infidel Seveners die. Let the steel of justice sever the thread of heresy."

Thus heartened, the youth with the dagger struck at the frantic boy. At the same instant strong hands closed about Omar's elbows from behind, dragging him back. Akroenos' voice whispered in his ear, "Come away, or my life also is forfeit. Come quickly."

By now the screaming boy had been stabbed several times in the stomach and his outcry was growing weaker. Akroenos' arm slipped under Omar's, drawing him away. "Talk to me — pretend to argue about the price received for the dates in Isfahan. Nay, it will do no good now to appeal to Nizam. Walk slowly."

But Omar could not help turning his head to watch the tumult in the square. Above the running men he noticed a plump man motionless in the saddle of a horse. Even at that distance he recognized the blue turban and the swinging rosary of Tutush, commander of Nizam's spies.

It had happened in two minutes. Then Omar found himself in the shade of an alley, staring into an open shop at a potter who was shaping wet clay upon a wheel, which he whirled with his bare foot. Ever and anon the potter thumped the clay rising between his hands as if endowed with life. But in the dust haze Omar still saw bright steel striking into human clay, and blood sinking into the dust.

"Gently," whispered Akroenos, "walk with me slowly. It is the chief of the secret police who follows. *Eight kantaras we sold, out of eleven, the rest being too spoiled for the market.*"

A horse stamped restively behind them, and bit chains rattled. Men were crowding from the shops to run toward the square.

"That dog!" Omar cried.

"Softly — that dog is Nizam's dog. Hast thou Nizam's favor still?"

"What if we have quarreled? I am no enemy of the Minister, and there is no need to fear him."

"But I fear the mob. Have you ever faced a mob egged on by mullahs scenting blood? *Look at these saddle bags of woven wool; they are what we seek.*"

Stooping beneath a mass of hanging saddle gear, Akroenos drew Omar into the shop of a wool merchant who was peering at the confusion outside.

"Haft," Akroenos whispered, pointing to a bag. "Seven, we seek."

Without a word, the shop-keeper rose and led them to the rear. Quickly he drew back the hanging that concealed a narrow door. "The owners of seven things," he remarked, "refresh themselves with wine at this hour." And he let fall the hanging behind his two visitors.

"Hold my girdle-end," Akroenos whispered. "There are steps that wind down, twenty of them."

And before Omar could speak, he began to descend into the darkness. In a moment around a curve in the stairs appeared a glimmer of light. A candle was standing in a wall niche, and Akroenos took it up with the familiarity of one who had passed that way frequently. Guiding Omar through the piled-up stores and rubbish of the wool merchant's cellar, he made for a great bale of wool standing apart against the wall. "Help me move this aside. Nay, just a little. We are neither of us as stout as that chief of police."

"But why run into a rat-hole? You are safe with me."

Akroenos glanced impatiently at the stairs across the cellar, and began to squeeze himself behind the heavy bale. "Perhaps, Khwaja Omar, in thy house I would be safe; but was that boy safe? This is not the first time I have fled from a religious riot, and I assure thee Tutush will do his utmost to track me down, to fasten some show of guilt upon me, and slay me out of hand. Then he and his followers would hasten to my warehouse and loot the goods there — thine as well as mine. Come thou after me. Ay, now pull the bale back against the wall by this rope."

They stood in a narrow passage concealed by the bale of wool. After listening for a moment, Akroenos led the way along the passage, which rose gradually to a closed door. This the Armenian opened without hesitation, placing his candle on a shelf beside it.

Omar stepped out into a cool cellar, odorous with wine. Its walls were lined with kegs and great tuns. Upon a carpet in the clear space sat a half-dozen men in talk, about an iron lanthorn. They glanced only casually at Akroenos, but they inspected Omar with interest.

After a deep salaam, the Armenian stepped aside respectfully, and a man who looked like a professor of the academy came forward to greet the astronomer.

"Welcome, O Master of the Stars, to this gathering of doomed souls."

"Every one of us," another explained lightly, "hath a price on his head this day."

Curiously Omar surveyed them. One spoke in the high-pitched cadence of Egypt, one wore the tattered robe and carried the staff and bowl of a dervish, while the others might have been wealthy merchants, but they were all alike in one respect — their eyes held the good humor of intelligence, and they bore themselves like men of action.

"Permit me, O Khwaja, to introduce these good companions who are temporarily in the shadow of the scimitar. I am the Professor; over there in the striped khalat sits the World Traveler, who can move mountains in his tales; the Dervish you will recognize; the fat man is the Seller of Sesame — and other disgraceful but pleasant drugs — and the twins are Gentlemen of Leisure from Isfahan. Do not trust them at dice. Now, sirs, I submit that we at last are Seven. And so we may depart, if the Master of the Stars will honor us with his company."

"I am honored," Omar smiled, "by your hospitality."

He had heard about the Seveners, who preached a new doctrine in Khorasan. But the tales conflicted, some relating that the Seveners were zealots who awaited the coming of a seventh prophet, some holding that they were heretics, preaching a new religion, while others maintained that they were magicians who possessed either divine or Satanic power. Omar thought it strange that these men could jest while the blood of their followers was being shed upon the square near at hand. Still, it would be foolish to wail and tear their garments.

"Is Hassan ibn Sabah of your company?" he asked. "I am looking for him."

As if by one impulse all the six turned to him, and even the Professor was silent. Akroenos spoke first.

"Hassan awaits you, Khwaja Omar. For months he hath awaited your coming."

The six relaxed, and the Professor found his tongue. "Hassan is not here. A little while ago he had occasion to visit Nizam, but now he is — in the mountains."

Something heard long ago tugged at Omar's memory. Hassan, who had first appeared to him on a mound of Babylon, had said that he haunted the heights. Hassan had been born in the mountains behind Ray, and people spoke of the leader of the Seveners as the *Shaikh al jebal*, the Master of the Mountains.

Omar wanted to meet Hassan, to find out why he received unsigned messages from a spy in Kasr Kuchik, by pigeon post. Moreover he had no desire to linger in Ray, under Tutush's eyes, or be summoned again before Nizam.

Leaning close to him, Akroenos whispered, "Hassan expects you, and he hath with him one whose beauty found favor in your eyes."

There had been many, Omar thought, whose fairness had found favor with him for a while; but his heart tightened at the memory of Ayesha.

"Well," he said, "will you take me to Hassan?"

Akroenos glanced at the Professor who had been listening in silence. "We are on our way thither now," responded that individual — and all amusement had vanished from his voice —

"Yet it is not an easy road nor a safe one for a stranger, even for Khwaja Omar of Nisapur, the King's astronomer. Bethink thee, we be *Rafiks* — Companions — of a new religion. That much thou knowest. Knowing that, and having seen us here thou mayest go forth into the street and say to the nearest spy of Nizam, or even to a mullah, *'There be certain leaders of the Seveners below in Ibn Khushak's cellar,'* and straightway our shoulders will be lightened of our heads."

"That is true," Omar assented.

"Too true. On our part we know that thou art no fanatic of Islam. Nay more, when thy word is given in any matter, it is always kept. So we ask only thy pledge that thou wilt not speak to anyone of what thou hast seen here, or of what thou wilt see upon the journey to Hassan."

Omar considered. "Yes," he assented, "I give my word."

"Good!" the dervish nodded. "Observe that we do not swear upon the Koran. We Companions are realists — we have long since ceased looking for the god in the machine of the world. Remember we Companions are likewise bound not to betray you. I do not think anyone ever broke the oath. And some," he added quietly, "were flayed alive to make them speak."

To Omar's surprise the taciturn Armenian busied himself in serving the seven with wine, producing glass cups, and drawing white wine from a keg.

"To amuse the police," explained the Professor, "we pretend to be a select band of tipplers, carousing upon forbidden wine in secret. The police are always ready to believe in a little sin and a little bribe. Now, up with the cups, because we know not whither we go, or —" he looked full into Omar's eyes — "why."

Then, one by one, they left the cellar — to meet at a rendezvous two days' journey within the mountains. Akroenos, who was to accompany Omar, insisted that he change his appearance. The King's astronomer, he said, could not leave Ray unobserved.

For an hour in one of the wineseller's upper rooms, Omar had to submit to the ministrations of a smiling woman who trimmed his beard and daubed it with henna. Then she swabbed the skin of his face and throat with walnut juice, until it was darker than the beard.

"Selma," the Armenian explained without amusement, "knows the faces of all men who journey upon the roads. She could make a Hindu fakir into an African marabout."

Selma giggled, and gasped that she had never had to deal with so handsome a type as this lord. Her husband smiled affably.

When the wineseller's wife had finished with him, Omar stood arrayed in voluminous khalats of padded silk, with broad shagreen breeches and riding boots that curled up at the toes. Upon his girdle gleamed silver plates, and his new turban was heavy with bangles. Akroenos turned him around critically, and suggested another silver armlet or two. When he was satisfied at last he announced that here was a Bokharan horse dealer, on his way to the hills to buy ponies.

"Swear in Turkish then," suggested Selma, "and spit often. Eat with both hands and blow thy nose — so — I ask the lord's pardon! Walk with bent knees, rolling a little, thus, as if from years in the saddle, and drink of mare's milk in public, and his own mistresses would not know the noble lord."

The Eagle's Nest above the mountains and the river.

IF ANYTHING WERE NEEDED to give Omar the feeling that he was ascending out of the known, familiar world, Akroenos supplied it by blindfolding him at sunset of the third day.

"Thy pardon!" the merchant muttered. " 'Tis forbidden that a layman should know the road up."

Mounted on mules, they were entering the hills above Kasvin. Omar's last glimpse had been of a rock-strewn ravine, and forested heights beyond.

"Then thou art of the Seveners."

"I serve the Lord of the Mountains." Akroenos leaned close to whisper, although they were alone upon the trail. "In these hills the name of Hassan ibn Sabah is not spoken. The Hassan thou knewest — he of Babylon and Cairo and Jerusalem — is no more. This Lord of the Mountains hath ten thousand who obey him in Khorasan. His power is not that of earthly rulers."

Remembering the eagle that had walked about the body of a man in the dust of Babylon, and the messenger pigeon brought down from the sky, Omar said nothing.

"Last week in Ray," Akroenos went on, "Tutush surrounded the hostelry into which the Lord of the Mountains was seen to enter, after his interview with the Nizam al Mulk. Tutush and two score police searched that place, leaving no bale or chest unopened, and they could not find him they sought. No one saw the Lord of the Mountains journey to his eyrie, yet he is there, awaiting us."

"Where?"

"In *Alamut* — the Eagle's Nest. The name is known, but who knows the road to it?"

"Evidently you do."

"Once," the Armenian admitted simply, "I saw the gate of Alamut."

"Was it a week ago that this Lord of the Mountains ordered you to bring me to him?"

"Nay, a year — two years ago. He said, 'The time draws near when the smoke of dissension will arise between Omar Khayyam and Nizam al Mulk. When that happens, seek him and bring him to the hills, where he will find sanctuary.' "

"Then Ha — the Lord of the Mountains is a worker of magic."

"He is wiser than any *man* I have known. He hath the secret of power. It is better," Akroenos added thoughtfully, "to obey him than to disobey. Some say that Nizam hath written in his book certain chapters of warning against him, and hath sealed these chapters until after the day of his death. Who knows? But it is true that Nizam fears him."

"And thou?"

Akroenos was silent for a while. "Down there," he observed, "in the plain we left the oppression of swords and taxes, and the tyranny of priests. Such things weigh little upon the favored Khwaja Omar, but they are like chains upon a non-Moslem seller of goods — ay, we Armenians be no more than slaves. Up here is freedom."

A strange eagerness crept into his voice. This worldly-wise merchant of the caravans rejoiced as he drew nearer to the rendezvous in the hills. Often he lashed on his mule or tugged at the halter of Omar's mount. Other beasts and men were moving along the track. Omar heard whispered greetings, a stifled laugh. But no one seemed to be carrying a light.

When they were stopped for a while by unseen sentinels, he

heard the whisper of a river below them. A cold wind buffeted them from above and Omar recognized the heavy scent of pines. The mules climbed steadily over broken stones, until a wailing voice challenged them:

"Stand, ye wanderers of the night!"

And a man beside Omar answered, "Nay, we are seven Companions."

"What seek ye?"

"The day that is not yet."

The mules went forward again, their hoofs grating on solid stone. They turned sharply upon their tracks, as if climbing a traverse up the face of a cliff; far beneath them, the river roared over rocks. Heavier gusts of wind clutched at Omar's loose khalat, and he gripped hard with his knees, feeling that he was swaying back and forth over emptiness.

Then lights flared about him, the mule stumbled to a halt, and he heard the creaking of giant hinges. Iron clanged behind him, and a hand lifted the bandage from his eyes.

For a moment the glow of a lanthorn blinded him; then he was aware of the stars overhead and the wall of a courtyard about him. Akroenos and his companions of the road had vanished. A grinning black boy held the mule's rein, and a little man in red silk of Cathay salaamed before him.

"May thy coming be fortunate, O Master. I am Rukn ud Din of the Cairo observatory, and my ignorance has rejoiced in the wisdom of thy books. Please descend, and seek rest in thy chambers."

Stiff with fatigue, Omar followed his guide into a postern door and through stone corridors that seemed to be deserted at this hour of the night, to a sleeping room where a brazier glowed comfortably beside a Bokhara rug. Sugared fruit and cakes stood on a tray near by, with a glass flagon of wine.

"This," Rukn ud Din indicated the black boy, "is thy slave. Now that thou hast escaped from peril, sleep with a mind at ease. May thy dreams be pleasant."

When the fellow-savant from Cairo had bowed himself out, Omar ate a little and gave the tray to the boy. He drank a goblet of the wine, which was strong and spiced. Then he peered out of the single embrasure of the room.

Only darkness lay beneath, and clouds scurrying across the stars above. Omar picked up a heavy coal that had dropped from the brazier, and tossed it from the window. Leaning out, he listened, but could not hear its fall.

Thoughtfully, he rolled himself up in his coverlets — for the mountain air was chill — and stared at the red embers of the fire. Drowsiness crept over him, and the red of the fire turned to the blue of sapphires. He looked over at the boy, curled up asleep against the door. The dark figure had altered to a shimmering white. And the room surely had increased in size — the ceiling had risen into the night.

But Omar had a sense of power and well-being.

" 'Tis a strange sleep, this of the mountains," he thought, closing his eyes.

Alamut, he discovered the next day, covered the summit of a mountain overhanging two sheer gorges. The path up which he had come was not visible from his side, because the cliff fell away almost sheer to the bed of the silver river. Beyond, towered ridge upon ridge of tawny rock resembling fantastic battlements and gigantic towers.

Since the walls of Alamut were built of natural rock, Omar reflected that from the other side of the gorge the castle must appear like the rocky summit of a mountain. Certainly no one — except the eagles that hovered about it — could see down into it. He noticed that the castle proper with its courtyard did not cover all the summit.

Midway across the castle rose what seemed to be a solid wall, with the tips of trees visible above it.

"Oh, that yonder is a garden," observed Rukn ud Din. "Later, perhaps, you will see it."

At times Omar saw sentries on the walls. They wore the same white garments, with red slippers and sashes, as the Seveners who had been slain in the square of Ray. There were numerous servants, mostly blacks and Egyptians. But he did not see any women, or any men of authority except those in Chinese garb, like Rukn ud Din. They seemed to converse in whatever language struck their fancy.

"We are merely the *Da'is* — the propagandists, you would say," Rukn ud Din admitted cheerfully. "Since we come from remote places and travel constantly, we necessarily know quite a few languages. I am a Cairene but you see that my Persian is quite fair. I know the library will please you. Come and look at it."

He led the way down the central stair to the first landing, entering a great room divided into numberless alcoves, all with oil lamps burning. A score of men were at work upon the reading stands, and Omar halted, surprised, before shelves of Greek manuscripts.

One, judging by the diagrams, was a copy of Aristarchus' work on the moon's orbit, and eclipses. Another was a volume of Plotinus.

"I have never seen these before," Omar cried.

"Yes. They were brought from Egypt, where they survived the fire that destroyed the magnificent library of Alexandria. Legend has it that all the volumes were fed by the Moslems into their cooking fires. Still, many were saved, and *Sidna* — our lord — discovered them. We have maps, too. Oh, we have our treasures. Two of the Da'is are from Byzantinum, and if you wish, they can translate the Greek texts for you."

Even in his excitement at the findings of Plotinus, Omar noticed that Rukn ud Din spoke of Moslems as if they were followers of a strange religion.

"Is this an academy," he laughed, "or a castle?"

"Both, and quite a bit more. Oh, yes. We seek knowledge without the taint of superstition. Look here."

The small propagandist pointed to a group of much-handled volumes. "The algebra, the third degree equations, the volume on eclipses, and the astronomical treatise of Omar Khayyam," he smiled. "All greatly in demand. I have read your mathematical works, but I confess the others are beyond my poor comprehension. But the *Sidna* has read them all."

"Has — the *Shaikh al jebal,* your lord?"

"Who else? Certainly. I have some skill in the seven fundamental sciences, which are: logic, arithmetic, music, geometry, astronomy, physics and metaphysics. But *he* hath mastered all the tradition of religion, the cabbala of the Jews, and magic itself. We obey him gladly because his is the perfect knowledge."

But Omar, turning the leaves of Plotinus, did not hear the last words. His mind had drifted away to a solution in cube roots.

The hours passed uncounted in Alamut. When Omar was

not absorbed in the treasures of the fabulous Alexandrine library he was seated with the Da'is — who seemed to have visited every inhabited corner of the earth — discussing the science of the Chinese, or the music of Byzantium.

Omar was amused by Rukn ud Din's interest in magical squares. The little man had worked out certain combinations of numbers that yielded fixed totals, no matter how they were added or multiplied. Omar, whose research had been devoted to solving actual problems, shrugged his shoulders. "Such squares are curious," he said, "but meaningless."

"They are not meaningless to common minds," Rukn ud Din objected; "they are miraculous."

Every night, however, Omar was visited by the fantastic half-dreams of the first evening. The walls of his room took on strange coloring, and he had a sense of well-being and power. He wondered if this came from the strong wine and the thin mountain air.

It did not keep him from making observations of stars low in the northern horizon which were not visible from Nisapur. He was up in one of the towers, late in the evening, when Rukn ud Din came to him agog with excitement.

"Our lord will see thee. But we must make haste."

Reluctantly Omar left the chart he was drawing. Rukn ud Din, however, was insistent. "Thou shalt see what no man from outside the walls hath seen before. Follow me, and say nothing except to me."

Almost running, he led Omar down from the tower, through the main halls to the library stair. This time he opened another door and began to descend a stair carved from solid rock.

"Look to thy footing," he cried over his shoulder, holding a round lantern high.

Omar needed no urging to do so. On the side away from the rock he could see nothing at all. A breath of cold air came up from below. The steps wound downward, and he felt that he was descending a great shaft in the mountain. Although the rock beneath his feet was hard basalt, hollows had been worn in the steps by the tread of innumerable feet.

At places the steps were so broken that he had to hold to the rock wall. Rukn ud Din seemed to know every foothold. He jumped down with the nimbleness of a goat, swinging the lantern in dizzying fashion.

When at last they stood on the bottom of the shaft, Omar drew a long breath. "These steps were not made yesterday," he said simply. "Is this a mine?"

The little philosopher glanced up at him curiously. "Thou art the first to come down and ask such a question. Yes, these steps were hewn in the time when men worshiped the sun — and fire. It was more than gold they sought here below. Now watch, but do not speak again."

Turning into a corridor — Omar thought it was a natural tunnel — he almost ran to the end, where Omar started at beholding a black warrior solitary in the darkness, leaning on a spear beside a low wooden door.

The guard paid no attention to them, and Rukn ud Din thrust the door open. Omar had to stoop low to follow, and when he rose he found himself in a vast space, in a multitude of other men.

Rukn ud Din took his hand and led him forward among the seated figures who muttered impatiently at the interruption. When he came to a clear space he whispered, "Sit here."

In front of them, beyond the dark ranks of heads and shoulders, a fire was burning. At least so Omar thought at first. But the flames leaped at intervals from fissures in the stone floor of the cavern with a bluish glare that was like no ordinary flame. They hissed and sang in cadence. And somewhere wailing music took up the cadence.

The music, Omar thought, came from flutes; but at times he heard the brazen note of a gong and the chiming of silvery bells that echoed faintly from unguessed heights of the cavern.

Although the throng moved from side to side in time with the distant wailing, every head was turned toward the space behind the leaping fires. For a moment Omar watched the spectators.

They were all young, and all wore the now-familiar white and red of the guards of Alamut. Some lean, dark heads showed Arab blood, and others might have been Hindus or Chinese.

"The *Fidais*," Rukn ud Din whispered, "the devoted ones. This is their night of freedom and joy. Soon they will look upon the face of the Lord of Life and Death."

Their eyes were distended, and at times one would wipe the sweat from his brow with a loose turban end. They were intent upon something happening behind the flames.

A dance was going on, a sword dance that whirled about a single half-naked man standing with his arms stretched above his head. Slowly he turned upon his heels, chanting:

"Allah illahi — allah illahi — illahi."

From the lips of the throng echoed the chant, in cadence with the swaying bodies and the chiming of the bells.

About the singer leaped and whirled a score of dancers, each swinging two swords in such perfect time that steel never touched steel, although the blades circled the heads of the other dancers, and seemed about to slash their bodies in twain. Sweat flew from their bare arms as the dance quickened and the gleaming steel became a shimmering arc of light.

". . . illahi illahi!" the crowd moaned, rocking upon its haunches.

How long the dance had been going on Omar did not know, but it was nearing its end. Rukn ud Din was gripping his arm and breathing hard. On the other side of him a boy was sobbing and chewing his lips.

"His hour is at hand!" screamed a voice through the monotone of the chant. "To paradise . . . to paradise."

Still the man with arms upstretched and head thrown back turned slowly among the whirling swords. And Omar became aware of something else behind the dancer. A form took shape in the leaping fires, a beast with clawlike feet, the legs of a lion, the trunk of a bull. High in the shadows reared its monstrous head of a man with a curling beard.

Wings towered on either side the head, and although the thing was stone, the flickering light gave it a semblance of life.

"Now," Rukn ud Din cried, "now, he goes to paradise!"

The revolving man stood still. The swords were touching him; they caressed his flesh, and blood ran down into the white cloth of his breeches. The stains spread, and he screamed with dreadful exultation. His upraised arms drooped to his sides. Steel swept against his neck, severing his head from his shoulders.

For an instant the body stiffened, the arms jerked, and then it collapsed to the floor.

As it did so, the chiming ceased, the chant was stilled, and every man except Omar and Rukn ud Din flung himself forward on his face.

"The Lord of Life and Death," a voice cried in the silence.

Between the claws of the bearded bull stepped a tall figure in gleaming white. From wrists to chin it was wrapped, like a shrouded mummy. But the dark head was that of Hassan ibn Sabah.

Bending down, he picked up the body that lay at his feet.

"Look, ye devoted ones," he called. "For this one hath gone to paradise."

Men around Omar rose to their knees. They saw Hassan between the claws of the stone beast. In his arms he held the limp body. But — and a sigh went through the throng at the sight — no scar marred the skin of the man in Hassan's arms; its head hung from its shoulders, and the white linen upon its legs bore no stain of blood. Line for line, hair for hair, the limp body was that of the dancer who had been struck down by the swords.

"Behold," the crowd murmured, "it is accomplished."

Still holding the body, Hassan stepped back between the feet of the winged beast and disappeared among the shadows at the back of the cavern. The sword dancers, still panting, circled the flames to merge with the crowd that had begun to take notice of Omar. Boys circulated among the white-robed figures, filling bowls with wine from the jars on their shoulders. Eager hands stretched forth for the bowls.

"By all the gods," whispered Rukn ud Din, "it is good to drink after a sight like that. Do not say anything aloud, for these swordsmen are in a mood to cut up the stone bull yonder. They do not know you are a privileged person. Ah!"

The little man's fingers trembled as he seized a bowl and drank down the contents. Omar noticed how one of the sword dancers wiped clean his weapon with a cloth.

"That, at least, is real blood," he said.

The warrior's lips twitched in a snarl and he thrust the naked scimitar before the Tentmaker's eyes. "Touch! Smell!" he grinned. "And if then you doubt, you will discover if your own blood be real, or not."

Others turned to stare at Omar, from haggard eyes. The dance or their own excitement had intoxicated them to the point where it would be a relief to do violence.

"*Y'allah*, how came he among us? Who brought him?"

Rukn ud Din took a bowl from a boy and handed it hastily

to Omar. "Drink," he whispered, "and be silent. Uncaged tigers are gentler than these." To the crowd he cried, "This is a guest of the Da'is. It was a command that he should come to behold the face of our lord."

"Who answers for him?"

A stripling staggered to the front of the circle forming about Omar. Thrusting aside the older men, he clutched the hilt of a dagger in his girdle. His mouth hung open and his eyes were blank in the head that swayed on his shoulders. "Who answers for him?"

"I do," cried Rukn ud Din, trying in vain to push the boy aside.

"He is no man of the mountain. Look, the dye upon his beard — look, the white skin on his hands. O ye who serve our lord, here is one in hidden guise."

Snarling faces pressed closer. Eyes glowed red with lust. Stench of blood and sweat stung the nostrils. . . . A sudden warmth flooded Omar's brain. The sides of the cavern were receding into space. He was looking upon a multitude of priests who had served the altar of the earth, here in the maw of the earth, since the beginning of time.

The stone beast had grown gigantic, and the stone wings moved. Between the claws lay the altar to which all bodies must come, the altar of Baal and the everlasting fire. He stood up and laughed, because it was ridiculous that his poor body should seek to protect itself against the power of the Beast.

"Way! Make way!"

Heavy footfalls drew nearer, and long staffs whirled against the heads of the crowd. A group of black slaves, moving shoulder to shoulder, forced its way toward Omar.

Strangely, the clamoring swordsmen submitted to be thrust aside and beaten by the blacks, who closed in upon Omar. He was picked up by strong arms and carried away from the fire. The muttering of voices dwindled behind him and the tread of the black slaves grew louder as they passed into a dark corridor.

Irresistible drowsiness crept over Omar. He was being carried through the darkness upon a litter of some kind. Once, when the motion ceased, he smelled strong incense and opened his eyes with an effort.

Turning his head he looked into the red coals of a brazier

from which smoke curled up, into his face. The smoke had a pleasant scent. A hand passed across his forehead. Hassan ibn Sabah was bending over him, and Hassan's voice repeated two words over and over, "To paradise . . . to paradise."

The distant winking stars grouped themselves into Orion's square. And beside it clustered the bright heads of the Twins. The eye of the Crab gleamed clear, and then its claws took shape.

Omar moved his head and sought for the other constellations. Yes, they were in their proper places, but something was wrong with the sky. He stared thoughtfully into the round face of a golden moon, low upon the horizon. There should be no moon in this sky, least of all such a full autumn moon. Moreover, he felt that if he reached out his hand, he could touch its face.

He sighed pleasantly and realized that he was lying down. His body felt light and when he sat up he moved with effortless ease, yet his head seemed to have a veil drawn about it. Triumphantly, he stood up.

A fruit tree attracted his attention. It was loaded with blossoms — he sniffed their fragrance — and that strange moonlight revealed all the colors of the blossoms. But the moon did not exist. Omar was quite certain of that.

Under his bare feet he felt soft grass. He extended his fascinating investigation to his arms. Sleeves of light silk covered them, and this unexpected beauty of his body filled him with delight.

The sound of running water attracted his attention next. With some difficulty — because his feet did not carry him in just the direction he wished — he arrived at the source of the water, and it was a fountain.

At least it ran from a rock, and he stooped to drink of it. After a taste he drank long and steadily. His throat had been parched and dry, and the water was red Shiraz wine.

"Good wine of Shiraz," Omar said aloud, and listened to his words receding into the night.

His roving glance fell upon a lion with a grinning head. Without trouble he walked to the lion, and touched its hard head, as smooth as porcelain. The lion, however, did not move. Omar climbed upon its back and still it did not move. He waited until that fact was established beyond any doubt. Now he had discovered three things about this garden of the moon.

"First, the moon is not real. Second, the water is wine. Third, this king of beasts is Chinese."

Having progressed so far, he felt himself to be at the threshold of a brilliant discovery. But his mind suddenly became weary of logic. His feet led him away from the lion toward a pool of water, still and inviting. White water blooms flecked its surface, and a white swan drifted far away, asleep with its head under its wing. This seemed to Omar to be a marvelously satisfactory way to sleep.

Then he became aware of sounds in the garden. Craftily he listened and was not deluded. "It is not a nightingale strayed into this garden of the moon. It is a woman singing." After a while he decided that she was playing upon a lute. Pleasant to hear, but not unwonted.

What really invited him was the house upon the water. Perhaps it floated, or perhaps it had been there when the pool came. No matter, there it was. If he could find his way to it —

Rushes tangled about his feet and he fell among them. There, beneath the trees this strange moon shed no light. Vines caught his knees, and for a while he lay hopelessly among them. "O Thou," he complained to the night, "who settest the pitfalls, wilt thou cry 'Death' to those who fall?"

No one answered him, and he thought that after all the vines were friendly things. By their aid he pulled himself to the water's edge and beheld a slender bridge. At the end of the bridge floated or stood the house or the boat. Not for purposes of scientific investigation but to satisfy his own whim he wanted to enter this thing shining upon the water.

Midway across the bridge he saw his shadow walking upon the water and stopped to watch it. When his shadow stopped also he laughed, because this was really amusing.

The house rocked gently when he stepped within it. He pushed aside a curtain, and gazed at another, silver moon lying upon the carpet. He touched it and found it to be a warm round ball of light. But he could not pick it up. Something stirred behind it and a voice whispered,

"The son of Ibrahim."

Omar sat down by the voice, on yielding cushions, and considered.

172

"Nay, not the son of Ibrahim," he announced, "but his High Excellency Khwaja Imam Omar, Master of the Stars and King's astronomer. Make salaam O creature of the night."

"Be merciful to thy slave! Behold, I make salaam."

The voice of this houri of paradise was low and strange. But then creatures in dreams did not speak in Persian or Arabic. They spoke to you, and you understood.

Long golden hair covered the head at his knee. It was soft as silk beneath his fingers.

"Does this boat drift," he asked, "through an endless night?"

"One night is like to another."

"And the moon," Omar assented with conviction, "never changes. It does not rise, it does not set; it does not wax or wane. And the demons sing to it."

After a moment it occurred to him to turn her over. The face upon the cushions was pale, the eyes looked up at him without expression, and the small lips drooped. It stirred Omar's memory.

"Zoë," he said at last, "and the great Khorasan road; and the night I wept for Rahim. . . . They took you away when I was the son of Ibrahim."

Cool to his touch was Zoë's body, lying so still in the silver light. Cool her lips, to his caress. Resting his head upon her arm he wondered what had frightened her and had taken her garments away. But Zoë was beautiful, even dead in a drifting boat, in a night that would have no end.

"I wanted to keep you," he mused, and suddenly he smiled. "Nay, I am no more than the son of Ibrahim."

The fright left Zoë's eyes and her lips curved. She pressed his head against her throat, and sighed. And the swan, asleep, drifted by on the still water, past the porcelain lion. Omar watched Zoë raise her arm and reach toward the light. She tossed something over it and the light grew dim as the wall of a tent.

Then Zoë took him into her arms again. And this time she was not dead — she was warm and living.

Hassan chose the hour of Omar's waking on the second morning to visit him. When he entered Omar's chamber, unannounced, the little black slave grew livid with fear and

173

fled. Closing the door carefully, Hassan seated himself on the carpet by the sleeper and spoke to him in a low voice until he stirred.

"Where hast thòu been? Tell me."

For a while Omar looked up at the ceiling. There were dark shadows under his eyes. "Asleep," he said, "and dreaming."

"Was it a dream?"

"Nay, only a little — not all."

"Then where wert thou?" Hundreds of times Hassan had asked this question of men roused from just such a sleep in this way, and he awaited the answer with confidence. In paradise, the hundreds had said with one voice.

"It was," Omar said thoughtfully, "a remarkable artificial paradise."

Not by a glance or a change of tone did Hassan betray his surprise. "Artificial?" he asked.

"Ay, the moon was too low in the sky."

"What else?"

Omar smiled in recollection. He was fully awake now. "The houri of your paradise was a girl I knew."

"That could not be. What girl was this?"

"Zoë the Byzantine, in the boat upon the lake."

Hassan had the ability, rare among men, to change his plans instantly; moreover he could do so without giving any outward sign of his intention. His spies had assured him — and they had not been chosen for their ignorance — that Omar could be enslaved by his senses, especially by wine and women. With a smile he dismissed this hope.

"I trust," his voice had a new note, "you found the wine of my paradise suitable?"

"Ah, it was good."

"I regret that the moon did not give satisfaction — to an astronomer. Unfortunately the light of day does not lend itself to illusion. But my *Fidais*, my devoted ones, never questioned it. After a visit to paradise they desire nothing so much as the opportunity to return to it. They are all young, of course. The *Lasiks*, the adherents, also crave it. As for the *Rafiks*, some of whom you met in Ray, I fancy they doubt its celestial nature, but they do not enjoy it the less for that."

"What of Rukn ud Din and his companion *Da'is*? Do they visit it?"

"Never. They are my brain workers; the library and the laboratory are their sphere. They find their own pleasures. You understand by now that my servants are divided into different classes."

"Four you have named."

"The laymen compose the fifth — merchants like Akroenos who attend to matters of trade, in the outer world. Oh, they make a profit out of me, being merchants. But they have never entered the gates of knowledge."

Omar thought of Akroenos, who had come as far as the gate of Alamut once.

"You bear many names, Hassan, son of Sabah."

"Why not? To the laymen and the devoted *Fidais*, I am in truth the lord of life and death. If you doubt that, you will have proof of it presently. They speak of me as the master of the mountain because our strongholds are being built, like Alamut, on the summits of the hills. Such places can be defended by few against many."

"And the *Rafiks*, what of them?"

"The zealots of the new faith, the champions, the apostles. *They* know me as the messenger of the Mahdi — as you did in Jerusalem."

"But now I no longer know you." Omar rose and went to the open window. "What do the two other classes of your converts believe?"

"Two others? I have told you of all five."

"Five, but not all," Omar said over his shoulder. "There are seven."

Amusement crept into Hassan's dark eyes. "For the moment I forgot that you were a mathematician. Enlighten my understanding: why do you say 'seven'?"

"Are you not known as Seveners? Your propagandists ask the unenlightened why there are seven days in the week and seven planets in the sky — counting the sun and the moon. I'll wager a dirhem against a Byzantine ducat that you have also seven classes of initiates."

Hassan smiled his appreciation. "Good!" he murmured. "Thou art tempered steel that cuts to the core! Akroenos swears thou wilt rise to great fame, but I say thou art worthy of more than fame. What other secret of Alamut hast thou discovered?"

Only for an instant did Omar hesitate whether to conciliate Hassan or to defy him. Alamut was not the place to show weakness.

"Thy secret of reading letters before they arrive by courier," he said.

"What dog saith that I use trickery? What lie is this?" Hassan's eyes contracted in sudden distrust.

"No dog. A falcon brought this down to me, on the way to Ray." Omar felt in his girdle and drew out the silver tube within which lay the message saying that he was on the road to Ray.

Swiftly Hassan read it, and glanced at the tiny tube. Sheer astonishment drove the rage from his face. "By Allah and by Allah! Ay, naught but a falcon could bring a messenger pigeon from the air. But what luck — what impossible luck is thine." He nodded as if making inward decision. "True, I have used messenger pigeons at times. Here in Alamut they bring the tidings of the world to me. Yet even the Da'is know naught of them. They come to the village, not to the castle — enough! Let us take our hands from the sword-hilt of strife, and tear apart the veil of dissension between us."

Striding to Omar's side, he flung his arm about his shoulders. "Thou art asking thyself — 'What is Hassan?' Then hear! Hassan is a wretched soul, once a student of life. What good is it to gain wisdom, where kings and their ministers rule souls as well as bodies? I have been lashed like a wandering dog by the armed guards of Cairo; I have tasted shame and have been flung mockery for consolation, ay, before I was of an age to beget a son. But in Cairo I learned wisdom at the feet of the masters of the Ismailite Lodge — the Seveners as thou wouldst say. I fled over the sea and sat at the feet of the cabbalists, those aged men in Tiberias by the sunken water of Galilee. Enough of that — I love not many words and thou also hast studied the mysteries when the stars grew dim over a weary land."

Hassan lowered his head. "I have tasted the bitter kernel of the fruit of wisdom. There is no God. The religions of the world are like aging women; their beauty and fruitfulness are gone. They are shrinking to the dry bones of superstition; soon nothing will remain of them but the scraps of hair and hide and bone that are preserved like precious stones in the reliquaries and shrines. What is the Black Stone of Mecca but a strange stone that is like iron? If I could cry a message to the listeners of the earth, I would say, 'Overthrow all altars and thrones. They who sit upon the thrones and they who guard the altars are no more than common men shielding themselves behind lies.' It is true that the Moslems who pray to Allah are no wiser than the pagans who made offerings to the sun in the beginning of time. Is it not true?"

"I know," Omar agreed, "that Malikshah is human enough. But if you take him from the throne, what will you put in his place?"

"The first thing would be to do away with the throne and its slavery of bodies. Thou hast more wisdom than four Malikshahs. Why should we submit longer to this king-worship? Men have been working up from ignorance toward reason. In the end men will achieve to perfect reason. . . . Well, I made converts, companions — dissatisfied souls. Secretly we preached the new propaganda."

For several moments Hassan was silent. "Thou hast seen the library, and thou has talked with the Da'is. Thou knowest we seek to perfect our understanding of all things. But thou knowest also — deny it not — that the mass of Persians have ears and eyes for nothing but the Koran. We needed converts among the masses, for a few intellectuals have never accomplished anything — except to get themselves imprisoned or burned. So to the vulgar we preach the coming of the Mahdi, which is an old superstition in Persia. To the intelligent ones, we preach scientific enlightenment."

Hassan shrugged, as if explaining the inevitable. "Is not life itself ordered in that wise? Does Nizam announce to the mullahs what he confides to you in his study?"

"He takes care," Omar smiled, "not to do so."

"You will find the doctrine made manifest in Plato. It is the very order of the universe. If you have light, you must have shadow. As a mate to man, you have woman. The twain fulfills one destiny. So our *talim* achieves unity by this very divergence — we have faithful converts among all classes."

"Yet you make use of magic."

"Why not? It is the highest wisdom."

"For the common man, perhaps. Your messenger pigeons and trained eagles appear miraculous."

"And for the intelligent ones, the *'arif*, there is a higher magic. Certain arts I learned in Egypt —" Hassan stopped abruptly. "By what art did you prophesy to the prince, who is now Malikshah, the death of his father and the Roman emperor fifteen years ago?"

On the point of answering, an instinct of warning checked Omar. "That miracle," he said calmly, "remains my secret."

"As you will. I have uncovered my secrets to your eyes."

"All but one."

Hassan looked at him intently. "And that is?"

"What the two highest ranks of your order believe — they who are above the Da'is, in Egypt."

"Bismallah! I did not say they were in Egypt."

"No," Omar admitted, "but I thought they might be."

"You thought!" Hassan turned to pace the length of the room and back. "If that is an idle thought, what will your reasoning be? Khwaja Omar, in Babylon I admired you, and in Jerusalem I desired you for a companion. Since then years have passed, while I have achieved much, and you remain in the same position at court — nay, I think you have forfeited Nizam's patronage. Your road will not be so easy now, with that aged Arranger of the World as petulant as a ruffled hen.

"Consider," he added, "what we of the new order have done for you. I bade Akroenos aid your fortunes, and he has done so faithfully. In the desert by the Euphrates he pulled you back from death; he has filled your palaces with luxuries, while he waited, and I waited for the moment when you should return to me. Admitted, that I watched your actions — as a friend seeking your friendship. Your new calendar, your books, the observatory at Nisapur — I admire every achievement. Do the leaders of Islam show favor to you in this manner? Does even Malikshah understand you as I do? Remember that in a change of mood or a moment's anger the Sultan may dismiss you from the Court. While to me you would be indispensable. Consider that, and come with me to see the strength of Alamut. Nay —" and Hassan smiled — "until now thou hast seen things only through the eyes of my followers. Now look through my eyes."

Omar wanted nothing more than to rest, because his head throbbed strangely and the sunlight that crept through the embrasure danced up and down before his eyes. To match his wits against Hassan's was an ordeal. But Hassan did not seem inclined to give him time for reflection. Instead he led him down into the bowels of the mountain.

Through corridors hewn out of limestone, Omar was taken to caverns where men labored at forges, and others tended furnaces wherein molten glass bubbled.

"They brought this secret from Egypt," Hassan explained. "Why should glass be a rarity only found upon the Sultan's walls? My merchants sell it in the bazaars where only clay jugs and porcelain dishes were sold before."

From the workshops he descended to storerooms filled with wine jars, bins of grain, and casks of honey. Summoning a slave with a torch he entered a space where sacks of rice were stacked to the ceiling.

"Enough," he said, "to feed my people for two years in case of a siege."

In the lowest level of the cellars they came upon wooden kegs beside the black mouth of a hole in the rock.

"Listen," Hassan said.

From the aperture came the splashing of water, falling into a pool.

"When the earth was young," Hassan observed, "this channel of water must have been a small river, at a higher level. It ate its way here and there through the limestone, making most of the tunnels and caverns thou hast seen. Centuries ago, some human beings found their way into the upper caves, and in time they cut the passages and steps over which we have come. Ay, they made a temple here in the heart of the mountain — we found their altar. Come!"

Omar realized that the structure of Alamut on the mountain summit might be no larger than another castle, but in the depths of the rock it formed a mighty labyrinth. Wayfarers might pass by the outside for generations without suspecting the secret of the bowels of the mountain. Then, too, thousands of men could live here unobserved.

Passing by one of the black sentries, who prostrated himself at his coming, Hassan opened a door at the end of a narrow tunnel and Omar found himself again in the cavern of the stone beast.

It was silent enough now, without the distant music and the stir of the assembled Fidais. But the yellow flame leaped up from the fissure in the rock in front of the natural dais where the dancers had performed, before the claws of the beast. At times the bearded head stood out distinctly against the shadows; then when the flames sank, the cavern was plunged into darkness. Omar noticed what he had not perceived two nights ago, that the air was warm and tainted with the odor of oil.

Even Hassan was silent a moment, contemplating the everlasting fire.

"Who knows its secret?" he murmured. "Down there, somewhere, is oil of the kind the Greeks burned in their lamps. But how did the fire come in the first place and why does it endure without change? Surely it is older than the worship of the god Ra in Egypt; it is older than Zarathustra, and the first sun-worshipers adored it because it seemed magical to them. Ay, they were Magians."

"They did not build the winged bull."

"No, that is the work of the early Persians, who likewise worshipped fire. I have seen figures like it in the ruins of Xerxes' palace down below Isfahan. The Persians simply believed this site to be sacred because it had been a shrine of the earlier worship, and they built their beast to honor or propitiate the sacred fire. Now I hold Islamic ritual here — with certain innovations of my own — to edify my Fidais."

The mood of meditation had left Hassan, and his cynicism returned. His words had the sting of steel.

"And why not?" he laughed. "Did not Muhammad make a holy place of the rock in Jerusalem that the Roman priests had cherished because the Judean king David dreamed there? And what was the rock, before David? Perhaps a well, perhaps an idol of pagans."

Yet in two minutes he looked and acted like another man. Striding from the cavern he turned into a dark passage that Omar had not noticed. A warm wind pushed them forward — and Omar realized why fire could burn and air be breathable in the maw of the mountain — around turn after turn until the darkness overhead became a half-light.

Soon a strip of blue sky was visible far above them, and the sheer rock walls of a chasm took shape on either hand. They had to climb over masses of broken rock until Hassan strode full into the glare of the setting sun at the end of the chasm. Then he stopped, flinging up both arms.

"Oh, my devoted ones! May the blessing of paradise be yours, and the strength of Allah strengthen your arms!"

He was standing above a natural amphitheatre. Behind him on either side the chasm towered the cliff wall that was Alamut's foundation. The amphitheatre was really a plateau half way down the mountain-side. It swarmed with white garbed figures, running from clay huts and throwing themselves face down before Hassan. Omar recognized the hundreds of Fidais who had watched the sword dance in the cavern. This shelf of the mountain apparently was their barrack, and he thought that there must be some way down from it to the valley below.

"To our lord — the peace!" they cried.

Poised so, his magnificent voice still echoing up the cliff wall, Hassan looked like a prophet able to lead his chosen ones to any promised land. He did not prolong the moment; instead he turned back into the chasm, drawing Omar with him.

Without slackening his pace he went from the lowest level of his stronghold up to the sheer summit. When Omar saw the sun again, they stepped out upon the broad rampart where the wind clutched at them.

The sun was setting, and three young Fidais who seemed to be sentries had laid aside their weapons to pray.

"Hast thou ever before beheld a miracle?" Hassan whispered to Omar. "Then watch."

Stooping above the youths he laid his hands on the bowed shoulders. They looked up, startled, into the face of their lord. Their eyes fastened upon his.

Then his voice rang out:

"Lo, your time hath come, and paradise awaits you. I release you. Leap!"

The last word was like the snap of a whip. Three slender figures quivered and jumped to the parapet. Omar saw one face transfigured with eagerness, and one distorted with a growing horror.

Two of the Fidais vanished over the parapet. The third swayed, his eyes closed.

"Thou also," Hassan urged, almost gently.

The third sentry fell rather than leaped into space. Clutching the paparet, Omar watched his dwindling figure spinning after the others — three white balls of fluttering cloth that bounced from the sloping cliff to vanish into the trees hundreds of feet below.

"You see," Hassan said, his eyes bright, "what obedience is given me. Is even Malikshah obeyed thus?"

"I saw three lives cast away for nothing."

"Nay, for a proof. What are three lives worth in themselves? Before this sun, that is sinking now, rises again, a thousand human maggots will have crawled into oblivion and another thousand will be spawned upon this dunghill that is our world."

With his foot Hassan thrust the discarded spears against the parapet. "Now thou hast seen a little, only a little, of my power. Wilt thou be my companion, and take thy place among the Da'is? Thy work will be in astronomy and mathematics as it is now."

"Here, in Alamut?"

"Nay, in the world. As thou wert before. Ask for what thou wilt — for the girl Zoë, or the Alexandrine books. I promise thee — and my promises do not fail — that the wealth and honor thou hast now is a small matter beside what will come to thee at my hand."

Omar looked down into the darkening valley. "And if I will not?"

"I cannot now send thee back to Nisapur. Until certain events have transpired, thou wilt abide here as thou art. Afterward, if it be thy wish thou mayest depart."

For a moment Omar was silent. "Give me a week," he stipulated, "to make the decision."

"Certainly," Hassan seemed relieved. "At the end of the week I shall await thine answer. Until then, my slaves within the walls are thine to command."

Within his chamber, Omar sighed with relief. It was good to

be alone for the first time, and he had learned some surprising things. He was filled with admiration for Hassan's genius, and he wondered how the leader of the new order had found the wealth needed to sustain his following. Hassan had mentioned some articles of trade, and of course Akroenos could draw a profit from a camel dying of the mange; but Hassan must have some other source of wealth that he had not chosen to explain.

A remark of Ghazali, the mystic, flashed through his mind: "Any shrine is better than self worship."

If human beings were in reality no more than intelligent animals, then Hassan's new order was logically the best that could be expected — a hierarchy of scientific minds directed by a single leader of unquenchable purpose.

"After all," Omar reflected, "Plato's republic would have been a stupid place. A lot of schoolmasters arguing about happiness."

It would not be so bad, to live in Alamut with such a companion as Zoe, in a place that was like an observatory of all the world. He would not have to dispute with Nizam or Ghazali or his own conscience. And that would be a relief. But he discovered that he did not wish to be the servant of a man like Hassan.

If he served Hassan, he could not get his own work done. And he had barely begun to test his theory, that the earth revolved through space instead of remaining motionless in the center of the universe.

"I do not think Hassan would release me, in any case," he mused. "No, he would not dare, after what I have seen. I would be kept here, a prisoner. That is certain. So I will have to escape, before the week is ended."

After making his decision, he thought regretfully of Zoë's loveliness.

Omar's first concern was with the unknown drug. This strange distortion of his senses and the following visions came not from wine alone — he knew the effects of wine too well, to think that. The thing that tampered with his brain was stronger; it came in the smoke of braziers, and in the cups he drank. He wanted to be rid of it, because he had need of all his faculties.*

It was simple enough to pretend to fall into a rage and command the little black slave never to put a brazier within his room again. But he suspected that if he refused the spiced wine brought to his room the drug would be administered in some other way. The unseen watchers must believe that he was taking the drug daily.

So he protested that the goblets brought to his room at noon and at night were not sufficient; he would like a jar of the precious liquid always beside him. A great jar was brought him — Hassan must have wished that during this week he should partake freely of the drug — and one cup of it convinced Omar that it had the same stupefying effect as the draughts given him at first.

"And now," he assured the jar, "every night the valley shall drink of thee."

When it became dark, while the black slave was out of the room, Omar filled the bowl from the jar and poured the drugged wine out the embrasure without tasting it. But he found, when he tried to sleep, that he craved his accustomed draught.

It was hard to lie there athirst and smell the fragrance of the jar beside him. Once he got up and went to it, only to throw himself back on his sleeping quilt, his limbs quivering with the effort.

The next night, although he felt the same desire, he made no motion to touch the jar, and by the fourth night he was sleeping normally without thought of it, except to wonder anew at its power over a human body.

Meanwhile under pretense of making observations of the sky, he had examined the wall of Alamut along the circuit of its ramparts, without finding any point where it would be

---

* Actually the drug employed by Hassan was "hashish," or Indian hemp. This was before the time of the use of opium in Persia, and "hashish" was almost unknown until Hassan introduced it. So its effect appeared miraculous to his "Fidais," who became habitués in its use and could, of course, obtain it from no other source. In time they became known as "hashishin," hashish users — hence the derivation of our assassins.

possible to climb down. In stories he had read often enough of gifted captives who wove ropes of women's hair or shredded blankets and slid over such walls, but it seemed to him that it was easier to tell such tales than to act them.

Several times he ventured down into the subterranean passages only to be turned back by the armed guards at the door of the fire temple. These guards had nothing to say, because they were mutes. And he satisfied himself that no weapons were kept within the castle — only the giant negroes and the Fidais who manned the walls and gates went armed, and they took their weapons away with them when relieved.

He could not make his way to the quarters of the Fidais. And as for winning over one of the guards, he might as well have entered into conversation with tigers. Besides, they were always posted in groups of three or seven.

"The logic of it is," he mused, "that if I can't go over or under the walls I must go through them. And the only way through is by one of the gates."

The great entrance gate was closed at night. A lantern glowed above it and seven Fidais sat there on watch. Only once did Omar see a man go out at night, by the small postern across the courtyard. This man was a tall Da'i and he showed a writing to the three guards, who unlocked the postern for him.

When Omar left his chamber after nightfall, he knew that watchers in the corridor followed him. Escape by night was impossible.

"Then it must be by day, and from the main gate," he assured himself. (The postern was locked shut from sunrise to sunset.)

After that Omar took to dozing on a roof pavilion from which he could watch the gate most of the day. He saw nothing that offered the slightest encouragement. No horses, and no men from outside were allowed within the gate; when villagers brought up stores they left them there for the Fidais to carry in. At times armed groups of Fidais emerged from underground and passed out the gate. In the same way others came in. More seldom a Da'i or two would enter or leave — they were always being sent on missions from Alamut, and returning to report. Hassan did not appear at all.

Yet the master of Alamut passed through the gate daily, unnoticed. Omar would never have suspected him, if he had not been scrutinizing every passerby.

For three days, a little after noon when the glare and the heat were greatest, he observed that the same tall Da'i who had left the postern the first night went out the main gate alone. After a half hour he returned and crossed the courtyard to disappear within the castle. This regularity stirred Omar's interest — as well as a certain familiarity in his walk. When Omar saw his hand lifted to open the inner door, he recognized Hassan in the dress of a Da'i. Hassan kept his eyes lowered and his hands — except for that one moment — in his sleeves, and his face had become that of a Chinese. Even the stoop of his shoulders and his knot of shining black hair proclaimed him Chinese. But he could not alter his hand, and he had not troubled to alter his walk, and Omar had a flawless memory for such things.

"But why does he disguise himself to leave his own gate?" he wondered. "And why does he go forth at the same hour?"

The answers occurred to him at once. The Rafiks had related that the master of the mountain came and went unseen. Evidently Hassan liked to impress his followers with his magical powers. Then Hassan himself had let slip the fact that his messenger pigeons were kept at the village — since he did not wish the men of Alamut to know how he received and sent messages. So he left secretly every afternoon to visit the pigeon-cote in the village.

To the Fidais and laymen outside he appeared to be one of the Da'is, while to the Da'is — Omar smiled as he glanced around. At this hour they were asleep or at work in the lower regions. If they happened to catch a glimpse of Hassan they probably took him for some new member from the outer world.

Omar who had drawn charts of half-seen stars could deduce another fact from Hassan's proceeding. The Fidais could not know all the Da'is, by face and voice.

"The chance of escape," he concluded, "is through the gate in the dress of a Da'is, in Hassan's footsteps."

After noon the next day he set about getting such a dress. Rukn ud Din had asked him more than once about the wine of paradise, and Omar remembered how eagerly Rukn ud Din had

grasped a bowl of the drugged wine during the sword dance —
and how Hassan had said that the scientists were not permitted
the delights of paradise. He asked Rukn ud Din to come to his
chamber, and he closed the door carefully upon them.

He did not need to pretend eagerness as he poured wine
from the new jar into the bowl. Raising it to his lips, he smiled
at the little philosopher.

"The wine of paradise!"

Rukn ud Din came hastily to the jar, his eyes intent.

"Is — is it the same?"

Omar held out the bowl to him. "Try, if it be not the
same."

With a glance at the door Rukn ud Din sipped of it and
sighed with almost painful relief. In a moment the bowl was
empty, and color had come into his plump cheeks.
Reluctantly, he surrendered the bowl.

"There is more, if it pleases thee," Omar observed
carelessly.

By the time the third bowl was half empty, the little man
lay stretched on the quilt, his eyes half closed. And he talked
without ceasing, his words beginning to wander. Omar, sitting
by him, asked quietly, as if they had been discussing it for
some time:

"The gold Hassan hath, and the power, whence cometh it?"

"By fear. By fear of the dagger that strikes, and the dagger
that strikes not. He hath taught us that men fear the unknown
more than the known. Likewise, he hath the secret —"

Rukn ud Din raised himself to his elbow, and seeing the
bowl, seized it and emptied it. "Allah be praised!" he
muttered and sank into stupefied sleep, breathing heavily.

In a few minutes Omar had discarded his own outer
garments, and had clad himself in the red satin khalat, the low
felt boots and the square velvet cap pulled from Rukn ud Din's
unconscious form. The coat was somewhat small, but the loose
sleeves and the wide skirts looked well enough.

A glance from the embrasure showed Omar that it was not
yet midafternoon. Probably Hassan had returned from the
village.

Throwing the voluminous khalats of the erstwhile Bokharan
horse dealer over Rukn ud Din, for the benefit of anyone who
might look in the door, Omar folded his arms in his sleeves and

187

stepped out into the corridor. In the distance he could hear voices, but no one approached the corridor.

Running silently, Omar gained the door into the courtyard. Through this he walked without haste, his head lowered as if in meditation. His skull felt strange without the accustomed turban. The glare of the limestone courtyard dazzled his eyes.

A pair of slaves passed him, carrying jars. Ahead of him the gate was empty, except for the guards. Omar's pulse quickened as he drew nearer.

The leader of the Fidais, who had a sword in his girdle, looked toward him casually. No one stirred, or showed any concern. Heat, reflected from the wall, quivered in the air. Four more steps would take him into the gate, Omar thought. One . . . two . . . three . . . four —

"The word of the day, what is it?" the leader of the guards asked irritably, and added, "master?"

Omar caught his breath. He had heard nothing and he had thought nothing of a password. Yet it would not do to hesitate. "I cannot recall it. Our lord himself hath sent me —" and he searched his memory for a possible reason — "to the village . . . with a message for the pigeons."

He felt beneath the satin robe and drew from his own girdle the unmistakable silver tube of Hassan's pigeon post. "See, it is here, and I must not delay."

The guards in the shadow glanced up curiously, and their captain looked puzzled. He was a man trained to use weapons, not his wits. Quickly Omar thrust the tube into his hand. "Do thou keep it, while I hasten to the house of the pigeons, and bring back a carrier. But take care of the message, or the anger of the master will fall upon thee."

The warrior grasped the tube gingerly, at loss for words. "Y'allah!" he muttered. "Be quick!"

Omar hastened down the path, leaving the guards clustered about the surety for his return, and as he had promised, he wasted no time. Of the village itself he had caught only glimpses from the castle wall — enough to know that horses were kept there, and that caravans came and went by several roads. Inwardly he prayed that he would not meet Akroenos or any one who knew his face.

Passing through hayricks and manure heaps he made for the pigeon house, beneath the circling birds. Only peasants and strange tribesmen sat in the shade along the street. To the first man within the courtyard of the house, Omar cried:

"Two pigeons in a cage, swiftly."

"Ah. Is it pigeons of Alamut the lord seeks, or —"

"What else? 'Tis the command of the *Shaikh al jebal.*"

The man looked startled, either because Hassan was not in the habit of sending for pigeons, or because the name itself frightened him. He lumbered off toward the rows of wicker cages.

"And a saddled horse from the stable. A good horse," Omar called after him urgently. "Send another man."

It was hard to pace idly back and forth, while the keeper of the pigeons shouted to the street at large that a red lord from the *kal'eh* demanded a fine, swift-paced steed from the stables at once, or calamity would come upon their heads. Drowsy men came to stare in at the courtyard gate, until the keeper ran up to Omar with a small wicker cage and a rope to tie it to the saddle.

"Here it is as the noble lord commands. See, one feather is clipped square on the inner wing, and also a circle in red ink is here on the tail. By those tokens these pigeons will be told from others, if the lord —"

But a rearing horse was led up then, and Omar cut short all talk by mounting it. He leaned down, picked up the pigeon cage, and — judging that those on the service of Hassan rendered no thanks for aid — tightened his rein and trotted out of the courtyard.

In the main street of the village he turned to the right, away from the river. Akroenos had brought him up the river road, and he remembered the guards posted there. Where the other roads went, he did not know, but they all led away from Alamut, and the only thing he wanted was to put as much distance as possible between himself and Hassan before dark.

Turning into a track marked by the pads of caravan camels, he found himself descending a narrow valley. In a nest of boulders, men rose suddenly with lifted spears. But after looking intently at his robe and the horse he bestrode, they sat down again with a shouted greeting:

"*Khoda hafiz!*"

"God be with you!" cried Omar.

Once he was out of sight of the outpost, he lashed his horse into a gallop, leaping rocks and swerving among giant pine trees. Suddenly he burst out laughing.

In that message tube held for him at the gate of Alamut there lay the written words that he had found there in the first place. *"Omar the Tentmaker is upon the road to Ray."*

At dusk, on a lathered, limping horse, he left the last foothills behind him and came out into the plain. There was light enough to see the white ribbon of a road where the trail ended, and beside it a broken-down tomb, by the lighted huts of a farm.

Dismounting by the first fire, he asked for the elder of the farm and demanded a fresh horse. "I ride upon the service of the *Shaikh al jebal*," he said, suspecting that these people at the end of the mountain road would have served Hassan's men before now.

"The one," the old peasant asked, "who is above?"

"Ay, in Alamut."

After whispering together the peasants went away from the fire, leading Omar's horse. Out of the shadows came a small girl and seated herself by the pigeon cage when she was sure the strange man did not notice her. She put her finger into the cage and touched the birds' wings.

Omar sat with his head in his hands, too weary to think of food. He had got away from Alamut, but he was not hopeful that he could escape the reach of Hassan's servitors.

"How," asked a child's voice, "did you make them go into this wicker house?"

When Omar looked at her, she drew back in fright. Still, she did not want to leave the pigeons. "I see them," she whispered, "flying up there, high in the air. Sometimes they sit in the trees but when I come they go away." And her voice drooped miserably.

"They eat grain in the fields, but they will not wait to play with me," she announced after a while.

"Would you like them," Omar asked suddenly, "to come down and walk around your feet here?"

"Oh, yes," she breathed, and clapped her hands softly.

Omar had reached down into the wet clay beneath his feet. There was a pool close at hand and the ground had been trodden by animals coming to drink. Taking a double handful of the clay he pressed it together upon a short stick and modeled the body and head of a pigeon. The girl-child drew closer to watch with fascinated interest.

Then Omar stuck two smaller sticks into the clay pigeon for legs, and set it aside. "Wait," he told the child, "and after the sun has dried this tomorrow, put it near the water. The others will come down out of the air to talk to it. But you must sit still, and not run after them."

"*Ai,* it is like them," the girl said with conviction.

When the peasants brought up a fresh horse, Omar noticed that it was no farm animal. He stretched himself and took up the wicker cage.

"Will it come soon," the elder whispered, holding his stirrup, "the day that is not yet come?"

"*Neh mi-danam; Khoda mi-danad.* I do not know; only God knows."

Omar rode through the night. When he came to a walled city that he recognized as Kasvin, he circled it and found the great Khorasan road again beyond it, for the riders from Alamut might well be in Kasvin looking for him by now.

When the first light touched the distant mountains, and the shadow of the plain gave way to gray hillocks, irresistible drowsiness came over him. Holding to the saddle horn, he began to nod, and the tired horse slowed to a walk. Omar Khayyam, his mind assured him, was on the road to Ray, the long Khorasan road that Rahim had traveled, leading nowhither. Clay pigeons walked over the desert plain, and why did children accept miracles as a matter of course until they were taught suspicion by old and stagnant minds? The clay pigeons were swooping through the air carrying messages of warning. Their wings drummed and drummed in his ears —

Hoofs thudded about him, and he woke with a start when a voice cried in Arabic, "What man art thou?"

Dust swirled in the full sunlight; scores of riders in the loose robes and head rings of desert men were passing by him, and some had stopped to stare. Omar also stared down at his dusty red satin.

"A wayfarer," he answered. "A wayfarer from beyond the Roof of the World, seeking the court of the great Sultan Malikshah."

"O Master Omar!" a familiar voice rang out. A bent man

flung himself from the saddle to seize Omar's knee in franti[c] joy. "Knowest not Jafarak?"

"But," Omar smiled, "Jafarak is at Kasr Kuchik."

"Nay," the jester laughed, "the army came. Malikshah'[s] riders came back from Samarkand, and so I joined them t[o] seek thee in Ray —"

A passing camel halted and knelt, rumbling protest, an[d] from its closed litter a woman climbed, running between th[e] horses to Omar.

"My lord!" Ayesha cried. "Allah hath preserved thee. I[n] the market of Ray they told us — thy fools of swordsmen tol[d] us — thou wert carried off by invisible devils." She caugh[t] Omar's stirrup. "They have changed thy shape — what hat[h] befallen thy beard? —"

"Master!" Ishak the gatekeeper cast himself on his knees "How could I prevent? This young person would not abide a[t] the *kasr*. She egged Jafarak on to follow thee, ridin[g] unashamed on the public road. I said to myself, 'Truly it rest[s] upon thy head, Ishak, to protect the honor of thy lord.' A[t] Ray she would not be stayed — she went to the commander o[f] these Arabs, and *he* went to our Sultan, upon whom be the blessing of Ali and Abu Bekr, and our Sultan said, 'Find Oma[r] Khayyam, if he be in the snow mountains or upon the sea itself —' "

"Be still, waggle-tongue!" hissed Ayesha, who suffered from no embarrassment at appearing before so many men — the Arab troopers had turned their backs modestly at sight of her — "It is by no doing of thine that our lord is restored unharmed. Thou wouldst have been yet picking thy nose at the gate post and pocketing the silver of spying eunuchs —"

"Peace!" said Omar sternly, for the officer of the cavalry clan was approaching.

Even Ayesha turned her veiled head away, when the young *rais* touched breast and forehead in salutation, looking curiously the while at Omar's strange garb.

"Say," he demanded, "art thou truly the King's astronomer?"

"Ay so," Omar assented, wondering how to explain his appearance. "I have been wrestling with magicians in those mountains yonder, and I came away in their garments."

"*Wallahi!* This is a time of marvelous happenings." The

Arab's curiosity changed to veiled alarm, and he reined back a pace. "Now hear the command of the King. Thou art to go with me direct to the presence."

"As the Sultan commands." Omar had hoped to return to the House of the Stars at Nisapur. "Where is his camp, O *rais?*"

"He rides to Isfahan, and we will follow."

When he was ensconced in the camel litter, at Ayesha's urging and the insistence of his own drowsiness, the Arab girl put aside her veil, and sighed comfortably. "Now thou seest — this is how a journey should be made, with a thousand swords to guard thy back, and the Sultan's favor to open the way to thee. . . . Were any women among those magicians of the mountain?"

Omar closed his eyes. "Only a demon girl, weeping upon a boat that floated on the lake of paradise."

"Paradise! Hast thou been carried out of the world to where the houris are?"

"It was only a dream, Ayesha. Verily the true paradise would be a moment's rest upon this road of life."

Ayesha was silent, pondering. Then she put her arms about him, and pressed her lips to his ear. "Nizam al Mulk is dismissed from his post. That is why the Sultan calls for thee."

Omar thought the girl must be mistaken. Nizam, who had administered the empire of the Seljuks for two ordinary lifetimes, dismissed from office!

"It was because of a letter," she added, seeing his incredulity. "Thou knowest how mighty Nizam had become, who placed even his grandsons as governors of cities. Well, someone wrote to the Sultan, 'Is Nizam thy Minister, or the partner of thy Throne.' And Malikshah, in anger, said to Nizam that verily henceforth he who wore the crown would rule without him who wore the turban."

A thought passed through Omar's bewilderment. If he had obeyed Nizam at the very first and had written long ago to Malikshah that the stars foretold misfortune if the Sultan returned to Khorasan, then Malikshah might not have dishonored the aged Minister.

"The letter," Ayesha went on, "was brought by a pigeon coming from those mountains."

After she said that Omar became silent. When they halted at the first walled town upon the Isfahan road, he descended from the litter and asked Ishak for one of the pigeons from the wicker cage he had entrusted to the care of the gatekeeper. When writing materials and a message tube had been brought him, he wrote upon a small square of paper:

> *"I have made decision. Thy road will not be my road, but concerning what was seen in thy house I shall say nothing, so long as no harm befalls those of my house."*

This message without greeting or signature he rolled into the tube and tied the tube upon the claw of the pigeon, after satisfying himself by the clipped feather and the red mark that the bird was one of the Alamut pair. When he tossed it into the air it swooped up and circled the town once. Then it darted off to the north, toward the distant mountains.

Ayesha and Ishak, who had been intrigued by his preparations, watched it open-mouthed.

"It goes toward the place of the magicians," observed the girl.

"Belike," hazarded the gatekeeper, "it was a prayer or invocation. 'Tis better to deal with the djinn-folk that way. But no good," he added ominously, "ever came of going into a sack with a bear."

PART V

The streets of Isfahan, at the end of the southern road, and the cellars of the Son of Fire.

TO AYESHA, Isfahan was one solid delight. The silks of the bazaar appealed to her woman's craving in their delicate coloring. She bought hugely of orange and magenta and glorious purple, while Ishak watched and grumbled that it was against all reason to let a handsome slave buy in the bazaar. Her ears were alert for every whisper of passing gossip, and Isfahan did not lack whispers. All this was much more exciting than sitting alone in a deserted garden. Even Ishak relished his new importance — he hired a pair of Dailamite swordsmen to follow them about for appearance's sake, when he was not sitting in majesty at the gate of Omar's new house.

His master was now the solitary favorite of Malikshah, and the entrance to his house was crowded with dignitaries who had favors to seek. Their horses and grooms could be seen waiting from the hour of sunrise until after the last prayer. Ishak's cup was full the day that the *Sipah-silar*, the Commander of all the armies, sent his chamberlain with a request, and Ishak kept the chamberlain waiting until Omar had finished reading a book.

"Don't stretch thy foot beyond thy carpet," Jafarak admonished the gatekeeper when Ishak related this, "or thou wilt know how scorpions sting."

"Well, my feet will never be where my head should be."

Jafarak spent his hours in wandering the alleys, and this seemed to Ishak a witless proceeding, when so much profit —

because every Isfahani who came to the gate brought some slight token for the keeper of the gate — could be made at the entrance of Omar's house. Ishak only regretted that his master had so little patience with visitors.

Instead of flattering the powerful nobles, and establishing mutually profitable arrangements with the wealthier merchants, and treating the poorer sort with becoming contempt, Omar listened to all of them impatiently and answered with a brusque word or two. He even assured them that he was not the Minister of Court — when his guests all knew perfectly well that he had the ear of Malikshah himself.

"Because he can't sit a-toiling and a-moiling over the stars," Ishak observed, "he is angry. Lo, he is the wisest of men, and still he does not know how to encourage an amir who is willing to buy the post of King's physician. *Wallahi*, what a pity!"

Ayesha did not reason about it, but she understood instinctively that if Omar had been an ordinary official, Malikshah would not trust him so utterly. The most satisfactory safeguard, she thought, was the favor of a man who could call four hundred thousand armored horsemen to his banner.

She loved to sit in the screened balcony of their house, overlooking the public square when Malikshah was watching a polo game in the late afternoon. Then she could admire the plumed and jeweled turbans of the highest amirs, the cloaks of damask and cloth-of-gold, and the Sultan himself, sitting opposite under the scarlet canopy, with Omar at his elbow. The horsemen wheeling before the massive marble goal posts, the shouting and the din of musicians when the game ended at a word from Malikshah — all this seemed to increase Omar's power. Ayesha nibbled sugared ginger and watched jealously the other veiled women who sought to catch the eye of the King's astronomer.

Only when she had overheard his remarks to a wool-clad Sufi, sitting on the roof one night did she protest. The Sufi had declared that from all eternity Allah had known what was to be.

"Then hath he known that I would drink wine," Omar answered. "And who am I to deny him?"

This frightened Ayesha, and when the Sufi had gone she came and rubbed her cheek against Omar's arm. " 'Tis ill, O heart of mine, to mock what Allah hath caused to be. Look at the wealth and the splendor he hath laid upon thy head."

Omar swept her with his eyes — the slave girl, fearful of some impending evil. "When you go out of the world, Ayesha, will you take all this wealth and splendor with you?"

"I do not know," she said, wistfully, fingering the silver on her arms.

"Well, enjoy what you can now, for — believe me — you'll not be back again."

Her lips drooped, and she stifled a sob.

"Nay, Ayesha!" He took her up in his arms. "I would not lose thee for all the promise of paradise."

"Not for the houri who waits in the boat on the lake?"

"For whom? Oh!" Omar considered, and shook his head. "Not even for that one."

Sighing with satisfaction, Ayesha ran her finger down his forehead and nose and lips. But she was careful to go every day to the great mosque to pray. Secretly she cherished a hope that after her life ended on earth, she might be allowed to dwell with Omar in paradise. The thought that an infidel dream-maiden with golden hair might be waiting at the threshold of the hereafter to embrace Omar filled her with deep anger.

Malikshah showed no inclination to release Omar from his attendance at Court. Since the dismissal of Nizam, the Sultan leaned more heavily upon the advice of his astronomer. He thought that the growth of the empire, and his own victories, had been brought about by Omar's inspired forecasts of events. Unquestionably the will of God had been the primary cause, but the interpretation of the stars had revealed to him what he must do.

"*Signs are in the power of God alone,*" he read aloud one day from the Koran. "And here it is said again: '*Though We had sent down angels to them, and the dead had spoken to them, they had not believed, unless God had willed it.*'"

"But if I should not read the signs aright, O Lord of the East and the West — what then? A man hath only human eyes to see, and he must fail often."

Malikshah considered, and shook his head. "By the Kaabah, I have no reason to fear that. A soothsayer with a little mind might fail, but thou art perfect in knowledge of the stars. How then would it be possible to fail in simple observation?"

When Omar would have answered, the Seljuk waved the matter impatiently from his thoughts. "See, here again it is written that even prophets have been given enemies, Satans among men, and djinn. I who am merely Sultan, by God's will, have many more enemies. So I have greater need to be guided aright."

Closing the heavy pages of the Koran and taking Omar's silence for consent, he added thoughtfully, "An ordinary astrologer might be bribed to deceive. That has come into my mind at times. But I know well that even a tower of gold would not lead thee to say 'Yea' when the answer is 'Nay.'"

Omar said nothing. No argument would shake the Sultan's belief in the stars. "Nizam al Mulk never betrayed your Majesty," he responded boldly.

"Nizam took into his hand too much of the power of the throne." As if remembering something, Malikshah drew a small slip of paper from the pages of the Koran. "This has to do with thee," he said.

The paper bore only a brief message in a fine, minute hand. *"If the Tentmaker garbs himself in a prophet's robe, look to it that there is not a jackal hidden in a lion's skin."*

"I do not need to look," Malikshah observed before Omar could speak. "I know thy worth. Since the battle of Malasgird our fortunes have been joined together."

Taking back the missive, he tore it in his strong fingers. Then with an angry hiss he tossed the pieces into a brazier.

"Spies!" he cried. "I would like to whip all such out of the land. Nizam said they were my eyes and ears. They sit down with my officers and rise up with my servants. So men who fear me and plot against the throne are careful to pay these same spies well, to report praise of them. And by Allah, they who love me do not feel the need of paying the spies. After a long time I hear much good of my foes and ill of my friends. But until now no one has dared lay blame upon thy name."

"I blame myself!" cried Omar. "I can do nothing here. Let me go back to the House of the Stars!"

Malikshah stared in surprise. "Allah! I have need of thee."

"Yet I have almost finished a new work. I have discovered something new about the sphere of the universe."

"Ha! A new star!" The Sultan smiled and leaned forward to pick up a choice bunch of grapes soaked in wine from the dish before him. The grapes he handed to Omar — a sign of rare approval. "Verily, our reign will gain luster from thy wisdom."

"It is not a star. I have seen — that the earth moves, turning upon itself."

For an instant Malikshah looked startled. Then he nodded understanding. "Who can escape such a nightmare? I myself dreamed once that I was falling, falling. The ground gave way and I fell through emptiness. Thinkest thou it was an evil portent?"

"That dream? Nay, thy Sign is favored by the planets. Have no fear." Omar wanted to tell Malikshah how for years he had been testing his theory that the earth, instead of resting motionless, revolved once in a day and night upon itself. That instead of being larger than the sun or the moon it was in reality a small speck in the universe. But Malikshah would never believe. So he began to eat the grapes slowly, praising their flavor.

"The other day," resumed the Sultan, "I counted the heads of game slain in one of my great hunts. There were more than nine thousand. I thought, 'Is it right to slay so many of Allah's creatures for my pleasure?' And now I think I shall give away in alms nine thousand pieces of silver, to make amends."

"Bism'allah — in the name of God."

"Ay, to Allah be the praise." Malikshah inclined his head devoutly. "Some time, perhaps, I shall let thee wander again. But now I would rather lose a slice from my liver."

Omar went from the Sultan's presence, through the crowded antechamber, in deep dejection. As he crossed the square, where lamps were beginning to wink through the dust haze, he was recognized. Behind his back he heard whispers.

"It is the Tentmaker, who measured the years. . . . Look, there goes Khwaja Imam Omar who tells what is to come to pass. . . . Companion of infidels . . . he destroys the verses he writes, lest. . . ."

Saying to those who still waited at his door that he would talk with no one, he climbed to the harem chambers, where Ayesha greeted him with a dancing girl's salaam, in mock solemnity. She had bathed, she had some sweetmeats from the bazaar for him, she had bought a casket of lapis-lazuli set in jeweled gold, she was burning ambergris to make the air sweet for him, and her heart had grown weary waiting for him.

But Omar lay down by his writing materials, in no mood for prattle, or pungent ambergris. When Ayesha saw his fingers move toward a quill pen, she made a face unseen.

For a while she occupied herself combing her hair, then she demanded jealously:

"What does it say, the writing?"

"Nothing."

"It is one of those things —" she peered over his shoulder — "that make you miserable. Is it a charm? What says it?"

> *"I was a hawk, uptossed to Heaven's gate,*
> *Therefrom to seize the book of human Fate,*
> *And now, with none to share my thoughts, I seek*
> *That very door from which I flew of late."*

"Falcons don't seize books," Ayesha observed maliciously. "They swoop at birds or hares. It's stupid, anyway. If you were a falcon you couldn't think, and if you were a man you couldn't fly." She yawned with ostentation. "Only scribes and priests write . . . such dull things."

Omar stared about the room, full of Ayesha's small treasures. The dish of stuffed dates before him had not been touched. She had waited for him to taste them and she was very fond of fresh stuffed dates.

She lay close to him, her body relaxed, her eyes closed. When Ayesha put on her finest silks and painted her face she looked like some strange bird of paradise, but lying thus unveiled — and unaware of him — he could not help but feel her loveliness.

Bending down, he kissed her lips gently. His kiss was instantly returned, and the girl's warm arms twisted about his neck. She had not been asleep or at all distrait, and her eyes flashed triumphantly at the paper with the four lines of writing that had fallen unnoticed to the floor.

"Master," said Jafarak, "the magicians of thy mountains have followed us to Isfahan."

At least, the jester maintained, marvelous things were

happening in the streets of the city. He had heard whispering at the mosque gates of nights. The whispers told of a man who had torn down the veil that separated the living from the dead. He had died, he had entered Muhammad's paradise and had returned to earth to tell of it.

"What," Omar asked, "did he find in paradise?"

"Wine flowing from fountains, and carpets spread upon the grass, and dark-eyed houris who intoxicated him with bliss."

"Is there no river in paradise?"

Eagerly, Jafarak shook his head. Often he had pondered what would await him on the other side of the grave. "The ones who heard this dead man speak — they say otherwise. It is no river but a lake under a silver moon."

Curiously he glanced at Omar. Often Ayesha had related to the jester how Omar had seen a vision when he was struggling with the magicians of the mountains, and in that vision there had been just such a lake. But unlike the man who had returned from beyond the grave, Omar had little to say about his vision.

"Ay," he assented, "a lake, and upon that lake a pleasure boat floating as silently as a sleeping swan."

"*Wallahi!* And what more, O master?"

"The awakening on the morrow."

Jafarak sighed. His joints were stiffening, and he felt his years. A longing had come upon him — an unvoiced hope that after the angels of death had stood over him, he might become youthful and strong and erect as other men, within Muhammad's paradise.

"Who has ever come back," Omar mused, "from that long journey?"

"Perhaps, at last, one has come back."

Secretly, Jafarak believed this had happened. Surely Muhammad had promised ever-flowing fountains, and Omar who never lied, had beheld in his vision — Ayesha was quite certain on that point — fountains flowing with wine. So, could he not believe this dead man who also told of the fountains? Jafarak wanted to believe, and he haunted the gate of the great mosque at night, his ears pricked for whispers.

A dervish spoke with him, a lean, tattered dervish who also believed. He confided in Jafarak that he had been present when the dead man appeared to some chosen spirits, and that the dead man would speak again on the coming Friday-eve, after the last prayer, in the house of Ibn Atash in the street behind the Jami Masjid. It seemed to Jafarak that if a dervish would testify to another man's miracle, it must be true.

He told Omar, who glanced at him thoughtfully and said nothing. But excitement gripped him, until he could not resist going to the street back of the great mosque and examining the houses to see which belonged to Ibn Atash. The next night he made his way back again, wondering if he might not by some chance behold the strange traveler.

Instead he noticed a man seated on a horse, watching from the shadows, who hailed him.

"What dost thou, O Jafarak?"

It was Tutush, but a harassed and suspicious Tutush. More miracles than one, the master of the spies related, had been happening in the streets of Isfahan.

For the last months, men had disappeared in steady succession. That, of course, was nothing remarkable. But these had been no common souls or mendicants. Rich merchants, noted visitors, heads of large families — five had vanished without a trace.

They had not been carried off by raiding tribesmen, because they had dropped out of sight within the city walls, and always in the late evening. All the five had been riding, or walking alone — most of them on the way home from the mosque.

Moreover — and here was a strange thing — the five had been the recipients of unusual gifts. By questioning the members of the households, Tutush had discovered that at various times the missing men had awakened from sleep to find two rolls of fresh bread by their heads.

"How could bread appear in that fashion by a rich man's couch?" Tutush demanded, in exasperation. "Ay, bread fresh-baked, as if carried that night from the oven?"

Jafarak shook his head. Such matters were unwonted, but surely Allah had caused them to be. They were not a miracle, like the one the dervish had beheld.

"Behold," grumbled Tutush — they were moving away from the mosque at a foot pace — "three of the five were last seen in the Jami Masjid. So must I watch all the gates, and post my men upon the roofs. What can we see? Have we eyes to

202

pierce the dark? The friends of the men who are lost have made great wailing and calamity at Court, and the governor — but what dost thou i' the alley yonder every night?"

"I wait for a friend who has promised to pay a debt. Nay, perhaps the five men went away secretly."

"Then where did they go? The guards upon the roads have not seen them. Moreover they were rich 'arif, not runagate thieves. When did rich men with full money sacks ever go off alone with nothing in their hands?"

Jafarak was glad that the stout master of the spies had stopped questioning him. "Perhaps if they were all wealthy, they were carried off by lawless men to be held for a ransom."

Tutush grunted, fingering the beads of his rosary. "They call thee fool, but I have known wise men who had less sense. Nay, it was not for ransom, because no demand hath come to the families of the five. Yet — Allah kerim — someone may come to ask for gold. The blame is upon my head in either case."

"May thy search be fortunate."

Jafarak left the master of the spies, and hesitated for a moment. He did not relish being watched by Tutush's servants; still he wanted to return to the alley, on the chance of meeting the dervish and hearing some more talk of the coming miracle. So he hurried off toward the mosque, deciding to look in at the gate first.

By then it was the third hour of the night and the last prayer had been finished. In the glow of the lantern above the arched entrance he saw only a pair of mullahs and a spearman who leaned drowsily on his weapon. A blind man was tapping with his staff in the shadows, and when Jafarak came abreast him, he turned with a supplication.

"Ai, wilt show mercy to the afflicted, and aid one who hath no eyes, to his door?"

"Ay, so," assented Jafarak. "Where is thy house?"

"It is behind the mosque." The blind man took the cripple's arm and went ahead at a faster pace. "The third door on the left hand, just beyond the well. 'Tis a little way, yet a stone's throw is a league for one without eyes. Ai, me!"

"The third house to the left," repeated Jafarak, with sudden interest. "Is it not the place of Ibn Atash?"

The blind man turned toward him, as if to peer into his

face. "Ibn Atash? What knowest thou of him, O friend of the afflicted?"

"I — I seek him."

"Ah, many seek him." The stick of the blind man tap-tapped on the hard clay, as they rounded the corner of the mosque and entered the narrow street. Jafarak heard the drip of the fountain, and searched out the third door in the darkness. Perhaps, if the blind man knew the secret of the house, he might learn something from him.

"Ay, the door." The blind man felt of it and tapped rapidly with his stick, until the door creaked back. "Come in with me," he whispered, "O friend of the night, and rest."

Leaning his weight on Jafarak's arm, he stepped forward. Something moved beside them, and a hand clutched the jester's throat. A flame of agony ran through Jafarak, and he fell forward into utter darkness.

Ayesha stirred in her sleep and woke. Her keen senses had given warning of something unwonted close at hand telling of danger. Outstretched on the carpet with Omar beside her upon the roof, she listened without moving.

Then she heard again the slight sound that had roused her — bare feet moving over the tiles. A third person was breathing deep so close to her that her nerves tingled. Paper scraped gently, and a strange smell crept into her nostrils. The girl screamed and sprang up, as a deer leaps from its sleeping place.

As she did so, she saw a dark outline against the stars. The bare feet pattered away, and Omar, climbing to his feet, was able to catch sight of a man slipping away toward the stair. With a shout, he followed.

But in the darkness of the courtyard below he lost track of the intruder. Drowsy servants came clamoring from their lairs, and lights were struck. The invader had vanished, although Ishak, who had slept upon the ground by the closed gate, swore by the ninety and nine holy names that the gate had not been opened.

"Look, my lord," Ayesha called down from the roof, "at what is here."

When the lights were carried up, Omar found two objects beside his sleeping quilt. A dagger without a sheath, and a roll of fresh-baked bread still odorous from the oven. Nothing of the kind had been there when he went to sleep, and he understood that the intruder must have risked his life to lay them there; or perhaps one of his own household had done it. Ayesha was quite sure the knife had not been dropped on the tiles; it had been placed beside his head, with care.

He examined the weapon and found it to be a *khanjur*, with a curved blade of fine gray steel. He had seen such knives before, in the girdles of the Fidais at Alamut, and he laid it down thoughtfully.

"But what does it mean?" demanded Ayesha, who was angry because she had been badly frightened. "That, and the bread?"

"One gives life," put in Ishak importantly, "the other death. Surely, it is a sign."

"Verily," Ayesha retorted, "if our lives had depended upon thy watching, O Keeper of the Gate of Snores, we would have been in our shrouds long before. *Ai-wah!* Thou art never asleep when visitors come with silver for thy hand, but when thieves come in the darkness — where art thou then?"

"Look!" exclaimed Ishak. "Here is a paper, and there is a writing on it."

Bending down, he handed a small square of rice paper to Omar, who held it close to a lanthorn. The writing was Persian — a single line without signature. "There is need," he read aloud, "thy tongue . . . between . . . thy teeth."

"Keep thy tongue between thy teeth," nodded Ishak sagely. "How true is the warning, O master. Without doubt 'twas meant for Ayesha — see the dagger is as pointed as her tongue. Better that she should bake bread and hold her peace."

But Omar knew the warning was meant for him. And it came, he felt certain, from Alamut, if not from Hassan himself. The paper was the same used by the messenger pigeons of the Lord of the Mountains, and who else would send a missive unsigned? Yet, in Isfahan, Omar had put Alamut out of his mind, and had told no one what he had seen among the Seveners. He wondered why Hassan had sent the bread, and the knife.

Soon after daybreak he learned the explanation. One of Tutush's spies came to the house and salaamed with long-winded greeting.

"What is it?" Omar asked impatiently.

"Who knoweth where his grave is dug? O Shadow of the Sultan, behold, at the first light we, who patrol the streets without ceasing, found one of thy household slain in the gutter. Lo, we have brought him."

Descending into the courtyard, he led Omar to a stretcher in the shade, beside which several of his followers squatted. The form on the stretcher was covered with a cotton sheet.

With a steady hand, Omar drew aside the sheet — and staggered back, choking down the nausea that rose inside him.

The body was Jafarak's, the face almost black, and the throat slit beneath the chin. Through this slit Jafarak's tongue had been pulled, until it must have been torn from all but its roots.

"Alas, Magnificence," sighed the street guard, "I have never seen one slain like this before. Yet he was old and misshapen."

Omar replaced the sheet and drew a long breath. But he remembered that the agent could not be blamed for this. "Thou art Tutush's man? Then send thy master to me, swiftly."

So rapidly did Tutush appear, that he must have been waiting for his men around the corner. Without a word the Tentmaker led the chief of the spies to a corner where they could not be overheard. Tutush wiped his cheek with his turban end, and clicked his rosary nervously — he had not forgotten how this same Jafarak had drawn Omar's wrath upon his head years before. Covertly he studied the face of his host, and drew no encouragement therefrom.

But Omar was thinking only of the slain Jafarak. With the death of the faithful jester the last tie that linked him with the carefree days of Rahim had been severed.

"Who would have done that?" he demanded. "He had no enemy — ah, God, he was harmless as a child."

Tutush almost touched the floor in a salaam. "By your Excellency's leave — 'tis indeed a mystery of the blackest. By the beard of Ali, he talked with me that evening near the Jami Masjid, and I warned him — may Allah do more to me if I lie — against wandering in the streets. Nay, I escorted him to a safe place —" as he pleaded, real misery crept into his words, because Tutush feared the wrath of Omar more than fire or sword — "and left him unharmed. I swear by —"

"Where did you find him?"

"It was one of my men, in a street near the river, far from the mosque. He was not slain there because no blood stained the dirt. Will your Excellency hear me, when I swear by Hassan and Hussayn, the blessed martyrs —"

"Be silent!" Omar clenched his teeth. Hassan! Hassan, son of Sabah. Hassan had just now warned him to keep his tongue between his teeth. And Jafarak's tongue had been pulled half out of his body last night. For what reason — for what earthly reason? Unless Hassan's men had thought he was spying on them. What had Jafarak been occupied with these last days? Nothing but that accursed miracle which fairly reeked of Alamut. The dead man who told tales of paradise, in the house of Ibn Atash, in — Omar frowned, straining his memory — yes, it was near the Jami Masjid. In the street behind the Jami Masjid, on Friday-eve. That was it.

Jafarak, then, had been slain probably near the mosque, and his body carried to a distant place.

"What knowest thou of a certain house of the Son of Fire (Ibn Atash) in the alley behind the mosque?" he demanded.

"Naught — the name I have never heard."

Omar half rose, to start off to the house in question and find out what it had to tell. Then he settled down again on the carpet, and Tutush breathed again. Useless to search the dwelling of murderers if they had just committed a crime. By now they would probably be praying with the dervishes in the mosque.

"Only one thing I know," he mused. "Last night a thief left a writing beside my head, warning me to keep my tongue between my teeth."

Tutush's jaw dropped, as he thought of Jafarak's death.

A voice from behind the distant lattice work interrupted them. "Thy forgiveness, my lord — tell him also of the dagger and the fresh-baked bread."

"Ayesha," said Omar quietly. "Go back to the harem."

A rustle of garments, then silence.

"A loaf of bread!" cried the chief of the spies.

"Yes — what of it?"

"*Y'allah!* And a knife?"

"Thou hast heard."

For a moment Tutush pondered. Then he explained how

five men of mark had disappeared some days after finding the bread beside their pillows.

"I think the bread was put by me after they slew Jafarak," Omar said slowly. "Surely it was the work of the same hand."

"Without doubt." Tutush considered and nodded. "Also, Jafarak waited of nights by the mosque, near which three of them were lost to sight."

"Then it must be the work of the Fidais," Omar said.

The words had a strange effect on Tutush. His mouth opened and closed again, and the skin beneath his turban visibly crawled. "Of — of what —" he stammered.

"The Devoted Ones, the drug eaters, the dagger bearers of the Lord of Life and Death, Hassan ibn Sabah. *He* is master of Alamut and is often called master of the Seveners."

Imploringly Tutush lifted his hands, glancing about in sudden fear. "Do not speak that name, Excellency."

Omar stared at him in silence. "Then thou knowest the Seveners, and that this is their work?"

"Oh, Master of the Stars, I know naught. Only, some tales. People fear the name of the one thou — your Excellency hath mentioned."

"And now, you will tell me what you know of these Seveners."

It was no easy matter to make Tutush tell what he had in his mind. His dread of the Seveners seemed to be as great as his fear of Omar. At last he spoke in broken whispers, eyeing the distant lattice as if it concealed serpents behind it.

Nizam had ordered the search made, he insisted, because Nizam believed Hassan's followers were heretics. Nizam had written about the secret order that had invaded Persia from Egypt in his book, and sealed the chapters until after his death. He, Tutush, was only a servant, who obeyed orders — he said this last in a loud, clear voice.

Hassan, they had discovered, gained power by inspiring fear in faithful Moslems and servants of the throne. He threatened rich merchants until they gave him large sums. His method of doing it was to have his Fidais leave the fresh-baked bread by the sleeping victim, as a sign that he must make payment to the lord of the mountains. Then the next day a beggar would come to the door, asking for bread from the hand of the master of the house. Instead of bread, the beggar would take away a sack of gold, and the giver would be free from menace.

"Yet we know not if it be Hassan's plan, or the work of others who serve him. We have tried to grasp him and hold him, in vain. Yea, he dared enter the Dar al Kuttub at Ray and sit down to talk with Nizam — no man knowing his face — and speak his own name. When we searched his lodging, he had vanished like snow on the desert's face."

Only recently had the people of Isfahan been threatened. And Tutush could discover nothing about the five who had not paid tribute and had disappeared. It was more terrifying to think of them simply snatched away from the very streets then to find their bodies, even slain like Jafarak. He thought the Assassins had a stronghold in the city, but he could not be sure.

"What did you call them?" Omar asked.

"Assassins — *hashishin* in Arabic — users of hashish. That is the drug that fires them to evil deeds."

Omar thought of the wine he had drunk in Alamut, and of the three Fidais who had leaped from the rampart into space. Yes, the men of Alamut were assassins, servants of hashish.

"Perhaps today," Tutush went on, "will come the dervish to beg. It — it would be wise to keep silence and give up a little money."

"I do not think they will ask me to pay them."

"Nay — I had forgotten. Already that man of affairs, Akroenos, hath made away with the goods and profits of your Excellency's caravans. He hath taken toll of your wealth. Still, they may desire more."

"It is they who will make payment, for Jafarak's death."

Tutush sighed, while his plump fingers played up and down the rosary. "Better to cover the embers of wrath with the water of discretion. What can your Excellency do, to oppose them? Preachers and great men of affairs have spoken in public against the Seveners, the Assassins. And then, in a little while they have become silent, except for praise of the Seveners. Who knows why — or how? Who can find a snake hiding i' the jungle? These assassins go about in the guise of camelmen, merchants, dervishes. By now at least one is working as a servant here, in the house of your Excellency."

Omar remembered the eunuch who had haunted Kasr Kuchik, and he wondered if one of his many servants had not placed the bread and the dagger with the message by him last night.

"Already," resumed Tutush, "they hold the mountain region behind Kasvin and Ray in the grip of fear. Their emissaries have come to Nisapur. And here in Isfahan they have been seen in the ruin of the ancient fire temple on the hilltop of Dizh Koh. And how did these five men of Isfahan vanish? My soul! If I could know! They were not slain openly as others have been; they raised no outcry; no word has come from them; they did not leave the gates of Isfahan, yet no sign of them remains. 'Tis a fearful thing to happen. Be wise, Excellency, and molest not these men of Ha — of the mountain."

"They make use of magic and trickery. So, there is one way to strike through their armor of secrecy."

"You — you will make search for them?"

"Nay, they will reveal themselves."

Tutush rose in haste. It was true, he reflected, that Omar the Tentmaker had a secret power, and Omar could oppose magic with magic. But Tutush wished to be far off from such a conflict. "Excellency," he whispered, "already is my life in pawn for saying what I have said this hour. I — I have naught to do with hidden powers. Grant me leave to go!"

When the sunset faded to full starlight that Friday-eve Omar left his house. He went out by a postern door, and only Ayesha of all the household knew that he had changed his shape. The man who crossed the great square with the swinging pace of the desert-born wore the black jellaba of an Arab of the Khoraish clan. The loose wool robes hid his figure and the short curved sword in his girdle, while the head-cloth veiled his face. Even his voice had taken on the harsh gutturals of the tribesmen.

By the hour of full starlight — in time for the last praying — Omar was in the Jami Masjid, with some hundreds of the faithful. Going out with the crowd, he turned aside, seeking the alley behind the mosque. Other figures went ahead of him in the near-darkness, and he slowed his pace until he could be certain that they turned into a door on the left of the alley.

A man was seated by this door who lifted his head in the manner of the blind, holding a staff in his hand.

Abreast him, Omar stopped and spoke.

"I seek the house of Ibn Atash."

"O companion of the desert, it is here. What has thou to do with Ibn Atash?"

"I have heard talk of one who knoweth paradise."

The blind man rocked on his haunches, chuckling. "Ay — ay, of paradise."

Since he said nothing more, Omar felt his way into the dark entrance. Near at hand a voice was chanting, but he could see nothing. His outstretched hand brushed a heavy curtain, and he drew it aside. A candle was thrust close to his face, and a lean dervish peered at him. Apparently the scrutiny was satisfactory, because the dervish motioned toward a curtain behind him, and Omar advanced into a large room filled with seated figures, all facing a heavy rug hung upon the far wall.

Before this carpet a *majdhub* stood, revolving slowly and wailing as he beat his chest — a half mad wandering dervish whose bleared eyes gleamed from a pockmarked face. As he turned, he chanted his mourning for Hussayn, one of the martyrs of Persia.

"How did Hussayn die? Oh, how did he die? He was slain with a sword and the earth drank his precious blood. Oh, believers, have pity for Hussayn — yes, for Hussayn. Lo, I strike my breast for Hussayn!"

The chant was familiar to Omar, and as he edged his way forward to a place near the *majdhub*, he scrutinized the crowd. No sign of the Assassins was apparent, anywhere. The listeners were townspeople, men-at-arms, even a few mullahs from the mosque — all afire with expectancy. Some of them beat their hands together in time with the *majdhub's* howling.

Incense curled up from a small brazier, filling the air with pungent scent. The light came from two great lamps on the floor by the chanter.

". . . have pity for Hussayn, yes, for Hussayn!" murmured the throng.

The room was packed by then, and suddenly the *majdhub* ceased his revolving.

"Lo," he screamed, "the voice of the dead speaks."

Reaching up, he jerked the rug aside. Sliding upon a long bar, it revealed an archway opening into an alcove. Upon the floor behind the lamps lay a great brass basin, half filled with blood. In the center of the basin rested a human head, its eyes closed, its skull shaven smooth.

Exclamations broke from the crowd. Save for its pallor this head, erect upon the basin, seemed to be that of an ordinary man.

"Be still!" cried the dervish.

And then the eyes opened in the head. They looked from right to left. There was no need to quiet the throng now, because utter silence held the room.

The lips of the head in the basin moved, and it spoke. "Oh, ye faithful ones! Hear the tale of that which is beyond sight."

"Oh, Allah!" breathed a mullah beside Omar.

While the low voice of the head spoke on, revealing one by one the secrets of paradise, Omar — unlike the others — watched rather than listened. The voice, he felt certain, came from the throat of the thing in the basin, and beyond doubt that was a living head, without sign of a body.

Except for the basin, the alcove was deserted, its walls covered with hangings. Then the voice ceased, the eyes closed, the face became rigid and the dervish jerked to the carpet that shut the alcove from the spectators.

"Karamat," exclaimed the mullah beside him, "A miracle!"

"A sign! A portent of great happenings." Others gave reverent assent. Men stirred and breathed freely again. But several were silent and Omar caught whispers of bewilderment. In a moment subdued argument began — the credulous affirming that they had heard the voice of the dead, while the doubters demanded proof that it was not the head of a living man.

The dervish surveyed them with a mocking smile.

"Proof!" cried a soldier at last. *"Wallahi,* if it be truly a miracle, give proof."

"Be still!" the dervish retorted. "Proof ye shall have."

He waited a moment, as if to make certain that all eyes were on him, then swung the carpet back again. Stooping down he grasped the head by both ears and lifted it high — turned slowly so that all should see, and replaced it in its basin of blood.

The mullah was the first to throw himself on his face, and a sigh went through the room. This was the head that had spoken to them, and it had no body.

212

"We believe! We have seen!"

Omar rose and stepped before the carpet and raised his hand.

"O my companions," his clear voice rang out. "This is no miracle but the trickery of a street juggler. The dead did not speak — he who spoke is now dead. Look!"

He had seen no slightest evidence of the trick, but only one thing could have happened. Thrusting back the carpet, he stepped toward the motionless head, and picked up the massive basin. Where it had lain he beheld a hole in the stone flooring, a foot square.

The dervish hissed angrily, and the men of Isfahan sprang up to stare in bewilderment. But Omar caught up a lamp and pulled down the hangings of the alcove. In one wall there was an open door. He ran through it, shielding the flame of the lamp against the wind. A few yards down the passage he slipped, and found the stones dark and moist with blood.

"By my soul, thou hast seen the truth, Arab." The soldier spoke at his elbow. "Something was slain here, and — that head is still warm. But the body has vanished."

Others pressed after them, fearfully as they searched the chambers in the rear. They found the sleeping quarters of several men, and a door open to the right. But at the foot of a stair leading to the cellars the lamp light shone upon the headless trunk of a man clad in the white robe of a Fidai.

"It was thrown down here," cried the soldier. "Look, brothers, if the dogs be not skulking below."

As he passed a closed door in the cellar, the warrior stopped with a grimace, smelling what was stronger than the scent of incense. "There was more than one body shortened of its head," he said. "Oh, the accursed dogs."

Kicking at the door, he broke it down, and thrust the lamp inside. "One, two . . . five. But they do not look like that other."

"Nay," echoed the mullah who had pushed to the front. "*Mashallah!* Here is the body of Anim Beg. And over there — that one was the merchant Shir Afghan who came often to the mosque. Verily these be the five who vanished from Isfahan. Hunt down the dogs who took their lives!"

But the dervish had slipped away in the confusion, and the now infuriated crowd found only the blind man, beating the darkness with his staff and crying to his vanished companions not to desert him.

Omar did not sleep that night, with the memory of Jafarak's mutilated body haunting him. He cared little for the murder of the five rich men, but the jester had shared the bitter and sweet of life with him, and the jester had been struck down as if he had been a stray dog. And unrequited rage burned in the Tentmaker like a fever.

While the hue and cry after the Assassins filled the streets the next morning — and Tutush galloped about with great show of zeal — Nizam al Mulk crept from his retirement, and had himself carried before Malikshah.

"Give command, my Sultan, that the Seveners who are Assassins be hunted down," he pleaded, "throughout the lands. See how their master defies thee, levying tribute in thy very shadow."

Malikshah had looked upon the Seveners as one of the numberless sects of Islam, too insignificant to notice. But the old Nizam urged that the real purpose of the Assassins was to overthrow the throne and cast the empire into disorder.

"Nay," the Sultan smiled, "am I to chase every dog that nips at the hoofs of my horse? These heretics have not arms or men enough to stand against a single *hazara* of my swordsmen."

Nizam pointed out that they had already fortified a strong castle called Alamut somewhere in the northern mountains, where they kept their treasure. Moreover the mysterious Hassan ibn Sabah had prophesied the downfall of the Sultan, and the coming of a new day for the people of Islam.

"If I were to crucify every prophet who proclaims a new day," the Sultan retorted, "I would have no time for hunting or other matters. Let this Hassan come out into the open and I will have him hewn into five pieces with swords."

"But what of his castle?"

Malikshah frowned irritably. "How can I tell which spy's tale to believe? Tutush swears upon his head and beard that the Assassins have neither head nor stronghold. If this Hassan seeks power, he is like many others in my realm. Thou hast leave to go."

As he made his salaam of farewell, the aged Nizam realized that since Malikshah had once looked upon him with suspicion, his influence was lost.

"It would be well," he pleaded, "to inspect the ruins on the Dizh mountain, overlooking Isfahan. For it is the policy of the Assassins to settle themselves in a fortified point commanding each one of thy great cities, and they have been seen on the Dizh."

During his hunts Malikshah had noticed the bare steep hill, upon which stood an ancient stone foundation — some said of the giants, and others maintained, of the fire worshipers.

"Yes," he assented, "that I will do, because it is in my mind to build a castle there for my men."

Instead of sending an officer, or even Tutush, Malikshah ordered Omar to ride from Isfahan with a troop of swordsmen to inspect the isolated ruin. Whatever Omar did, the Sultan believed, would be fortunate, and, besides, he had heard rumors that Omar himself had unearthed a nest of these strange heretics, overcoming their magic by his arts. He could trust whatever Omar said.

The Dizh hilltop proved to be inhabited only by shepherds and wandering families which had taken refuge in the ruins. Although the Sultan's guards searched every corner of the ruins and thrust their spears down the dark well-mouths, they came upon no trace of the Assassins.

No weapons were hidden in the cellars, and the frightened people swore that they had never heard of Alamut or a false prophet Hassan ibn Sabah.

Still Omar was troubled by a vague doubt. Here was an altar of the fire worshipers, as at Alamut. And the rendezvous of the Assassins in Isfahan had been the house of Ibn Atash (Son of the Fire). In an echoing cleft between rock walls a stream took its rise.

The whole place reminded him of Alamut. And he thought that there were overmany young men among the families of the shepherds. So he scanned every face closely, without recognizing one.

"If the Khwaja please," one of the soldiers told him, "there are strange figures carved in the round tower. Belike they are pagan gods or portents of magic."

When Omar dismounted, and entered the base of the tower, the soldier pointed to a ring of carvings at the height of a man's head. They ran all the way around the circular wall, apparently without beginning or end. And Omar saw what they were at a glance.

A giant Scorpion, an Archer, a Goat — here were the twelve signs of the zodiac hewn in the stone by unknown hands. Beneath each sign was a bronze point projecting upwards, as if something had been hung from it.

"They are signs of the stars," he assured his men, "but they were made before Islam."

"Then, master," observed the one who had found them, "they must be pagan and evil. Shall we shatter them with a battle-hammer?"

"Nay — they can do no harm."

What purpose had they served? Surely they had not been carved so carefully in a single frieze upon the otherwise blank wall just as an ornament. They had been placed there for some reason, perhaps by the fire worshipers who had built the tower. No doubt they had played a part in some ceremonial, now forgotten.

Going to the center of the tower, he turned slowly on his heel, keeping his eyes on the zodiac figures. Yes, they began with the Ram, and ended with the Fish. Perhaps through an opening in the tower, the sun had shone upon them in a certain way, marking the seasons ... still he turned slowly, while his men watched, breathing heavily — thinking that the Master of the Stars was invoking some supernatural power. Suddenly, Omar laughed.

"What hath come upon thee, Khwaja?" demanded the one who had made the discovery. "Is this a message? Is a treasure buried beneath our feet?"

"The message," Omar said, "is from God. And it is not to be spoken now."

With reverent *"Aman — aman!"* they gave back, and Omar strode from the tower. He had seen how he could convince even a dogmatic mullah that the earth revolved.

From that moment he ceased to brood upon the death of Jafarak, or the Assassins. And he labored to one end — to be dismissed by Malikshah to return to the House of the Stars, where he could experiment with his new idea.

Slowly the Wheel of Fate turned. The lives of men who had reached their appointed hour were snuffed out like candles in the wind. Other human mites came wailing into the world.

The Sultan was journeying toward Nisapur. Each evening the imperial *ferrashes* raised the pavilion wherein he was to sleep, and each morning struck it, and bound it up for the journey.

Nizam was writing new pages for his book. Slowly the Wheel turned, but in every hour struggling men achieved fortune, or disgrace; they found fleeting happiness, or they were plunged into pain. . . . A comet appeared in the sky over the Sultan's camp, and Malikshah sent in haste for Omar to explain its portent.

It was, the astronomer answered, a sign of peril. Fiery red, it came from the west into the Sign of the Dragon. Malikshah saw that this was so. And, pondering it, he ordered an amir to set forth with a division of the army to find and destroy the castle of Alamut, the eyrie of the Assassins in the northern mountains behind Kasvin.

It seemed to Malikshah that this was the only danger close at hand. And without doubt Hassan had come from Egypt in the west. Because, for a moment, the hardy Turk felt afraid, he kept his great camp in the plain under pretense of hunting, and would not go to Nisapur. Nor would he allow Omar to depart.

That moon waned and before a new moon stood like a silver scimitar in the sky, the daggers of the Assassins were drawn in the camp.

It happened at the hour of midnight. A youth dressed as a Dailamite came to the pavilions of the nobles crying out as a suppliant. He sought Nizam al Mulk, and before any one could prevent, stabbed the old man. He was seized by guards and hacked to pieces, crying out deliriously something about paradise.

"Verily," Malikshah marveled, "calamity came to us, and the omen is fulfilled."

He mourned Nizam sincerely, and sent couriers to his army in the hills — already besieging the mountain on which Alamut stood — with orders to spare no effort to tear down the nest of the murderers. He had read the sealed chapters of Nizam's book, and had satisfied himself that the new religion was an actual menace to his reign.

"Nizam al Mulk," he confessed to Omar, "was a faithful

servant. For a month I will hold mournings for him, here."

And he released Omar from his attendance upon him, fo[r] that month, knowing his eagerness to visit Nisapur.

Riding toward his home with Ayesha beside him, Omar reflecting on the power that Sultan after Sultan had held wrote:

> *This world of ours, this caravanserai*
> *Wherein night enters on the heels of day —*
> *It is no more than Jamshid's banquet hall*
> *Above the grave where Jamshid's bones decay.*

On the hillside beneath Alamut siege engines reared thei[r] massive arms. Great stones flew up and crashed against th[e] walls, falling in fragments in a cloud of dust, rolling down t[o] the river. Iron pots of flaming oil soared into the air, fallin[g] upon roofs and courtyard.

From the walls the men of Alamut cast down javelin[s] flights of arrows and stones that dismantled the engines below The garrison was hemmed in by the Sultan's army; but th[e] besiegers could make little impression on the mountai[n] stronghold.

At times Hassan ibn Sabah showed himself within the walls By some secret way he was able to come and go as he pleased and he made his presence felt outside. His emissaries rode a[t] night toward Ray and Nisapur and distant Balkh, preaching t[o] restless crowds that calamity, heralded by the flaming come[t] was at hand. In such an hour the invisible and long-awaite[d] Mahdi would appear to those who sought him.

Along the great Khorasan road dervishes whispered t[o] peasants that the appointed day was at hand.

In mosque, gateway, and caravanserai, men talked of th[e] murder of Nizam al Mulk. Some believed that Nizam had bee[n] slain by Malikshah's order, and others insisted that he ha[d] been struck down by a supernatural agency. For two lifetime[s] the aged Minister had governed the empire, and now he was i[n] his grave.

Uncertainty and dread as subtle as poison seized the citie[s] and spread into the open country. No one knew the exac[t] cause of this unrest, but it spread as swiftly as the plague. I[f] Malikshah had shown himself with his Court at Isfahan or Ray the fear of the multitudes might have been appeased.

Malikshah, however, would not give up his hunting. And at times he refused to mount his horse, staying instead within his tent. His officers believed he was grieving for Nizam, but they did not understand his moodiness.

In the House of the Stars Omar Khayyam worked at a new device. His mathematicians who had been engaged on a geometrical treatise rejoiced at the arrival of their long-absent master. They found that Omar was intent upon this new experiment which appeared to them to be so simple that only a child could find amusement in it.

It was nothing more than a Chinese shadow-lantern effect. Only it was visible from within the lantern, instead of outside.

Omar had removed everything from the first story of the round observatory tower. At the height of a man he had built a shelf around the wall and had placed a hundred small oil lamps upon the shelf. Then he had covered shelf and lights with a shade made of parchment, so at night the only light in the chamber came from this circular band of parchment, which he had a painter ornament with the figures of the zodiac.

When the mathematicians inspected it gravely the first evening it was lighted up, they could make nothing of it. True, it enabled one to see the twelve divisions of the great ring of the zodiac, but every child knew that much.

"Ay, a child!" Omar assented, smiling. "A child can see what we are too blind to see."

Although the mathematicians looked at it again carefully, turning slowly on their heels, they beheld nothing they had not seen before. They talked it over among themselves and agreed it was nothing but a crude representation of the heavenly band of the zodiac — which every one knew was the pathway of the sun and the moon and the planets across the inverted bowl of the sky. Why Omar had taken such trouble to light it up, so it could be seen at night, they did not understand.

He went to greater trouble. Under his direction workmen labored in the chamber of the zodiac — as they called it now — taking some stones from the floor. Then Omar barred everyone except the artisans from the tower. Boards and a great wooden pillar were carried in. The carpenters bored some holes in the round pillar near one end, and made handles to fit into these holes — long handles like those used to turn the massive grindstone of a gristmill. All of the artisans went away except two who seemed to find plenty to do in the callar below the chamber of the zodiac.

Then to the stupefaction of his assistants, Omar invited Ghazali the mystic, who was now the foremost teacher of the Nisapur academy to visit the House of the Stars, to watch a new Chinese lantern show.

The guests did not arrive until after full starlight, and they came with great expectancy. For, whatever whimsical displays Omar gave, no one had ever found the Master of the Stars dull.

Ceremoniously his assistants greeted the dignitaries from the academy, and they salaamed low before Ghazali, who wore only his inevitable gray wool. Years had added poise and authority to the mystic, and he was now called Hujjrat ul Islam — the Proof of Islam. It seemed incredible to the assistants of the House of the Stars that Omar would dare bid Ghazali come to look at a lighted zodiac.

Omar greeted the mystic with frank delight, and offered him sherbet and fruit with his own hand. The young leader of Islam answered with constraint.

"I have heard," he said, "how your Excellency departed from the guidance of Nizam al Mulk — upon whom be blessings — and how at Isfahan you practised magic after the manner of infidels."

"Of late," Omar answered gravely, "many tales have been told. But tonight in my house I wish the Proof of Islam to tell me in his kindness only one thing that he beholds. Will you come with me?"

"*Bismallah,*" assented Ghazali. "In the name of Allah."

When they entered the first chamber of the tower the disciples of the astronomer and of the mystic gazed about them curiously. There was no light except from the great band of illuminated parchment with its crude drawings. At a word from Omar the others seated themselves against the wall, leaving the two leaders together in the center of the room.

"What is this?" Omar asked. "Will you turn once from left to right and tell me?"

"Verily it is the zodiac. Ay, here the Ram and there the

Bull ... and the Fish. I see no more than the twelve signs, ranged in order."

Omar nodded agreement. "Now will the Proof of Islam stand here, in the center — nay, upon that round piece of wood. Ay, so — facing the first sign."

The disciples, stirred into expectancy by what seemed to be a new ceremonial, leaned forward to watch the better. They were half-concealed in the shadow under the lighted band. Ghazali was reserved, almost indifferent.

"Now," said Omar without raising his voice, "do not move, or step aside. There is no harm — only the thing to be seen. *For now the whole tower will revolve about thee.*" And he clapped his hands once.

Half smiling, Ghazali waited — knowing that such a thing would not happen. It was a jest — he drew in his breath sharply. The lighted band was turning.

Something creaked and strained beneath his feet. His muscles contracted, and he cried out involuntarily. With a distant rumble and rush the tower revolved, the signs on the parchment swept past his eyes. Then, with a slight jar it stopped, and he fell to his knees.

"*Aiwallah!* What — in God's name —" he sought for words. What, indeed, could turn a massive tower on its foundations? "I saw it turn."

Omar waited without speaking, as he raised Ghazali to his feet, and the mystic's disciples hurried forward.

"Master," one said, "surely this tower did not move. We — we saw thee turn slowly at first and then swiftly upon thy feet."

"Nay, I moved not."

"You moved not," Omar assured him, and the confused babble of voices quieted, "but you turned once around. Verily, such a mass at this building could not be moved like a wheel."

"But how —"

"This pillar head can be turned from below like any mill post. When I clapped my hands my servants walked once about it thrusting the handles before them."

"And why," Ghazali gathered his robe about him, lifting his head, "was this child's trick played upon me?"

"Because thou art one of the wisest of us, and I wished to

hear thy word tell what thine eyes beheld. Listen now! The first time thou didst turn upon thy feet, the second time thou wert turned — thine eyes beheld the same lights and signs in the same manner. But the second time it seemed to thee *that the tower turned*. Why was that?"

"Because I moved not — I was deluded by a trick. Is this what the infidels taught thee?"

"Every night —" and Omar's voice rang out urgently — "thou seest the real band of the constellations, the great band of the starry zodiac, pass over thy head, and thou sayest 'Because I move not, these stars revolve about me.' Yet the stars move not. The delusion is in thy mind." Ghazali was silent, frowning, and the disciples stared, unbelieving.

"It is the earth that turns, as this round pillar turned, once in a day and night. Think, Ghazali, how for uncounted ages men have thought that the sphere of the heavens revolved. Some must have seen the truth, opening their eyes to it. Perhaps children, new-born, feel that they are in motion beneath the far, fixed world of the stars — whirling through space. They see with open eyes, but they cannot make clear to us what they see."

"Nay," cried the mystic, "Allah caused the world to be as it is, motionless in the center of the universe."

His disciples murmured assent, and the boldest of them exclaimed, "This was no more than a trick, O Master of the Stars, to make the Proof of Islam fall to his knees before thee. What is it but lights and evil, painted signs? Where is the proof that the stars move not?"

"Ay the proof," the others echoed.

"It is clear," Omar answered gravely.

"Then reveal it."

Briefly, almost impatiently, Omar explained. The planets were nearer to the earth than the fixed stars — Mars, Venus and Mercury very near, and the moon also. The sun as well. That was manifest during an eclipse, when the moon passed between the earth and the sun, or the earth passed between the sun and the moon. But the stars themselves were far distant in the sphere of the heavens.

"And where," asked someone, "is the proof of that?"

A man, Omar explained, standing at Cairo at night could see almost all the stars, among the thousands, that a watcher could see in Nisapur. A great distance on the surface of the earth revealed only a slight fraction more and less of the vast sky sphere. So the size of the earth must be infinitesimal compared to the universe.

He was speaking now with assurance, knowing that it was the truth. But, while some of the mathematicians became thoughtful, the men of the academy waited in hostile silence.

"Some of the stars," he said, "must be a thousand times a thousand leagues distant. They appear small because they are remote, as the sun seems large to us because it is near and blinding."

"If that were true," a listener cried, "where is even a shred of proof in that? Small or large, the stars revolve about us, as Allah willed."

"They could not," said Omar quietly. "Because to circle the earth at such a distance they would have to move through infinite space at such a speed that they would disappear in flames, as we see a star that falls from its place vanish in flames."

"What blasphemy!" cried a disciple. "O, believers — hath not Allah power to turn stone into fire, or fire into stone?"

"Yea," Omar said. "The power that moves our earth upon its orbit! The power that hath set worlds beyond worlds in outermost space! That same power moves us through our tiny lives." He turned impulsively to Ghazali. "And we will not understand."

"All knowledge," Ghazali answered, "is from Allah. Verily, Allah is our sun, and all other intelligence no more than the sunlight."

"*Yek zarra az hukm-i-tu jahan khali nist* — no particle of the universe is outside his power. The sun? The sun rests as impotently in its place as thou or I — and we were created when Eternity was. What can the sun teach us, if we will not see it as it is?" Omar stretched out his hand appealingly.

Suddenly the mystic called for one of his disciples to bring water in a jar from the well. Then he bade the man pour the water upon his hands, and feet. When he had cleansed himself, Ghazali gathered his robe about him and stepped to the door.

"Omar Khayyam," he said, "take heed of thy words, for this is blasphemy. I dispute not thy proof of the distance of the stars, or of eclipses. But it is written in the

Book-To-Be-Read, 'God is the LIGHT of the Heavens and of the Earth. . . . He guideth whom He will.' What hath measurement or time itself to do with human souls? Be warned!"

"I have been warned." Omar could not help laughing as he remembered. "A writing came that bade me keep my tongue between my teeth. So, tomorrow I shall go to the *divan* of the academy, to explain to the teachers the result of my life's study."

Ghazali considered him curiously. "Art mad, Tentmaker?"

"No. But a man can not live forever — and the thread of my life may be cut any hour. I would like to speak while I am still alive."

"A jest! Guard thy tongue, Tentmaker — for only a poet or jester may speak as thou hast spoken. I shall pray that the enlightenment of God will come to thee, in time."

Omar stared disconsolately after the mystic and his followers — who made no secret of their anger. He had not meant to jest.

"Master," one of his assistants observed, "it was ill done, to make the Proof of Islam fall to his knees before thee. The tale will spread through Nisapur."

"He would not have fallen," Omar answered absently, "if he had not thought the tower was turning round."

"Do not go to the academy. It may be written that calamity awaits thee there."

"If the moving pen hath written it — it will not be rubbed out for thee or me."

Rumors crept out of Nisapur. In the bazaar it was related how the King's astronomer had summoned the Proof of Islam to a meeting, to test their powers.

By using his magical art, the tale ran, Omar Khayyam nearly succeeded in rendering the beloved Ghazali unconscious. But by invoking the Koran, Ghazali's power was restored and in the end Omar was reduced to shame and silence. Some men maintained that Omar had wrestled bodily with Ghazali and had cast him to his knees. Others were equally certain that Ghazali had discovered an infernal machine built secretly within the tower.

Ishak the gatekeeper heard the tidings from a passing

caravan of wool merchants bound for Balkh. One of the camelmen leaned down to spit within the gateposts.

"Dirt-eater!" roared Ishak, asserting his dignity. "May dogs litter on thy father's grave."

"This house is full of such dogs. Ay, the master here is a blood-drinking infidel. *Wah,* his name is dirt."

"What is upon thee?" demanded Ishak, too astonished to retort fittingly. Always the caravan men had stared admiringly into the gate of the Master of the Stars, and sometimes they had left gifts with the keeper of the gate — hence Ishak's appearance at that moment.

"Hast thou not heard?" The camelman checked his donkey with a jerk and sat sideways to watch Ishak the better. "First, this unbeliever, thy master, dug a pitfall in his accursed tower. *Hai* — it was to catch and impale men alive, this pitfall. But a certain holy man — I forget his name, but he is a veritable living saint — cast the blessed Koran into the pit and destroyed its power for evil. Then I heard from the daughter of the serai keeper how this ill-omened one, thy master, made a talk for a day and a night in the college of the long-beards. Such a talk! May Allah never cause the like to be again."

The camelman paused to take a pomegranate out of his girdle and pry the skin from it.

"He said the stars had ceased moving."

Ishak stared, unbelieving.

"Moreover —" the bringer of tidings munched the crimson heart of the fruit — *"umh,* he said that the sun did not move. Now I have heard the talk of Samarkand where the Chinese are, ay, and the talk of the House of Allah in Mecca, and much wisdom hath passed into my ears. But never have I heard doctor or dervish say that the sun did not rise and set. May the dogs bite thee, and the curse of the death of Kerbala be upon this house."

With this parthian shaft, he kicked his donkey's ribs and departed. Ishak rose to go and complain to Zuleika of the bad news.

"Did I not say," the stout mistress of the kitchen observed, "that no good fortune would come out of the talk about Cosology and Capulation?"

"Wallahi, what is that?"

"Well, perhaps it is Cal-cupation — 'tis all the same. Ay, me, why did the master try to measure time?"

From the kitchen Ishak went to the lattice screen of the harem — Ayesha having been sent to Kasr Kuchik to escape the heat of the city. Not without malice, he explained to her how the master had roused all Nisapur to anger. Ayesha thought it over, with misgivings.

"If our lord says that the sun stands still," she observed finally, "it is still. Who should know if he does not?"

This quarrel with the learned men might be unfortunate, she decided, but so long as Omar enjoyed the favor of the Sultan, his enemies could do no more than bark at his heels like dogs.

Ishak went back to his gate sorely perplexed. Attentively he watched the red ball of the sun as it set beyond the distant plain. There was no doubt about it; the sun had not altered its habits. It was sinking out of sight just as it did that night when Omar's new calendar began, years ago — Ishak counted the years on his crooked fingers, and found there were thirteen. What had the mullahs said about a bad omen, in the first hour of that new calendar?

The banners of death had been in the sky, even as they were this evening, in their scarlet shrouds. No, the sun had not changed.

Ishak took to waiting outside the gate, to pick up more news from Nisapur. He heard from a slave merchant that Khwaja Omar was at work in the House of the Stars with his mathematicians, and that the academy still buzzed with his preposterous talk. The merchant, who was a kindly man, thought that perhaps Omar had been drunk at the time, and that by making a pilgrimage to the shrine of the blessed Imam at Meshed he could expiate his heresy.

Then, in swirling dust, a courier from the Court galloped by, shouting to peasants and shepherds to clear the road, as he was riding to Samarkand.

"With what news?" Ishak called.

Over his shoulder the courier flung an answer. "Bad. Sultan Malikshah is dead."

From Balkh to Baghdad the word of Malikshah's end was carried as swiftly as hard-ridden horses could travel. The Sultan had been taken ill while hunting, and, although his physicians had let blood copiously, he had died within a few days, naming no successor.

The bazaars were closed in Nisapur and Isfahan, and the larger caravans turned back from the road, while armed forces gathered under the powerful amirs at different places. The division besieging Alamut withdrew because its commander hastened at once to join the camp of Barkiyaruk, a son of Malikshah who was supported by the sons of the slain Nizam al Mulk.

At the same time Muhammad, another son of the Sultan, was acknowledged successor to the throne by the Kalif of Baghdad. As the days passed, the fighting men of the empire gathered in two rival camps, and civil war began.

Hassan ibn Sabah, once Alamut was free from capture, retired unnoticed to Cairo to take counsel with the leaders of the Assassins in Egypt. It suited his plans to have civil war devastating Persia, while his followers spread their propaganda unmolested in the growing confusion. Whether Barkiyaruk or Muhammad gained the throne, Hassan would be the gainer by the strife. Meanwhile, there were castle sites to be acquired in Syria — already his followers had cast aside their disguise and were fortifying the Dizh Koh at Isfahan — and plans for a world empire to be perfected with the masters of the Assassins in Cairo.

It was years before his hand was seen in events in Persia, and then his followers failed in an attempt to assassinate Barkiyaruk, who was gaining ascendancy over his rival.

At the first tidings of Malikshah's death, Ayesha had made Ishak take her back to the small Nisapur palace by the park, and the Street of the Booksellers. Here she could be near Omar, who spent most of his time at the House of the Stars at work upon a revision of the geometry of Euclid.

Ayesha had gathered together a number of armed retainers, mostly Arabs — lean and reckless men who cared little what the Persians did, so long as they were well paid and fed. Ayesha also bought swift-paced horses and baggage camels from the bazaar. Now that Omar's protector had passed to the mercy of Allah, she thought it best to have swords of their own to guard their backs, and horses in readiness to carry them from Nisapur at any moment. She did not trust the

Persians who acted after the manner of sheep, now flocking here, now rushing off there.

Except that crowds no longer gathered at Omar's gate to beseech his patronage, Ayesha did not notice any great change in the people of Nisapur. Now that civil war had begun, the nobles naturally were seeking new alliances, and the crowds in the mosques talked of nothing but the armies on the march from Baghdad, or Ray. At night the gates were closed, and mounted patrols rode through the streets.

True, after a time, the imperial treasurer ceased paying the salary of the King's astronomer. But when Omar needed money for his followers he sent his steward to borrow in the bazaar, and there was always plenty of gold in the chest Ayesha guarded jealously.

Once she tried to persuade Omar to travel to the camp of Barkiyaruk who had just defeated the Baghdad army. It seemed to her a splendid chance to make new prophecies — had not the King's poet, Mu'izzi, written an ode celebrating the victory, at the same time sending secretly to the defeated party a poem of consolation? Especially now, when Omar assured her an eclipse of the moon was at hand, and that it would be visible from Nisapur.

But Omar wore the white of mourning for Malikshah. The young Sultan — Malikshah had been only thirty-nine at his death — had been his companion since boyhood. Now he had joined Rahim and Yasmi and Jafarak — and where were they?

He did write a quatrain that aroused no enthusiasm in Ayesha.

The friends who drank life's draught with me have gone.
Content with less than I, they one by one
Laid down their cups to take Death's waiting hand
In silence, ere the Feast was well begun.

"But it says nothing in praise of Barkiyaruk," she pointed out. "You should not think so often about the dead. They are in their shrouds and they can do nothing more. You are little more than forty years in age, and I for one," she added tenderly, "know well that your strength is no whit diminished. Why do you not ride with the nobles instead of sitting in that everlasting tower making marks on paper?"

228

"Once I rode with Malikshah. It is enough. Nay, tonight thou'lt see the moon vanish, Ayesha."

"Will Satan eat it all?" She shivered in pleasant anticipation.

"Watch, and you will know."

That night Omar spent on the summit of his observatory. Ayesha lay on her roof in Nisapur, staring at the crowds in mingled excitement and dread. It was a full moon, and when the shadow began to creep across its face, a murmur went through the multitude.

Straightway horns began to blare and the saddle-drums reverberated. Cymbals clashed and women wailed on the housetops. They all understood, as did Ayesha, that the Devil with evil intent was trying to devour the moon.

The shadow deepened, and groups of mullahs came forth with torches to recite, loud voiced, the ninety and nine holy names of Allah, to take power away from the Devil.

Still the light failed. A cold breeze came in from the desert, and the wailing increased. The most zealous Moslems hurried forth to beat brass basins and shout, to frighten away the evil power in the sky. In spite of their efforts, the shadow covered the moon and before long the city was utterly dark except for the dancing torches.

Then — and Ayesha cried out with joy — a rim of light appeared, like a scimitar in the sky. The drums and cymbals beat with new vehemence and slowly, slowly, the Devil was forced to disgorge the moon that he had swallowed.

Not until the full moon was restored did the tumult cease. Ayesha curled up and went to sleep satiated with excitement. She wondered if Omar in his tower had beaten a drum, but she thought that probably he had done nothing of the kind.

The religious fervor roused by the moon's eclipse lasted for some time, and the *kadis*, the judges of Islam, sat in consultation. They sent a message to Omar bidding him appear before them the following day. And the guards who brought the message remained sitting within sight of the House of the Stars until the hour when he was to be escorted before the judges.

Strangely, no one had warned Omar that he would be summoned. His friends all seemed to be occupied with their own affairs — although his assistants besought him to say nothing to anger the *kadis*. After all, they were the judges of Islam, and it would be best to assent to any complaint they might make, until he had secured the favor of a new Sultan, or perhaps of the Kalif himself.

When Omar entered the *divan* a glance showed him that the whole council of the academy was ranged upon the seat about the wall, with the heads of the departments of philosophy and theology. Facing him sat the *kadis* in their white turbans, with Ghazali the mystic, and a *mufti* or maker-of-decisions from the Ulema itself. So crowded was the room that only a small space had been left for him to kneel before the judges.

He had often come there to lecture to the professors, or to advise the council, and most of the faces were familiar. Now, however, they gave no sign of recognition, and Omar understood that he was to be tried, even before the oldest of the judges spoke the first words — *"Bismallah ar rahman ar rahim*" — in the name of Allah the Merciful, the Pitying."

While he listened, his mind became alert, weighing not the formal words but the feelings of this council of judgment. Had Malikshah been alive they would not have dared call him to judgment. Now in the eyes of mullahs and professors of the Law he read an old hatred, no longer concealed.

One of the mullahs recited the charges against Omar the Tentmaker, son of Ibrahim, once astronomer to the King, upon whom be blessings.

The mullah said that first the books of Omar must be judged, since those books had been taken into the schools throughout Islam.

It was charged against the books — which had been written without question according to teachings of the infidel Greeks — that their author was *mulhid* — an unbeliever.

He was manifestly a heretic, on many counts. First, he had prevailed upon the late Sultan to set aside the proper calendar of Islam and to measure time anew in accordance with infidel ideas.

Then, he had established his work-place near a cemetery, so that he could walk among the graves and hold unhallowed commerce with the dead.

Also, he had blasphemed against the word of God, saying that the earth was not the center of the universe, and that the stars which Muhammad had declared to rise and set in fact did not move. Most of those who were present — faithful followers of the road of God — had heard this *mulhid* speak these very words. That, in itself, was sufficient cause for a judgment. In fact, the mullah concluded, there could be no argument. All these circumstances were known beyond doubt. Hundreds of witnesses could testify to every point. The only question for the council to decide was — what punishment should be measured out to the books of Omar Khayyam, and what to the author of the books.

When the mullah was silent, a doctor of the academy spoke. He agreed that the facts already related were beyond need of testimony. The hand of Omar Khayyam had, however, committed another offense not so generally known.

From time to time Omar Khayyam had written *rubais* which, although never gathered together in a book, were repeated in all quarters. The Sufis, especially, quoted these quatrains, and impious souls voiced them in challenge to the Koran and the Traditions of Islam. The speaker, a humble servant of the Ulema had collected several of these quatrains written down by various hands in Persia, yet composed by Omar Khayyam.

If the doctors and learned kadis would permit he, the speaker, would read aloud these impious verses, asking their forgiveness for uttering words so evil in meaning.

There was a stir of interest, and heads craned forward. Not every one had known of the quatrains. And here the maker of the verses would be condemned by his own words.

"Read, and fear not," said the oldest judge.

Slowly, the doctor of the Law read the verses, and Omar smiled faintly in recollection . . . with Yasmi beside him, how could he spare a thought to paradise . . . indeed, wine had eased his grieving . . . a hawk uptossed, to seize the book of human Fate. . . .

"That is sacrilege," the doctor said, "but here is one clear line of blasphemy. *'O Thou to Whom we cry, "Forgive!"' —
Say, where wilt Thou forgiveness find?' "*

Omar looked up, surprised. "I did not write that."

No one answered. The bearded faces beneath the white turbans were stern. Ghazali rose, avoiding Omar's eyes, and made his way to the nearest door. As clearly as if written on paper before him, Omar could read their judgment — that he was condemned.

He also rose to his feet and as he did so something relaxed in his mind. He did not want to struggle any more with these intent doctors and judges.

"Wilt thou speak to us, Omar Khayyam?" the *mufti* asked

"Yes. That verse is not mine. But here is one that has not been read:

> *If at the dawn of the last Judgment day*
> *We will arise with what beside us lay*
> *Within the tomb — O put by me a jug*
> *Of wine of Shiraz and a mistress gay.*

"That verse was not written before," Omar added, "but it came into my mind as something appropriate to the moment."

A murmur of anger answered him, and the mufti lifted his hand.

"Go thou, and await the decision of the judges."

As he was led through the door that Ghazali had left, a pockmarked dervish leaned toward him to whisper under his breath. "Sanctuary is in Alamut."

When Omar made no response the dervish slipped away and the guards led him to an alcove of the mosque where the shadow of the minaret lay upon the stones. With a sigh Omar seated himself comfortably.

He was no longer the son of Ibrahim, and no longer Khwaja Imam Omar, the favored of the Sultan, the bestower of favors. For long years he had heard great argument, and here he was at the courtyard of the mosque wherein he had studied at the feet of the learned, and now he was not Khwaja Omar but a prisoner being judged.

The mufti himself came to tell him of the verdict.

"All thy books are pronounced contrary to the Law, as being the work of an unbeliever. They will be forbidden in the schools, and those that are here will be burned.

"The House of the Stars is confiscated; henceforth it will belong to the council of Nisapur. Thou art forbidden to set foot within its walls, or to speak in public within the government of Nisapur."

"I hear," Omar replied. "But what of me?"

The mufti considered, stroking his beard. "Some of the judges hold that thou art mad, being afflicted of Allah. As to that, I do not know. Thou art free, but thou must depart from Nisapur, and the academies of Islam."

"For how long?"

"For ever."

When the guards had gone away, Omar went from the gate. Taking no heed of the whispering crowd that gathered to watch him, he turned instinctively down the familiar Street of the Booksellers.

"O unbeliever!" a voice mocked him. A band of students trooping down toward the park fell silent at his approach. Faces appeared in the bookstalls as he went by. At the turn in the street, he stopped by the fountain. The water trinkled from it just as it had done twenty-five years before, and women sat gossiping on the rocks. One of them uttered an exclamation, and a girl who was filling a clay jar at the basin turned, startled, to find him standing behind her. The jar, half lifted, fell and broke upon the stones.

"Thy forgiveness!" he said impulsively, and turned to go on.

Twenty-five years ago when he had waited at the fountain for Yasmi, he had been real and all those other people only shadows that came and went like shapes on a Chinese lantern. Now they were real, and he had become a shadow moving without purpose. That had happened when they had taken the House of the Stars away from him.

Ayesha, weeping, besought him that evening to take what followers remained, and the chest of gold and her belongings and flee to Kasr Kuchik with her. Here in Nisapur, she was afraid. The talk she had heard in the alleys, the jeering of the crowd at the mosque! There was time to go — she had horses ready at hand, and camels for the baggage — before fresh misfortune came upon their heads.

But Omar felt no desire to go from Nisapur. He had not finished the commentary on Euclid — all his work was waiting at the House of the Stars.

"Nay," he said, and went to sit on the roof, to think of what he must do. Nothing occurred to him, however, except to watch the glow of late afternoon change into sunset.

It was nearly dark when Ishak came running up.

"*Ai*, master, a great crowd is going toward the House of the Stars. They are soldiers, mullahs, worthless ones. They make outcry against thee, and perhaps they will loot the tower. Let us hasten and take what we can and ride to Kasr Kuchik before the gates are closed. *Wallahi*, there is no safety here."

"Saddle one horse," said Omar, rising.

When he had mounted, he rode from the courtyard, after ordering Ishak to keep the household within doors. Crossing the park, he trotted through the river gate of the city and whipped the horse into a gallop.

At that hour the road was almost deserted. When he came out from under the trees, his eyes fastened on the height of the observatory. Instead of a dark line against the stars, he saw a red glow rising and sinking.

As he drew closer, he made out flames beneath clouds of smoke. Digging his stirrups into the horse's flanks, he plunged up the slope, through scattered groups of men. At the garden entrance he flung himself from the saddle and ran in. Smoke eddied about him, and flames licked in and out of the embrasures of the tower. A breath of hot air scorched his face, and he was pulled back by hands that grasped his arms.

"*Y'allah!* Art blind, O man! The fire is in there."

"It rages, now."

"Ay, 'tis well lighted. See, how it eats the tower."

The men who had pulled him away from the observatory door were talking, elated by the spectacle. Some of them had bundles of hangings in their arms, and two of them were quarreling about the screen with the dragon embroidered on it — arguing whether it was worth carrying to the bazaar to sell.

Omar was only half-conscious of the shouting and running about as the crowd made off with its loot. The first story of the observatory was a roaring furnace, and the fire was eating upward.

All his books and papers were there, on the third floor — the star tables, the records of the years of observation, the half-finished Euclid.

"The books — what of the books?" he cried, shaking the nearest man.

"Eh, what? The books made good food for the flames.

Ay we piled them below there."

A boy ran past holding something under his shirt. The soldiers hacked the dragon from the screen with their knives. It would be easier to carry off, without the frame. They looked up with interest when the first floor of the tower fell in, and sparks whirled up.

When the roof of the tower fell, the thing became no more than a chimney of fire, above a bed of glowing embers. The glare diminished and the air grew cooler. The voices quieted down as the crowd departed, hastening to get back before the city gates should be closed.

A party of horsemen, entered the garden and reined in to look at the scene. They went over to inspect the great bronze globe of Avicenna which had been carried out of the tower and stood in safety, with the astrolabe lying by it. The globe, then, would serve other watchers of the stars.

"Will your Excellency compose an ode upon this burning?"

Omar glanced up, startled. But the speaker was one of the newcomers and he addressed a man who wore a court robe and bestrode a fine white horse. Something about the rider was familiar to Omar, and after a moment he recognized Mu'izzi, the Glorifier, the King's poet.

Mu'izzi pretended to take no notice of the astronomer. Instead he made some jest about the fire and turned his horse away, reminding his companions that they were late. After their hoof beats passed down the road Omar was left alone.

It did not occur to him to go away. His work had been there, and it was smoldering now among those blackened stones. He wondered what had happened to his assistants, and decided that they had fled from the mob.

The bed of embers was like a mass of roses lighted from within, growing bright and then dim, as the night air stirred. Still, in his mind the flames roared, and he felt a desolating heat. This had happened to him before, when the tent burned on the bank of the Euphrates just a little while ago. It had never been extinguished, that fire, and he felt again its warmth, watching the smoke make a veil across the sky.

But here a round moon looked down from a clear sky. Omar paced up and down the ruined garden. Some of the rose bushes had scattered their petals along the walk, and a white lily bloomed in the shadow. Omar felt that he must be careful not to step on the flowers, which were growing indistinct. It would be better to mount his horse and go away from this ruined place.

His horse, however, had been stolen or had wandered off. So he walked back along the road with the moon above him, and his shadow keeping him company, stride for stride. . . .

The city gate was closed, and the guards warned him away. So he wandered through an outlying village until he came to a light in a doorway. When he heard a subdued burst of laughter and the tinkle of a guitar, he stopped.

Within the open shop he saw only a potter's wheel, with dried clay upon it, and a rug with a jar or two. Yet the place was fragrant with the scent of wine. Omar entered, and pushed aside the curtain at the rear.

Jars upon jars were ranged along the walls. A peasant girl, unveiled, smiled at a man who was plucking the guitar with clumsy fingers. An old man held a jar in his arms, as if embracing it, while he poured wine from it into a bowl.

"Take care," cried Omar. "Spill it not."

When he took the bowl in his hand the cool red wine rolled cheerfully, and he sipped it while the three stared at him.

"Mashallah," the white beard said, bowing low, "hath his Honor lost his way?"

Omar glanced down at his robe covered with dust and ashes. Then with a sigh he emptied the bowl. Here in the wine shop it was cool, and the old potter with the crooked hands was an angelic shape. Seating himself beside the jar, Omar considered.

"Today," he answered, "I have divorced religion and learning from my bed, and taken the daughter of the grape to bride."

"What strange names," the girl laughed.

"Sing," Omar demanded, "and you with the open mouth, play. Such a divorce happens not every day."

He did not say anything more for a long time. The wine gurgled musically from the jar, and Omar felt inclined to call attention to it. He put his hand upon its cool side, and turned to the potter. "What if this clay like me a sighing lover was — its lip to the lip of the lovely sweetheart was, and its arm about her throat?"

"Who knows?" responded the old man drowsily.

Omar listened then for the girl's singing but it had ceased. The place was dark, and he had been asleep. He sat up and shook the jar, but it was empty. So he turned over to sleep again in the dark.

When someone touched his shoulder he opened his eyes and found the room filled with gray light. The old man looked troubled and afraid. "Wake, my lord," he urged, "for the muezzin calls to prayer from the tower."

"Heed him not," Omar said, "for he calls to you from ambush, hidden in his tower. Beware of him."

And he turned over again beside the empty jar. Why should he get up when the gates of Nisapur were closed to him? And the House of the Stars, that lay in ashes —

"Listen, master," begged the old man.

"... *Come to prayer, come to prayer ... to the house of praise*. ..."

The distant call echoed within the potter's room, and Omar got to his feet, swaying a little. In the entrance he stopped to think for a moment. It was dawn, and here he was in a tavern door — so he called to the muezzin:

> "*At dawn a voice cried from the tavern door,*
> '*Come sots and little fools, fill one cup more.*
> *Awake and come, before your cup is filled*
> *By Fate, and all your drinking days are o'er.*'"

Then he went back to sleep.

By day the potter's wheel whirled, scattering cool drops of water. The potter's crooked hands molded the wet clay into fantastic shapes. By night Omar cooled the fire within him with wine, until the rows of jars so motionless in the sunlight became human faces that could talk with him. When he tired of talking, he slept, and he did not try to count the days.

"They trouble me not," he explained shrewdly to the potter, "the days that have gone by, and the days that have not come."

One day, however, brought a disturbance. Ayesha and Ishak stood by him, and Ayesha's voice was shrill with anger.

"What new madness is this? Knowest not that we have sought thee for weeks? *Aiwallah!*" She wrung her hands. "Is it not enough that they burned the House of the Stars, and the moneylenders of the bazaar took the city house for thy debts?"

But all that must have been yesterday. Surely the fire had died down to cool ashes by now.

"Ay, they have taken Kasr Kuchik. Now thy name is a mockery in the Court of the new Sultan, who hath done away with thy calendar and restored the lawful months of the moon —"

"My calendar?"

"Ay, they will have no more to do with it. Is it not enough that women point at me in the bath, saying 'Behold the slave of Omar Khayyam?' Is it not enough that Mu'izzi's harlots ride in palanquins with black slaves to clear the way, when I have only a horse and Ishak, and thou art wallowing in wine with a potter's girl —"

"It is enough," said Omar, sitting up. "Ayesha, I promise thee that women will no longer mock thee with the name of Omar Khayyam, and Mu'izzi's peacocks will not have brighter plumage than thine henceforth. Ishak, thou hast store of silver put by?"

"Allah alone knows how much!" said Ayesha.

"And Ayesha hath the chest of gold with other things?"

The slave girl and the gatekeeper exchanged eloquent glances. Long ago they had convinced themselves that Omar could read their minds, but still they were surprised.

"Jewels she hath," assented Ishak promptly, "and the case of thy coins."

"Then be witness, O Potter, that all this property of mine I give to my slave girl who is here, and my servant. Go and testify before the mufti of Nisapur that I do so."

There was a moment's startled silence, and Ishak asked curiously, "But, master, what of thee?"

What remained, Omar wondered, of all that had been his? His books forbidden in the schools, his records burned, his calendar forgotten and he himself exiled from the academies of Islam?

"Beyond the outermost spheres," he answered thoughtfully, "there is hidden a cup that all must drink. Sigh not when it is thy turn to take it in hand, but quaff it joyously. That is all I know."

Ishak nudged the potter, and touched his head significantly.

"Tell that same mufti," Omar resumed, "that I shall set out with the caravan going to Aleppo. Now, begone to Nisapur — all of you."

When they were at the horses, still arguing in whispers, Ayesha began to weep under her veil. Ishak helped seat her in the saddle, exclaiming, "Woman, what is upon thee now?"

"I do not know. But are — are the chests really to be mine?"

"Certainly. The master hath said it."

Slowly Ayesha dried her tears. On the way to the mufti's house she could not help glancing into one of the entrances of the great bazaar where veiled women thronged about the silks.

In the gate of the caravanserai two days' journey upon the Khorasan road Omar squatted, stirring the fire that had kept him warm during the night. Over his shoulders hung a torn camelhair coat. His bare feet he stretched out to the embers.

In the night sky, the Dragon was descending to the western hills. Two hours more and his watch would be ended, because it would be dawn. A wind gust stirred the leaves, the dead leaves, whirling like souls in torment. Omar gathered them from the ground into his hands and dropped them on the fire which blazed up for a moment. His chest itched, and he scratched it comfortably. The hour was drawing near.

But something disturbed him. The hoofbeat of a horse on the hard clay of the road ceased, and a solitary rider approached the fire. "O watchman," the stranger asked, "is this the caravan Aleppo-bound?"

"Ay," said Omar.

The man dismounted, stretched his saddle-bound legs, and yawned. "Oh, Allah, it is a long gallop from Nisapur. Is there a Khwaja Omar Khayyam traveling with this caravan?"

Putting some thorn bush on the fire, Omar considered. Hearing the voices the serai keeper came out from his nook in the gate and squatted down by the rider. "Nay," observed the keeper, "there is only one merchant here, and he is neither Khwaja nor Khayyam."

"I am he," said Omar after a moment.

The two men looked at him, and laughed.

"Oh, Allah," said the rider. "Am I to give a Kalif's letter to a watchman with uncut beard? It is the Kalif of Cairo who writes to Omar Khayyam, bidding him come to cast his horoscope. And I shall escort him with honor to the court of Cairo."

"*Inshallah,*" said the serai keeper. "Is it true?"

From his girdle the courier drew a folded letter, tied and sealed with a great seal. "Look!" he said.

"Is it not also true," Omar asked, "that Lord Hassan of Alamut is at the court of Cairo now, in the confidence of your lord the Kalif?"

"Who art thou, to know that? Eh, he is there, as thou sayest. But what —"

"Bring me a pen, with ink," Omar ordered the staring keeper.

Taking the letter, he turned it in his fingers. It was heavy and no doubt it was long. It would be simple enough to cut the cord and find out what it said. Omar closed his eyes, weighing it in his fingers.

Why had these two men come to his fire to disturb him at this hour? Now, in his mind's eye he saw Nizam again, asking him to measure time anew, and Malikshah seeking a prophecy, and Akroenos enriching himself by him. Everything was quite clear to him now. Hassan had sought to make use of his brain, the kadis of the academy had exiled him, and the Sultan's courtiers had mocked him.... All that time he had been drifting, as purposeless as a leaf driven by the wind.

Once he had been so sure of himself, so certain of the power he held. He had stretched out his hand toward the curtain of the Invisible, and, lo, the Invisible was as remote as before.

"The pen," said the voice of the serai keeper. And Omar felt the quill within his fingers. "If he writes," the keeper whispered to the messenger, "he can be no watchman."

He must make haste to get these two away, before the time of the warning drum. Yes, he must write an answer to the Kalif of Cairo from Omar the Tentmaker who had sewn himself so many tents of learning. Bending close to the fire Omar wrote four lines upon the back of the letter.

> *Khayyam, who stitched at study for so long,*
> *His thread of life is severed. Right or wrong,*
> *Fate's shears have clipped him, and he's up for sale,*
> *Cried by the Broker, "Going, for a song."*

When he handed it to the courier, the man exclaimed, "But thou has not read the letter!"

"I know what is in it."

Staring, the man stepped back from the fire. Thus they had told him Omar would be — a worker of magic, a reader of human fate. Drawing his horse after him, he went with the keeper into the gate.

Cautiously Omar glanced over his shoulder. The Dragon was at the edge of the hills, and the dawn chill was in the air. Now at last he was alone, without friend, companion or consort.

What had Yasmi said about that hour? *It is cruel to be alone in love when the stars are sinking.* Was Yasmi a shadow on the veil of the Invisible? And Rahim — Rahim's blood that had sunk into the clay would not flow again. He must not think of that. They would never be back again. They would not come riding, like that courier, along the great Khorasan road again.

He took his head in his hands, rocking upon his knees beside the road. "Oh, be merciful," he cried.

For the hour of their coming was at hand. The shadows were gathering in the darkness, whirling along the road. They were thronging about him now, their faint voices crying, like the voice of the cold wind.

Stretching out his hands, he could not touch them, or keep them from hurrying away from him. He could not see them. On the heels of the darkness they were speeding away, looking back at him. Their thin voices were urging him to follow, toward shoreless space.

And he must make haste. He looked up, and the stars had faded. It was time. Staggering to his feet, he ran to the drum by the sleepers. When he struck it with his fist the serai walls echoed its reverberation.

From man to man he hurried, rousing them from their quilts. Bells clanged as the kneeling camels stirred. A man coughed and spat, and a bucket splashed into the well. . . .

"But," said the serai keeper, counting the coins in his hand, "I saw him write the verse upon the Kalif's letter."

The master of the caravan knotted up his wallet and stowed it into his girdle. "Ay, he is afflicted by Allah. Yet he never oversleeps the sun. Listen, now." And, swinging into his saddle, he called out, "O watchman, whither goes the caravan?"

Omar, tugging at the nose cord of the leading camel, looked over his shoulder. It was full day — the sun shone through the rising dust in the serai.

"Where the night hath gone," he answered eagerly. "But we must make haste."

"And where is that?" asked the caravan master, smiling.

Wearily Omar passed his hand across his eyes. "Nowhere," he said. And, pulling his ragged cloak over his head and taking up his staff, he drew the leading camel with him through the gate.

AUTHOR'S NOTE

The last anecdote.

A certain Nizam of Samarkand has the last word to say about Omar. This writer of Samarkand had met Omar, and had heard some tales about him. He says:*

"In the year 506** Khwaja Imam 'Umar Khayyam and Khwaja Isfizari had alighted in the city of Balkh, in the Street of the Slave-sellers, in the house of Amir Abu Sa'd, and I had joined that assembly. In the midst of our convivial gathering I heard the Argument of Truth *(Hujjatu' l-Haqq)* 'Umar say, 'My grave will be in a spot where the trees will shed their blossoms on me twice in each year.'

"This thing seemed to me impossible, although I knew that one such as he would not speak idle words.

"When I arrived at Nishapur in the year 530 — it being then some years since that great man had veiled his countenance in the dust — I went to visit his grave on the eve of a Friday (owing to the fact that he had the claim of a master on me), taking with me a guide to point out to me his tomb. The guide brought me out to the Hira cemetery; I turned to the left, and his tomb lay at the foot of a garden wall, over which pear-trees and peach-trees thrust their heads. On his grave had fallen so many flower-leaves that his dust was hidden beneath the flowers.

"Then I remembered the saying which I had heard from him in the city of Balkh, and I fell to weeping. Because, on the face of the earth, I nowhere saw one like unto him. May God have mercy upon him!

"Yet although I witnessed this prognostication on the part of that Proof of the Truth, 'Umar, I did not observe that he had any great belief in astrological predictions; nor have I seen or heard of any of the great (scientists) who had such belief."

* The following is quoted from Edward G. Browne's translation of Nizam-i-Samarqandi's "Chahar Maqala" published in the Journal of the Royal Asiatic Society for 1899. The author is indebted to Professor Browne's fine history of Persian literature for many points given in this book.

** 1112 - 1113 A.D. The Moslem year 530 would be 1135 - 1136. So Omar died, apparently, some time after 1113 and "some years" before 1135. Since he was given his observatory in Nisapur in 1073 - 74, he must have lived about seventy years. He must have been at least twenty years old when he assumed charge of the observatory. This observatory may have been at Merv, the city that was Malikshah's capital.

Several things in this anecdote are interesting: the evidence of devotion on the part of a few of Omar's followers: the fact that while his grave was known, it was not revered by the public; and Omar's own whimsical prediction as to his resting place.

A delightful instance of this lighter mood — or, if you will, his irony — appears in a much later anecdote. It seems that Omar came upon workmen repairing with bricks the academy of Nisapur. A donkey laden with bricks refused to enter the building in spite of all prodding. Omar laughed and, going up to the donkey, spoke to it.

> "O lost and now returned, 'yet more astray'
> Thy name from men's remembrance passed away,
> Thy nails have now combined to form thy hoofs,
> Thy tail's a beard turned round the other way!"*

Without more ado, the donkey entered the building, and the workmen asked Omar how he had made it do so. He replied that in a former life the donkey had been a lecturer in the academy, and therefore was unwilling to enter it again, until recognized!

In Nizam's *Chahar Maqala* there is an enlightening bit about soothsayers and their royal masters. This particular anecdote deals with Sultan Mahmud and one Abu Rayhan, a scientist and astrologer who was unfortunate enough to make a twofold prediction, doubly displeasing to his royal master. The prediction came true. Mahmud imprisoned Abu Rayhan, but eventually recovered his good humor and released the talented culprit.

"Kings are like little children," Sultan Mahmud explained frankly, "in order to receive gifts from them, it is necessary to speak according to their wishes. It would have been better for Abu Rayhan that day if one of his two prognostications had been wrong. But give him a horse caparisoned with gold, a robe of honor, a satin turban, a thousand dinars, a slave, and a handmaiden."

Then he scolded the offender, saying, "If thou desirest to profit from me, speak according to my desire, not according to the dictates of thy science."

The chronicler adds that after that day Abu Rayhan altered his practice, and agreed with the king, right or wrong.

* Edward G. Browne's translation.

From this *Chahar Maqala* — Four Discourses — of Nizam of Samarkand I have taken many incidents of this book, such as the riddle of the four doors, propounded to an astrologer.

The main events in this book, the major incidents, the scene itself, and perhaps half of the actual dialogue, are drawn from the reality of that day. They are retrieved from contemporary writings, or traditions, and are not invented.

Reality in the book.

Most of the characters are shown as they appear in the evidence of that time. Hassan ibn Sabah is easy to draw; his peculiar genius left its stamp on the writings and thoughts of his generation; although his own commentary on events was lost when the Mongols burned Alamut more than a century after his death — destroying at the same time that extraordinary library of the Assassins* — many writers have quoted from his book, and I have been at pains to collect these references hidden in the Persian and Arabic chronicles. The details given about the "magic" of the Assassins are all actual, although they are attributed to another remarkable leader Rashid ad Din, grand master of the Syrian branch of the order. Even the trick of reading sealed letters by judicious use of messenger pigeons is true, with the really ingenious and rather bloody trick of making the head of a dead man speak from a blood-filled tray.**

(By the way, these anecdotes of the magic of the masters of the Assassins appear in these sources as actual miracles written down by zealous disciples. I am responsible for the explanations, but I am pretty sure of them.)

Nizam is presented as he appears in the historical sources, as is Malikshah, although occasionally as in the latter's remark upon the evils of spies, the actual words were spoken by his father Alp Arslan. Ghazali's life is known sufficiently to indicate his character. Jafarak, Mai'mun, Isfizari, Mu'izzi are historical characters, portrayed as the evidence reveals them. But except for Mu'izzi, little is known about them.

Tutush is imaginary, but as with Rukn ud Din and Ishak, he is the personification of a definite character of the time. The women are imaginary portraits, drawn from the poetic literature and legendry of that other side of the world, long ago.

* Details of the overthrow of the Assassins by the Horde of Hulagu Khan, and the general history of that time, are given in my "The Crusades — The Flame of Islam."

** "Journal Asiatique" for 1877, Guyard's "Un Grand Maitre des Assassins."

So this book is a pattern of old mosaics, set in their proper places. It is not a portrait, because we have no sitter for a portrait, and the book had no plan at its beginning.

It is a story, told in the oriental manner. It is a *Maqamat* — a collection of episodes told as a story. Little was written in Asia at that time, and much was repeated from man to man. So we have more spoken tradition, like the *hadith* of the Arabs, than written records. So, likewise, when we study Omar's time, we are confronted with the recitals of eyewitnesses rather than historical records. History as an art was almost unknown in medieval Persia before the coming of the matter-of-fact Mongols with their Chinese secretaries. And certainly the European novel was undreamed-of.

This book is called a life, because the author did not know what else to call it. It is a work of pure imagination, based upon reality, in the oriental manner.* Its author believed that, as Genghis Khan could be portrayed more faithfully by turning back the clock to the twelfth century in the Gobi Desert than by modern character analysis or a historical dissertation, so something of Omar might be revealed by a re-creation of the incidents and setting of his time, told in the manner of that time and place. And for this attempt I can best apologize in the words of Cunninghame Graham, in the latter's Preface to Wayfaring Men:

"So I apologize for lack of analysis, neglect to delve into the supposititious motives which influence but ill-attested acts, and mostly for myself for having come before the public with the history of a failure to accomplish what I tried; and having brought together a sack of cobwebs, a pack of gossamers, a bale of thistle-down, dragon-flies' wings, of Oriental gossip as to by-gone facts, of old-world recollections."

Our knowledge of Omar.

History yields us almost nothing that is certain about Omar. We believe he was the court astrologer of Malikshah's reign; we are convinced that he wrote most of the quatrains popularly ascribed to him; we know his work upon algebra, his

* This adherence to the oriental manner, as it varies with the time and subject matter of Genghis Khan, Tamerlane, the Flame of Islam and even the author's occasional Cossack tales, may account for the readiness with which his efforts have been translated back into the various Asiatic languages and their — to him — surprising popularity in those languages. It is needful to remember that while the modern Asiatic reader inherits the imagination of the past, he insists upon reality.

commentary on Euclid, his research into the deep intricacies of mathematics and astronomy, and his creation of a new calendar. He had the House of the Stars in Khorasan. Malikshah, it seems, esteemed him, while Ghazali quarreled with him. His grave is at Nisapur; he was past his boyhood in 1073, and he died "some years" before 1135.

So much for established fact. We have traditions, beginning with Nizam of Samarkand's recital, and ending in vague latter-day remarks of the sixteenth century. These inform us that he was:

An unhappy philosopher.

A defender of Greek learning, and a follower of Avicenna's (Abu Ali Sina's) teaching.

The arch freethinker of his time, indolent and yet a great worker upon occasion, brusque in manner, endowed with a caustic wit, a quick temper, and a keen memory — once he rewrote a volume word for word after reading it seven times.

The greatest thinker of his time.

Other traditions have it that he avoided argument if possible, but gave tongue without restraint when aroused, that other scientists respected him — at his approach people would give back, saying "Here comes the Master" — while the religious groups in general disliked and perhaps feared him. Apparently he was spied upon by the rival sects. And at times his life was threatened.

It is said that he never married, and there seems to be no record of children.

These traditions yield a fragmentary but clear impression of a man's character. We can add to them the negative conclusions that he did not meddle with the politics of his time; that while he accompanied Malikshah at times, upon that Sultan's travels, he did not appear to be a courtier such as Mu'izzi. In fact he appeared to be the exact opposite of Mu'izzi.

So we have certain indications of a man going his own way in solitude, appealed to by others but independent of their thought. Next, by his remarks scattered through the Algebra, we discover that he had mastered such advanced processes as equations of the third degree solved by geometrical means, and the use of hyperbolas, which he did not learn from the Greeks, and which were not relearned in Europe until Descartes. He also had studied still more difficult problems — "some of them impossible," he says.

247

In the introduction to his Algebra he writes:

"However, I have not been able to concentrate my thoughts on it, hindered as I have been by troublesome obstacles. We have been suffering from a dearth of men of science, possessing only a group as few in number as its hardships have been many. Most of our contemporaries are pseudo scientists, who mingle truth with falsehood, who are not above deceit, and who use the little that they know of the sciences for base material purposes only. When they see a distinguished man intent on seeking the truth, one who prefers honesty and does his best to reject the falsehood and lies — avoiding hypocrisy and treachery — they despise him and make fun of him."*

Shahrazuri, who wrote the "Recreation of Souls" about a century after Omar's lifetime, supplies us with an interesting afterword upon his character:

"His eminence in astronomy and philosophy would have become a proverb, if he had only been able to control himself."

There is no doubt that we are dealing with a penetrating mind of extraordinary ability. That he suspected that the earth revolved upon its axis is simply an assumption. Some of the Moslem scientists of his century did believe it. But in expressing such an opinion they would be faced with the antagonism of orthodox Islam.

The Wheel of Heaven quatrain.

At least once Omar suggests in a quatrain that he conceived of the earth as turning upon its axis. The *rubai* beginning *In chark-i-falak,* I have taken as follows:

> *This Wheel of Heaven by which we are amazed*
> *A Chinese lantern like to it we know —*
> *The Sun the candle, the universe the shade,*
> *And we like its unheeding shadow forms.*

The Persian here is difficult to translate. The first two lines end in verbs of exactly opposite meaning — the first, that we do not comprehend at all, the second that we know, familiarly. Omar apparently meant that we are confounded by the Wheel of Heaven — which is probably the starry band of the zodiac — while a Chinese, or ordinary, lantern we understand readily enough.

*From "The Algebra of Omar Khayyam," by Daoud S. Kasir Ph. D. A recent and very able translation undertaken at the suggestion of Professor David Eugene Smith, and published by Teachers College, Columbia University.

The third line is clear. All the translators agree that the sun is the light, or the candle or lamp, while the earth or world is the shade. But I wonder if the Persian 'alam does not mean the universe here, instead of the earth? It is an old word, signifying the world, the whole world. If Omar had meant, as I believe he did, the universe, he could have used no other word.

And certainly no astronomer would ever have conceived of the sun as a candle within our earth. In fact no man of ordinary intelligence would have written that. On the other hand the concept of the sun as the candle of the great universe is crystal-clear.

The last line is interesting, and has been given various meanings by the translators. Nicolas says that, like figures on a lantern shade we remain in stupefaction, while Whinfield slurs it with his "trembling forms" and Garner and Thompson both give the final verb a more active meaning with their "While mortals are but Phantom Figures traced — Upon the Shade, forever onward hurled," and "We are like figures that in it turn about." M. K. is even more emphatic "And We the figures whirling dazed around it."

Except for Nicolas and Whinfield, I do not know if these translators had command of Persian. It is evident that the quatrain stumps everyone including FitzGerald. But if we grant that Omar conceived of the earth as revolving through space, lighted by the sun, while we cling to its surface in ignorance, the thing is clear behond doubt. Remember that he uses the Chinese lantern* for comparison. And Chinese lanterns are not magic lanterns, nor do they revolve. They do have inanimate figures painted on their shades.

FitzGerald, as usual, suggests Omar's thought beautifully by sheer fantasy without literal translation.

> *"We are no other than a moving row*
> *Of Magic Shadow-shapes that come and go*
> *Round with the Sun-illumined Lantern held*
> *In Midnight by the Master of the Show."*

Omar and the orthodox of Islam.

That Omar did come into conflict with orthodox religious opinion is beyond doubt. For one thing he was accused of fellowship with the infidel Assassins. Traces of that conflict are noticeable in Persia today. Often during my stay in that

* Curiously enough the word for lantern, "fanous," appears to be Greek instead of Persian.

country I asked, why Omar was so little recognized by them today, and they answered in effect: "We Persians have our religion. We esteem the writings of Jallal ud Din Rumi for example because he is animated by a devout spirit.

There is no evidence that Omar had any intercourse with Hassan or the Assassin propagandists. But the legend of the Three Schoolfellows — which makes out, long after they were all dead, that Nizam al Mulk, Omar and Hassan went to school together and formed a compact that they would aid each other thereafter — pictures him as intimate with Hassan. Omar and Hassan were two of the leading spirits of Persia in their generation; they appeared on the scene at the same time, and they died within a year of each other; Hassan is almost ubiquitous in his traveling about, and it was his custom to invite distinguished men to Alamut. So there is a strong probability that Omar may have been one of the guests of Alamut.

Moslems of that time traveled more than they do now. The current of intellectual life ran strong, after that great eleventh century in Baghdad. Every one who could, performed a pilgrimage; the travels of Ibn Jubair, al Biruni, Nasir-i-Khusrau and many others of that time have become famous; Malikshah was in the saddle the greater part of his reign. Mighty caravans from China, India, Constantinople, passed through Khorasan. All Islam was, so to speak, on the go.

Omar Khayyam made a pilgrimage, whether to Mecca or Jerusalem, we do not know. His quatrains give the impression that he did not dwell, most of his life, like Hafiz, in one place; without doubt he accompanied Malikshah upon occasion, and Malikshah was in Syria in 1075 when his Seljuk Turks conquered Jerusalem.

When I was in Persia I found very few people acquainted with the grave of Omar, although they had plenty to say about the tombs of Hafiz, outside Shiraz, and that of Avicenna in Hamadan. One man did say that he had known Meshed-bound pilgrims to go out of their way at Nisapur to find the grave of Omar Khayyam — and spit upon it.

In Persia today the verses of Hafiz, Ja'mi, the epic of Firdawsi, and the extraordinary work of Rumi, the *Mathnawi*, are favored far beyond the quatrains of Omar which are little known and less regarded. In fact, although I had no difficulty in finding good manuscript copies of Hafiz, Ja'mi and Rumi, I did not see anywhere a single copy of Omar's verses.

It is known that Omar's calendar was discarded after Malikshah's death, and that Omar remained in partial exile — whether voluntary or involuntary — from the court and the academies in his last years.*

Knowing all this, the impress of his character becomes clearer to us. We have still one more measure by which to measure him, the *rubaiyat* itself.

The Quatrains.

I have read in the original Persian most of the verse believed to be Omar's. My translation of that verse is scattered in Omar's dialogue throughout this book. Only eight quatrains are translated complete in an attempt to show Omar's verse in its varying moods.

But in studying the quatrains a clearer impression of his personality is obtained. Not by comparison with modern ideas, but by comparison with the writings, and the known characters, and the thought, of men of his time.** By taking, as it were, the shadow shape of the Omar revealed in the quatrains, and *placing it upon the clear pattern of the aspirations, the follies, the dogma, the superstition and the longing of his time* the impression is clear.

It is that of a man who, like Avicenna, revolted against the fixed ideas of his age. While Avicenna's revolt was intellectual, Omar's was passionate in its intensity.

---

* In two details this book departs from the conjectures of scholars.

First, Omar's birth. It is placed about ten years later than the usually accepted date (about 1052 instead of c. 1043-44). Omar's life coincided almost exactly with that of Hassan ibn Sabah, and even at the later date of birth, the two would have been over seventy years at their deaths. A study of the dates of men who knew Omar in the life seems to indicate that he was younger than has been generally believed, at the time when he undertook his astronomical work at the observatory.

Second, that Omar was part Arab. This is indicated by his name, by his father's name, by the nature of his early studies and by certain characteristics such as his brevity and bluntness of speech, his patience in carrying work to its end, and the almost savage clarity of his quatrains — traits not usually found in the Persian. It is possible that his father was an Arab.

** Nizam al Mulk for instance wrote a dissertation on the conduct of Sultans, known as the "Siasset nameh:" Ghazali's writings, notably his Revival of Religious Knowledge, are numerous. Then there is the Lament of Baba Tahir, the Travels and the "Divan" of that extraordinary Nasir-i-Khusrau, and the effusions of blind Abu 'l Ala, the memoirs of Usama, the "Chahar Maqala" abovementioned, which is full of anecdotes, and many others, as I found to my cost.

Oriental scholars and the Persians themselves assure us — in spite of the many cults, and schools of thought that claim Omar for their own nowadays — that Omar's poetry is the expression of his own life. It is the fruit of his experience, written down from time to time. It was not, therefore, as our saying goes, written for publication.

Reading the Persian, one cannot escape the conviction that this is pure realism. When Omar speaks of wine, he means wine; he is not using the hidden allegories of the Sufis and mystics of his time. When he speaks of a girl, it is a girl of flesh and blood.

At the same time a powerful imagination is at work upon the objects of reality. When Omar considers a cup, he reflects that a maker of such a cup would not dash it into pieces upon the ground — yet the loveliest human bodies are mangled, or decay in sickness, by inevitable fate. He pours wine from a jar, and wonders whether this clay were not once a sighing lover like himself, its lips to the lips of the beloved, its arms about her throat. A drunken fancy? Very likely. But there it is.

It is not the almost brutal realism of Nasir-i-Khusrau, who could exclaim beside a dunghill, "Behold the luxury of the world, and here am I the fool who craved it" — or wonder — "O why didst Thou make the lips and teeth of Tartar beauties so fair to see?"

Nor is it quite the melancholy typical of so many Persians, who were often wittier and more fluent than Omar Khayyam. True, the concept of the foxes breeding and the lions making their dens in the palace where once Jamshid lifted high his cup is usual enough. But the following image of Bahram, who set so many snares for hunted beasts, caught at last by the snare of death is not so typical.

Many Persians of that time might have written, "See how the nightingale clings to the rose!" Yet in Omar's mind the wind strips the beauty from the rose and scatters its petals upon the ground — and a human body might well rest beneath such a rosebush that grows out of the earth and sinks into it again. Did he remember that, when he told Nizam of Samarkand that his grave would be where blossoms fell twice in the year?

Omar's verse escapes the patterns of his time. It suffers a sea change into something not easily explained. There is, for one thing, the fire *motif* which creeps in so frequently — "Khayyam hath fallen into grief's furnace" — and —

> *"O, burning, burning, burnt, O, thou to be*
> *Consumed in fires of Hell made bright by thee!"**

Omar grieves for youth forsaking him; he cries to the cupbearer to hasten to bring wine because the night speeds by with its revelry; he mourns the friends who have left him solitary at the banquet of life. He echoes the refrain of Villon, *"Or beuvez fort, tant que ru peut courir."* Yet Villon could write his own epitaph, as a hanged man swinging at the wind's touch, with a plea for deliverance to *"Prince Jhesus, qui sur tous a maistrie"* while Omar can only question, question, question God.

His cry of agony is heard in almost every quatrain. The moon he loved will rise and set when he is no longer there to see; the flowers blooming at the edge of a stream — he must not step upon them because a lovely head may be buried there; the body of the loved one, it is no more than the clay from which the flowers bloom; his companions have left him — they will never be back again.

In spite of the versions of a few translators, Omar does not beseech forgiveness, nor does he voice any accusation. He wonders why wine should be a sin, but wine brings forgetfulness. At times he lashes out with mockery at the reassuring ones who offer nepenthes other than the wine which transmutes pain into nothingness. What else can relieve his agony?

So incessant is this note of pain that one who follows it closely from quatrain to quatrain becomes obsessed by it. There is no relief. You want to ward it off, to give respite to the agony of the struggling spirit. There is no respite. You feel that the man is dying before your eyes, and that he knows it. "Do not blaspheme wine; it is bitter only because it is my life."

Perhaps this simple human suffering is the thing we have not understood in Omar.

FitzGerald.

More than seven centuries after his death, a moody kindred spirit in another land gathered together the remnants of Omar's verses, and from them created one of the masterpieces of our literature.

* Thompson's translation.

The enormous popularity of Edward FitzGerald's *Rubaiyat of Omar Khayyam* brought forth in turn volumes of discussion and comment upon the Persian astronomer and the English poet. The question as to how much of this Rubaiyat is Omar and how much FitzGerald has been debated for years.

But one who reads the original Persian cannot escape the conviction that FitzGerald has created something new and whole out of the fragments of Omar's verse. In doing so FitzGerald took a little from Hafiz, a little from Avicenna. He did not translate Omar's quatrains but he paraphrased them beautifully.

FitzGerald wrote nothing else that can be compared to this paraphrase of Omar, and the ablest scholars have not been able to make a translation equal to FitzGerald's inimitable rendering.

Perhaps in brooding over Omar's quatrains, that taciturn Englishman had for a brief moment the gift of knitting cobwebs together, of weighing thistledown, and weaving a magic tapestry of dragon-flies' wings.

SURGEONS DON'T CRY by Albert R. Greenfeld   *Fiction*

When postoperative complications developed, the young resident surgeon's career was threatened by petty in-fighting and incompetency!
00105-095N   240 pps.   95¢

THE LAST ONE by Dion Henderson   *Fiction*
Author of *On The Mountain*

Whimsy, treachery, and bared politics scorch the lives of all involved . . . as vivid and touching as *The Last Hurrah!* First time in paperback!
00113-095N   240 pps.   95¢

Should you be unable to obtain any of these titles from your local bookseller, they may be ordered directly from the publisher.

LEISURE BOOKS, INC.
Department A
6340 Coldwater Canyon
North Hollywood, California 91606

Please send me_____copies of each of the books I have checked. I am enclosing the payment plus 10¢ per copy for postage and handling.

Name_____

Address _____

City_____ State _____ Zip_____